CURRENT TOPICS IN

DEVELOPMENTAL BIOLOGY

VOLUME 18

GENOME FUNCTION, CELL INTERACTIONS, AND DIFFERENTIATION

CONTRIBUTORS

DOROTHEA BENNETT

SALVATORE BOZZARO

LUISA CASTAGNOLI

GENNARO CILIBERTO

ROBERT L. COFFMAN

RICCARDO CORTESE

IRA HERSKOWITZ

ROLF JOHO

SCOTT LANDFEAR

CHARLES D. LANE

P. LINSER

HARVEY F. LODISH

GIORGIO MANGIAROTTI

A. A. MOSCONA

CAROL NOTTENBURG

STEPHEN S. WACHTEL

IRVING L. WEISSMAN

CURRENT TOPICS IN
DEVELOPMENTAL BIOLOGY

EDITED BY

A. A. MOSCONA

CUMMINGS LIFE SCIENCE CENTER
THE UNIVERSITY OF CHICAGO
CHICAGO, ILLINOIS

ALBERTO MONROY

STAZIONE ZOOLOGICA
NAPLES, ITALY

VOLUME 18
GENOME FUNCTION,
CELL INTERACTIONS,
AND DIFFERENTIATION

1983

ACADEMIC PRESS

A Subsidiary of Harcourt Brace Jovanovich, Publishers
New York   London
Paris   San Diego   San Francisco   São Paulo   Sydney   Tokyo   Toronto

ACADEMIC PRESS, INC.
111 Fifth Avenue, New York, New York 10003

United Kingdom Edition published by
ACADEMIC PRESS, INC. (LONDON) LTD.
24/28 Oval Road, London NW1 7DX

LIBRARY OF CONGRESS CATALOG CARD NUMBER: 66–28604

ISBN 0–12–153118–X

PRINTED IN THE UNITED STATES OF AMERICA

83 84 85 86   9 8 7 6 5 4 3 2 1

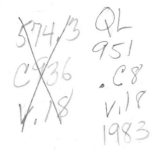

CONTENTS

CHAPTER 1. Cellular Differentiation, Cell Lineages, and Transposable
Genetic Cassettes in Yeast
IRA HERSKOWITZ

CHAPTER 2. Immunoglobulin Gene Rearrangement and Expression
during Lymphocyte Development
ROLF JOHO, CAROL NOTTENBURG, ROBERT L. COFFMAN,
AND IRVING L. WEISSMAN

CHAPTER 7. Development of the Heterogametic Gonad: A Model
             System for Embryonic Induction
             STEPHEN S. WACHTEL

CONTRIBUTORS

Numbers in parentheses indicate the pages on which the authors' contributions begin.

DOROTHEA BENNETT, *Memorial Sloan Kettering Cancer Center, New York, New York 10021* (xiii)

SALVATORE BOZZARO, *Max-Planck Institut für Biochemie, 8033 Martinsried, Federal Republic of Germany* (117)

LUISA CASTAGNOLI, *European Molecular Biology Laboratory, 6900 Heidelberg, Federal Republic of Germany* (59)

GENNARO CILIBERTO, *European Molecular Biology Laboratory, 6900 Heidelberg, Federal Republic of Germany* (59)

ROBERT L. COFFMAN, *DNAX Research Institute, Palo Alto, California 94304* (15)

RICCARDO CORTESE, *European Molecular Biology Laboratory, 6900 Heidelberg, Federal Republic of Germany* (59)

IRA HERSKOWITZ, *Department of Biochemistry and Biophysics, University of California, San Francisco, San Francisco, California 94143* (1)

ROLF JOHO, *Institute of Pathology, Division of Experimental Pathology, University Hospital, 8091 Zurich, Switzerland* (15)

SCOTT LANDFEAR,* *Department of Biology, Massachusetts Institute of Technology, Cambridge, Massachusetts 02139* (117)

CHARLES D. LANE, *Laboratory of Developmental Biochemistry, National Institute for Medical Research, London, England* (89)

P. LINSER, *Laboratory for Developmental Biology, Cummings Life Science Center, University of Chicago, Chicago, Illinois 60637* (155)

HARVEY F. LODISH, *Department of Biology, Massachusetts Institute of Technology, Cambridge, Massachusetts 02139* (117)

---

* Present address: C. V. Whitney Laboratory, University of Florida, St. Augustine, Florida 32084.

ix

GIORGIO MANGIAROTTI, *Cattedra di Biologia Generale, University of Turin, Turin, Italy* (117)

A. A. MOSCONA, *Laboratory for Developmental Biology, Cummings Life Science Center, University of Chicago, Chicago, Illinois 60637* (155)

CAROL NOTTENBURG, *Laboratory of Experimental Oncology, Department of Pathology, Stanford University, Stanford, California 94305* (15)

STEPHEN S. WACHTEL, *Division of Pediatric Endocrinology, New York Hospital-Cornell Medical Center, New York, New York 10021* (189)

IRVING L. WEISSMAN, *Laboratory of Experimental Oncology, Department of Pathology, Stanford University, Stanford, California 94305* (15)

PREFACE

These are exciting times for biology and for developmental biology in particular. New discoveries on genome organization and expression, and technical advances in DNA manipulation, are having a profound impact on our views of developmental processes. At the same time, new possibilities for studying differentiation are opening up thanks to the powerful methodology of monoclonal antibodies. The impact of these new approaches is not limited to analysis of differentiation at the cellular level; it extends to the processes of cell interactions, morphogenesis, metaplasia, and malignant transformation.

A full coverage of the many aspects of these problems would require a multivolume treatise. Hence, consistent with the policy of this series, the present volume contains selected topics focusing on those current developments that should be of immediate interest to a broad spectrum of scientists in diverse fields of modern biology.

The editors thank the contributors to this volume for stimulating accounts of their work and views, and the staff of Academic Press for expert cooperation in the preparation of this volume.

Alberto Monroy
A. A. Moscona

CONSPECTUS

Dorothea Bennett

MEMORIAL SLOAN-KETTERING CANCER CENTER
NEW YORK, NEW YORK

This volume offers a wealth of facts and ideas that can lead to flights of fancy on the part of a developmental geneticist who has had a longstanding interest in trying to define mechanisms of differentiation in mammals, and in trying to understand what kinds of gene expression and organization regulate this process. Viewed in its totality, embryogenesis requires enormously complex sets of decisions which result in the transformation of the fertilized egg into an individual with hundreds of different cell types in complex morphological arrangements. Yet one can speculate quite reasonably that this whole process is really no more than the summation of many quite simple decisions on the parts of specific cell groups; these very probably represent no more than binary choices to maintain membership in, or to diverge from, specific cell lineages. The ultimate basis of differentiation is of course differential gene expression, as was so elegantly pointed out by Jacob and Monod in 1963 when they said "two cells are differentiated from one another when they harbor the same genome but synthesize different sets of proteins." We must ask, however, not only how this state is achieved but how it is maintained. In multicellular organisms like a mouse, for example, it is clear that differentiation also implies maturation, which can best be defined as an increase in the complexity of organization of cells and tissues during development, which is accompanied by differential gene expression, and which, very importantly, results in communities of cells whose individual potentialities are restricted to a rigid constellation of functions.

One way of trying to dissect this complexity that has been attractive to me, and to others who call themselves developmental geneticists, has been to try to use mutant genes as probes to pinpoint key events in development processes. The idea has been that, since genes and their appropriate regulation must control specific developmental events, a retrospective study of embryos afflicted with genetic disorders of development should reveal first the morphological end result, then the cell types involved, then the process affected, then the biochemical defect impeding the process, and eventually the ultimate holy grail, the identification of the abnormality in gene product responsible for the

xiii

whole cascade of events. It should be pointed out first of all that in
principle this is by no means a new idea; in fact, the first clear descrip-
tion of this kind of strategy can be found in a statement by Sir William
Harvey in 1657, "Nature is nowhere accustomed more openly to display her secret mysteries than when she shows traces of her working
apart from the beaten path. . . . For it has been found in almost all
things that what they contain of useful or of applicable is hardly perceived unless we are deprived of them, or they become deranged in
some way." And second, it has to be confessed that this kind of approach has only recently even begun to fulfill its promise, and, where
that is true at all, it has been limited to situations which the developmental geneticist would consider relatively trivial events of terminal
differentiation, such as the thalassemias (Weatherall and Clegg, 1982).
This is not to say that understanding the molecular, biochemical, and
physiological basis of thalassemia is trivial, because of course it is not,
but simply that it presents a relatively trivial problem to solve, since it
involves the abnormal production by a terminally differentiated cell of
a high abundance luxury protein. It will clearly be far more difficult to
understand more complex morphogenetic events which must often depend on the transitory production and fleeting interactions of minor
gene products. And unfortunately the understanding of morphogenesis
has hardly yielded at all to the conventional approaches of developmental genetics. This is certainly true of the system I have struggled
with for years, namely the T/t-complex in the mouse, which has tan-
talized generations of developmental geneticists since its components
were first described in 1927 by Dobrovolskaia-Zavadskaia. The $T/$
t-complex contains a number of apparently related mutant genes that
subvert specific morphogenetic events during early embryogenesis,
and also impair both the morphogenesis and the function of male germ
cells; it has thus promised to provide keys to understanding these
processes. Furthermore, these mutations come as a package in a segment of chromosome held together by its inability to undergo recombination with wild type chromosomes, and thus the T/t-complex has also
offered the possibility of providing insights into the structural organization of genes that apparently regulate sequential developmental
events. While we are not even close in any instance to defining pathways leading from gene regulation to gene product to morphogenesis,
we have learned a lot, established some general principles and some
facts, and certainly defined new questions that are now approachable
with the techniques of modern biochemistry and molecular biology. It
has to be emphasized, though, that a developmental geneticist who
takes a gene mutation (or in the case of the T/t-complex a complicated

set of genes) and runs with it, has to be in a sense a jack of all trades and a master of none. Furthermore, he is one who is foolhardy enough to try to deal simultaneously with two of the least understood problems in biology, i.e., cellular mechanisms of differentiation and the regulation of eukaryotic gene expression—and moreover at the organismal level!

With this in mind, I thought it might be amusing (certainly) and instructive (maybe) to provide a kind of personal and informal conspectus of this volume in the context of how the elegantly focused studies reviewed here might impinge on the more diffuse world of developmental genetics and especially the T/t-complex.

Until recently, it would have seemed quite a good bet that in general all cells in a multicellular organism harbored the same genome (outside of trivial departures such as sperm and red cells), and that differentiation implied the switching on (or off) of particular batteries of genes appropriate to specific cell types. Nevertheless, a few examples, thought to be dead-ending evolutionary peculiarities, were known which could have been used to predict that differential gene expression could also be achieved by the abandoning of specific chromosomal segments by particular cell types. For example, in both the roundworm *Ascaris* (Boveri, 1910) and Cecidomyiidae (Geyer-Duszynska, 1959) wasps, the DNA content of somatic cells is substantially less than in the germ line, a situation that certainly offers the possibility that different somatic cells contain different constellations of genes; broadly viewed, this situation could be both a result and a determinant of differentiation. Now, of course, as first shown by Hozumi and Tonegawa (1976) and discussed in this volume by Joho *et al.* (Chapter 2) it is abundantly clear that sometime during the pathway of differentiation that leads to mammalian B lymphocytes, some portions of immunoglobulin genes are deleted and others are rearranged. Joho and colleagues present the very interesting information that rearrangements in heavy chain genes occur first in pre-B cells, and that this is followed by rearrangement to produce the light chain genes. Thus in this case it seems clear that the entry of lymphocytes into the pre-B cell state elicits a definitive act of differentiation which involves the rearrangement and discarding of some chromosomal material, and subsequent differential gene expression. In fact, Joho and co-workers point out that immunoglobulin gene reorganization may itself function as an activator of the expression of the newly created gene.

A different level of complexity in the regulation of gene expression is introduced by Herskowitz (Chapter 1). Genetic and molecular studies of the mating type locus in yeast have yielded information that has intriguing implications for mechanisms of genetic control of development in general. A very much oversimplified version of the picture is as follows: There is a locus called *Mat* which contains a regulator that allows the expression of either of two mating type genes, *a* and *α* when they are next to it. At a distance from the *Mat* locus and from one another are two loci composed of silent cassettes (HML and HMR) which contain respectively *α* and *a* genes that are not expressed. Under ordinary, but circumscribed, sets of conditions, the *a* and *α* gene associated with *Mat* is discarded, and replaced preferentially by the alternative allele from HML or HMR, which is then expressed. This appears to be a unidirectional conversion process since the *α* or *a* gene, which has "moved" into the *Mat* locus, also remains in its original association with HML or HMR, and can be used again in subsequent division cycles. As Herskowitz points out, such systems may well exist in other higher eukaryotes, and the number of cassettes obviously need not be limited to two. It is just this sort of system, in which a functional cassette could simultaneously lead a given cell to a specific state of differentiation *and* program its own replacement with a cassette appropriate for the next step in differentiation, that could account for the orderly sequence of events that occurs during embryonic development.

In fact, it is almost inescapable to consider in this context the series of recessive lethal mutations in the *T/t*-complex of the mouse, which appear to govern sequential switch points in early embryogenesis (Bennett, 1975). The implication is that these mutations must identify the existence of wild type genes that operate in some coordinated fashion to regulate cell commitment in the early stages of development when totipotency is being curtailed, the three germ layers are being established, and all cells come to have only limited options for further specific differentiation. Especially relevant to our thinking about *t*-lethal mutations are new findings that these mutations map widely separate from one another (Artzt *et al.*, 1982) but yet show defective complementation so that they appear to belong to the same "genetic unit" although this has the surprisingly large dimension of about 20 cM (Shin *et al.*, 1982b). Thus they are clearly related to one another in some way that requires an arrangement of wild type genes in cis, i.e., on the same chromosome.

It is quite within the realm of possibility that functional genes in the *T/t* region could be produced by rearrangements similar to those that occur to generate immunoglobulin genes, and that events similar to the class switch may occur at specific transitional points in early development. Perhaps an even more attractive hypothesis is that the relationship among *t*-genes might be based on a system similar to the mating type systems in yeast, in which case one would predict self-programmed sequential replacement of one gene after another into an expression locus, by conversion acting over the chromosomal segment that they span. There is no evidence for or against either of those speculations at the moment, but a variety of probes are already available for chromosome 17 genes, and these could be used right now to search for chromosome rearrangement in restricted cell lineages during embryogenesis. Furthermore, in due time there will certainly be probes to *t*-specific genes (Shin *et al.*, 1982a) and these will provide definitive answers to these questions.

While our knowledge of the rules of genetic regulation of embryogenesis in mammals is, as indicated above, sorely deficient, we do know some of the phenomenology of the cellular mechanisms that must elicit differential gene expression; specifically, we know that environmental influences (other cells, extracellular matrix, small molecules such as hormones) can alter cellular gene expression. These observations give strong clues that a fertile area to concentrate on experimentally is the cell surface, which must have both receptors for identifying components of the environment and signals that affect other cells. In this volume, Wachtel (Chapter 7) reviews a number of examples of known and postulated cell surface interactions that may regulate specific developmental events. Moscona and Linser (Chapter 6) give many important experimental insights into interactions of glial Müller cells and neurons in the developing neural retina. Most significantly they demonstrate that not only is the expression of specific phenotypes dependent on specific histotypic cellular relationships, but that even after a differentiated phenotype is attained, its maintenance requires continued specific cell interactions.

Mangiarotti *et al.* (Chapter 5) add information highly relevant to the Moscona and Linser chapter. In studies of cell contact and gene expression in *Dictyostelium,* Mangiarotti and colleagues show that the formation of specific cell contacts is dependent on a number of developmentally regulated cell surface proteins, and furthermore that the cell associations thus formed are essential both for the subsequent transcription and the stability of about 2500 mRNAs that are important in further differentiation.

Returning now to the mouse, and to the possible relevant of *t*-mutations for understanding environmental influences on the regulation of gene expression, let us consider what is to be a most striking example of the importance of the environment, which is contained in the "inside–outside" theory for the differentiation of the morula stage mammalian embryo to a blastocyst (Tarkowski and Wroblewska,

1967). This is an important event, since it represents the very first obvious step in the differentiation of mammalian embryos; in the morula all cells are equivalent and totipotent while in the blastocyst the outside cells are morphologically distinct, and have embarked on a pathway of terminal differentiation that will lead to their death when embryonic development is completed. Good experimental evidence demonstrates that the important difference between these two cell types is established by their relative positions. Outside cells, having one surface in contact with the fluid medium surrounding the embryo, differentiate into trophoblast; cells on the inside, completely surrounded by other cells, apparently remain in the original genetic state and retain totipotency. It also appears that subsequent events in early development depend on entirely comparable conditions, for example, the initiation of primary endoderm differentiation. An interesting corollary reinforces the importance of environmental influence for orderly early development; if the morphology of young embryos which still contain totipotent cells is disrupted, for example by transplanting them to ectopic sites, they readily produce teratocarcinomas, which contain a population of pluripotent malignant embryonal carcinoma cells (Stevens, 1964; Skreb *et al.*, 1972).

Interestingly, the lethal *t*-mutations that have been studied all have lethal periods during very early development, exactly during the time when totipotent cells are being channeled into definitive pathways of differentiation. In fact, it can be speculated that *t*-genes represent a genetic system specifically designed to crank down cells from totipotency to commitment, and a good deal of evidence suggests that this regulation is achieved through cell–cell interaction (Bennett, 1978). Although this conclusion is logically consistent with morphological data, it has been argued with by several authors who proposed an alternative hypothesis that *t*-mutations result in general cell lethality. On this hypothesis the apparent stage specificity of *t*-lethals was interpreted as an artifact produced by some generalized metabolic insufficiency, which eventually was limiting in some specific group of cells whose requirements for that particular metabolic pathway were by chance higher than other cells in the embryos. The cell lethality notion was based primarily on statistical evidence that cell lines from mutant embryos homozygous for t^0 or t^{w5} could not be established in tissue culture (Wudl and Sherman, 1976; Wundl *et al.*, 1977), although it could have been argued quite reasonably that adequate conditions had not been achieved for the survival of compromised mutant cells. In any case, the cell lethal hypothesis can clearly be dismissed now, since cell lines homozygous for t^{w5} have recently been reported (Magnuson *et al.,* 1982). An amusing aside to making conclusions about cell lethality from observations of cell lines derived from cultured embryos can be found in a recent paper by the group that originally proposed the idea that homozygosity for *t*-mutations results in cell lethality. In this case embryos were cultured from litters segregating *T/T, T/* +, and +/+, and t^{w18}/t^{w18}, $t^{w18}/$+, and +/+, and cell lines were produced that were either homozygous or heterozygous for *T*, or for t^{w18}, but none that were homozygous wild type (Hammerberg *et al.,* 1980). Thus following the previous reasoning with respect to cell lethality of t^{w5} homozygotes leads to the intriguing conclusion that under certain culture conditions the wild type genotype behaves as a cell-lethal!

But now to return to some details on cell interactions in *t*-mutants. The most dramatic example, perhaps, harks back to the first step in mammalian differentiation mentioned above, the morula-to-blastocyst transition. The earliest acting *t*-lethal known prevents this transition from occurring, apparently by interfering with the cell–cell interactions necessary for compaction of the morula and subsequent trophoblast differentiation. At least what we see is that in normal embryos junctions begin to form in maturing morulae, and eventually "zipper" the outside cells together with occluding junctions, while in t^{12} homozygotes only minimal and ineffective junctions appear at best.

It of course has been a high priority for us to try to identify the relevant cell surface molecules, so here let me emphasize again that the use of mutants provides a great potential advantage, since it should help us pinpoint the essential biochemical difference that determines success or failure in blastocyst development. The first approach we used was an immunogenetic one, and we prepared alloantisera against testicular cells on the principle that, since they are also affected by *t*-mutations, they could serve as an experimental substitute for embryonic cells, which we could not obtain in large enough quantity for immunization. To make a long story short, we succeeded in obtaining antisera which recognized unique constellations of antigens on sperm from heterozygotes of each of the different lethal *t*-mutations that we examined (Bennett *et al.,* 1972; Yanagisawa *et al.,* 1974; Artzt and Bennett, 1977). Furthermore, and very importantly, even though these antisera were operationally weak, we were able to use them in cytotoxicity inhibition assays to decide that the antigens they detected were primarily carbohydrate in nature (Cheng and Bennett, 1980). This finding raised a question that is as yet unanswered, namely, whether the mutations in the *T/t*-complex code for structurally abnormal proteins which are targets for aberrant glycosylation by normal glycosyltransferases, or whether the t-mutations code directly for abnormal glycosyltransferases.

So far we have pursued the information that t-antigens are carbohydrate only with respect to the antigen associated with the t^{12} lethal mutation, whose major immunodeterminant was defined as terminal galactose, and which we were therefore able to partially purify by Ricinus affinity columns. Heteroimmunization with the partially purified antigen yielded a quite specific rabbit antibody that was cytotoxic for $t^{12}/+$ testicular cells but not for wild type cells. Immuno-precipitations with this antibody from both testicular cells and embryos yield specifically an 87-kd glycoprotein that is about half carbohydrate from both $t^{12}/+$ and $+/+$ cells, but which is more heavily galactosylated, by a factor of two to three times, when it is obtained from t^{12}-bearing cells. The expression of this molecule is developmentally regulated in embryos and its expression peaks before morula compaction occurs (Cheng et al., 1982). In any case, because of its developmental regulation, as well as its different glycosylation pattern, it seems very likely indeed that the 87-kd protein plays a role in preblastocyst development, and is altered by the t^{12} mutation. Work in progress now to determine the protein and carbohydrate structure of this interesting molecule should give us additional insights into its genetic specification and developmental function.

So far the questions addressed in the conspectus have concentrated on how genes may be organized or reorganized to permit and promote their function, and the phenomenology of how cells receive and utilize information coming from outside that ultimately affects gene expression. The hard question that follows upon these two is how transcription is actually regulated in eukaryotes, and that is an area in which there are many experimental observations but relatively few satisfactorily complete answers.

Lane (Chapter 4) explores some intriguing aspects of transcription of foreign genes in *Xenopus* oocytes, which have traditionally been so useful as translation machines for foreign RNAs. The new information given here shows that isolated genes injected into oocyte nuclei are both transcribed and translated, apparently within the limits of the processing equipment available within the oocyte, even when they come from other species or are genes that normally would be expressed only in specific differentiated cell types. On the other hand, intact nuclei even from differentiated cells of other species, when injected into the cytoplasm, lose the expression of products typical of their differentiated state and begin to produce oocyte-specific proteins. The most important message here must be that under normal circumstances genes are prisoners of the cell they reside in, and that the nuclear or chromosomal organization, upon which they are dependent for expression, depends in turn on cytoplasmic conditions acquired during the developmental history of their cell. The other side of the coin is that when they are stripped of whatever nuclear or chromosomal baggage they acquire during differentiation, and added naked to a functioning nucleus, genes are in most cases readily expressed but, significantly, are most often refractory to the usual positive and negative controls. As Ciliberto *et al.* (Chapter 3) point out, these naked genes can be dissected with recombinant DNA methods and used in the *Xenopus* oocyte transcriptional system to identify and define specific promoter sequences necessary for transcription.

One wonders in the context mentioned above, of intricate interplay between cytoplasm and nucleus, whether developmental genetics could offer some way of dissecting the rules that determine gene expression. It is well known for example that many developmentally important genes, and the mutations in the *T/t*-complex are no exceptions, often have pleiotropic effects, e.g., they produce diverse and often seemingly unrelated abnormalities. It could be speculated, in such situations, that one mutant gene, with an abnormal or absent gene product, might set up cellular conditions which result in inappropriate expression of other, normal, genes. Time will tell.

This review is being written at a time when both information and insights relevant to developmental biology are emerging in an explosion of new experiments in molecular biology. This reviewer regrets the necessity, as I am sure all other authors in this volume do also, of writing a story that no doubt will be sadly incomplete by the time this volume is published.

REFERENCES

Artzt, K., and Bennett, D. (1977). *Immunogenetics* **5**, 97–107.

Artzt, K., McCormick, P., and Bennett, D. (1982). *Cell* **28**, 463–470.

Bennett, D. (1975). *Cell* **6**, 441–454.

Bennett, D. (1978). *In* "Birth Defects" (J. W. Littlefield, J. de Grouchy, and F. J. G. Ebling, eds.), pp. 169–177. Excerpta Medica, Amsterdam.

Bennett, D., Goldberg, E., Dunn, L. C., and Boyse, E. A. (1972). *Proc. Natl. Acad. Sci. U.S.A.* **69**, 2076–2080.

Boveri, T. (1910). *Arch. Entwmech.* **30**, 101–125.

Cheng, C. C., and Bennett, D. (1980). *Cell* **19**, 537–544.

Cheng, C. C., Bennett, D., and Artzt, K. (1982). Submitted.

Dobrovolskaia-Zavadskaia, N. (1927). *C.R. Soc. Biol.* **97**, 114–119.

Geyer-Duszynska, I. (1959). *J. Exp. Zool.* **141**, 391–448.

Hammerberg, C., Wudl, L. R., and Sherman, M. I. (1980). *Transplantation* **29**, 484–486.

Hozumi, N., and Tonegawa, S. (1976). *Proc. Natl. Acad. Sci. U.S.A.* **73**, 3628–3632.

Jacob, F., and Monod, J. (1963). *In* "Cytodifferentiation and Macromolecular Synthesis" (M. Locke, ed.), p. 30. Academic Press, New York.

Magnuson, T., Epstein, C. J., Silver, L. M., and Martin, G. R. (1982). *Nature (London)* **298**, 750–753.

Shin, H-S, Stavnezer, J., Artzt, K., and Bennett, D. (1982a). *Cell* **29**, 969–976.

Shin, H-S., McCormick, P., Artzt, K., and Bennett, D. (1982b). In preparation.

Skreb, N., Damjanov, I., and Solter, D. (1972). *In* "Cell Differentiation" (R. Harris, P. Alin, and D. Viza, eds.), pp. 151–155. Munksgaard, Copenhagen.

Stevens, L. C. (1964). *Proc. Natl. Acad. Sci. U.S.A.* **52**, 654–661.

Tarkowski, A., and Wrobleska, J. (1967). *J. Embryol. Exp. Morphol.* **18**, 155–180.

Weatherall, D. J., and Clegg, J. B. (1982). *Cell* **29**, 7–9.

Wudl, L. R., and Sherman, M. I. (1976). *Cell* **9**, 523–531.

Wudl, L. R., Sherman, M. I., and Hillman, N. (1977). *Nature (London)* **170**, 137–140.

Yanagisawa, K., Bennett, D., Boyse, E. A., Dunn, L. C., and DiMeo, A. (1974). *Immunogenetics* **1**, 57–67.

CURRENT TOPICS IN

DEVELOPMENTAL BIOLOGY

VOLUME 18

GENOME FUNCTION, CELL INTERACTIONS, AND DIFFERENTIATION

CHAPTER 1

CELLULAR DIFFERENTIATION, CELL LINEAGES, AND TRANSPOSABLE GENETIC CASSETTES IN YEAST

Ira Herskowitz

DEPARTMENT OF BIOCHEMISTRY AND BIOPHYSICS
UNIVERSITY OF CALIFORNIA, SAN FRANCISCO
SAN FRANCISCO, CALIFORNIA

I. Introduction

Understanding development in multicellular organisms requires an understanding of the mechanisms responsible for production of stably differentiated cells. Studies of the unicellular eukaryote, the yeast *Saccharomyces cerevisiae,* provide new information on mechanisms responsible for producing specialized cells, mechanisms that may operate in multicellular eukaryotes as well. In yeast, a single genetic locus—the mating type locus (*MAT*)—codes for regulatory proteins that control expression of cell-type-specific genes elsewhere in the yeast genome. Cells with the α allele (*MATα*) thus express the specialized functions of an α cell, cells with the **a** allele (*MAT***a**) express the specialized functions of an **a** cell, and cells with both *MAT***a** and *MATα* express the specialized functions of an **a**/α cell. A remarkable feature of yeast is that cells can switch to the opposite type of cell, in a process involving rearrangement of the genetic information at the mating type locus (Harashima *et al.,* 1974; Hicks *et al.,* 1977a). In addition to the block of **a** or α genetic information at the mating type locus (what we call a genetic "cassette"), the yeast genome contains **a** and α cassettes that are silent. Replacement of an α cassette at *MAT* with an **a** cassette leads to a switch of cell type from α to **a**. Switches from **a** to α similarly occur by substitution of the **a** cassette at *MAT* with an α cassette derived from the silent locus. The process of cassette substitution is exquisitely controlled, taking place only in certain cells of a clonal

1

population (so-called "experienced" cells), at a particular stage of the cell cycle (early S), and only in certain types (in a and α, but not in a/α cells). Yeast cell types are thus determined by a genetic locus which is itself subject to control by genetic rearrangement.

This article shall consider current work and views on three topics: (1) cell type determination by the mating type locus; (2) switching of cell types by cassette transposition; and (3) control of the switching process.

In general, only the most recent references have been cited in the text; others can be found in two recent reviews (Herskowitz $et\ al.$, 1980; Herskowitz and Oshima, 1981).

II. Cell Type Determination

Yeast has three cell types—a, α, and a/α—that differ from each other in several respects. Cell types a and α are the mating types: haploid cells of opposite type mate efficiently with each other to form a/α diploids. a/α cells are unable to mate with either a or α cells, but unlike a or α (or a/a and α/α diploid cells), can be induced to undergo meiosis and sporulation (which yields 2 a and 2 α spores). These three cell types also differ in several other respects, for example, in pheromone production and in agglutination. Each haploid cell type produces an oligopeptide pheromone—α-factor by α cells and a-factor by a cells—that acts specifically on cells of the opposite mating type to cause arrest in the G_1 phase of the cell cycle. These factors appear to coordinate the cell cycles of mating partners prior to cell and nuclear fusion. a/α cells produce neither factor and respond to neither factor. a and α cells likewise agglutinate with each other; a/α cells do not agglutinate with any cell type. A primary goal in our work has been to understand the molecular mechanisms which determine that these three cells produce their particular constellation of phenotypes.

It has been known for decades that one locus, the mating type locus (MAT), determines the cell type: $MAT\alpha$ cells are α, $MAT a$ cells are a, and $MAT a/MAT\alpha$ cells are a/α. MacKay and Manney (1974) identified four genes unlinked to the mating type locus that are necessary for mating and proposed that the mating type locus in some way controls expression of these genes. We have studied mutations of MAT and elsewhere and formulated a specific hypothesis (the "$\alpha1-\alpha2$ hypothesis"; Fig. 1) by which this control occurs (Strathern $et\ al.$, 1981).

$MAT\alpha$ codes for two putative regulatory genes, $MAT\alpha1$ and $MAT\alpha2$ (Strathern $et\ al.$, 1981; Nasmyth $et\ al.$, 1981b). The $\alpha1$ protein turns on expression of certain unlinked genes (α-specific genes, "αsg"), which are required for mating by α cells; $\alpha2$ turns off expression of certain

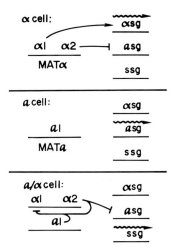

Fɪɢ. 1. Control of cell type by the mating type locus: $\alpha1-\alpha2$ hypothesis. The three panels show genes expressed in α, **a**, and **a**/α cells. αsg, α-specific genes; **a**sg, **a**-specific genes; ssg, sporulation and other genes specific to **a**/α cells. Wavy line indicates expression of the genes; line with arrowhead indicates stimulation of expression; lines with blunt head indicate inhibition of expression. Expression of ssg genes is described further in Fig. 2. Expression of genes that are expressed in **a** and α but not in **a**/α cells (nonmating type-specific genes, nsg) is not shown; they are proposed to be negatively regulated by **a**$1-\alpha2$ (as shown for the $MAT\alpha1$ gene). Other details are given in the text. Reprinted from Strathern *et al.* (1981) with permission.

other unlinked genes (a-specific genes, "asg"), which are required for mating by **a** cells. α cells thus express their proper set of α-specific functions.

MAT**a** codes for one regulator, **a**1, whose role is discussed below. MAT**a** cells express a-specific genes because they lack $\alpha2$ to turn these genes off; they do not express α-specific genes because they lack $\alpha1$ to turn these genes on.

MAT**a**/$MAT\alpha$ cells express their unique set of phenotypes because of the actions of both **a**1 and $\alpha2$ products. These products—perhaps acting as a complex (**a**$1-\alpha2$)—turn off transcription of $\alpha1$ (Nasmyth *et al.*, 1981a; Klar *et al.*, 1981a). Hence, α-specific genes are not expressed. a-specific genes are turned off by action of $\alpha2$ as in $MAT\alpha$ haploid strains. **a**/α cells are thus unable to mate. Why do they sporulate? An appealing hypothesis (Rine *et al.*, 1981b) is that the **a**$1-\alpha2$ complex turns off expression of a sporulation regulator, the product of the RME 1 gene, which inhibits sporulation (Fig. 2). In other words, **a** and α cells produce this sporulation inhibitor, whereas **a**/α cells do not and are thus able to sporulate.

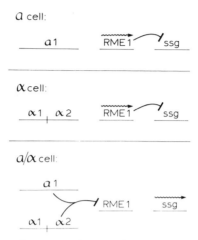

Fɪɢ. 2. Control of sporulation-specific genes by the *RME*1 gene product. The three panels show expression of the *RME*1 gene in **a**, α, and **a**/α cells. Symbols are as in Fig. 1. The *RME*1 gene product is produced in **a** and α cells but not in **a**/α cells. Reprinted from Rine *et al.* (1981b) with permission.

A variety of genetic tests of this hypothesis have been performed (Strathern *et al.*, 1981; Sprague and Herskowitz, 1981; Sprague *et al.*, 1981) and will not be discussed here. We have recently cloned an α-specific gene (called *STE*3) and studied control of its transcription (Sprague *et al.*, 1982). We find that *STE*3 RNA is produced only in α cells and not in **a** or in **a**/α cells. Furthermore, this RNA is synthesized by $\alpha2^-$ mutants but not by $\alpha1^-$ mutants. These results show that the mating type locus controls expression of the *STE*3 at the level of RNA production (for example, by controlling transcription initiation or RNA stability or processing). Likewise these results show that $\alpha1$ is a positive regulator of RNA synthesis; in other words, $\alpha1$ is a putative activator protein. We have also recently cloned the structural gene for α-factor (which is synthesized as a precursor with multiple copies of the mature α-factor) (Kurjan and Herskowitz, 1982) and are now in a position to assay its transcription in different cell types and mutants. Future studies on $\alpha1$ and the other mating type locus products should prove informative in understanding the mechanisms by which these regulators turn on and off genes such as *STE*3 and α-factor.

III. Mating Type Interconversion

Yeast strains differ in the stability of their mating type. Those carrying the *HO* gene (and appropriate accessory genes discussed below) change mating types nearly every cell division. In contrast, cells

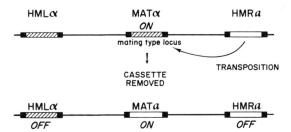

FIG. 3. The cassette mechanism of mating type interconversion. The structure of chromosome III of an α cell is shown on the upper line; the structure of chromosome III after switching to become an **a** cell is shown on the lower line. Open and cross-hatched rectangles indicate DNA segments unique to the **a** and α cassettes, respectively. Black rectangles indicate homologous sequences flanking the unique regions that may participate in the transposition event. *ON* and *OFF* indicate expression of the cassettes located at *MAT, HML,* and *HMR.*

with the recessive, *ho* allele change mating types only at low frequency, approximately one per million cells. The switch in mating type in both cases reflects a change in the mating type locus itself. Thus a switch from α to **a** is caused by a genetic change from *MAT*α to *MAT***a**. The switch from one mating type to another indicates that all yeast cells must contain the information for both *MAT*α and *MAT***a**. An original proposal was that the mating type locus itself harbored both **a** and α regulators which were expressed mutually exclusively. Another hypothesis (Fig. 3) proposed that the mating type locus contained only one type of regulatory information, an **a** regulatory block or an α regulatory block, and that elsewhere in the genome were silent copies of this regulatory information (Hicks *et al.,* 1977a). The silent α mating locus information was proposed to be present at the *HML*α locus, which had been identified as required for switching from **a** to α (see Harashima *et al.,* 1974), and the silent **a** mating locus information was proposed to be present at the *HMR***a** locus, which was required for switching from α to **a**. We termed these genetic blocks "cassettes" because they are expressed only when located at the mating type locus, which acts like the playback head of a tape recorder, and not expressed when the cassettes are located at storage loci *HML* and *HMR*. Mating type switching thus occurs by removing the cassette at the mating type locus and replacing it with a cassette derived from *HML* or *HMR*.

We have shown that the cassette that is removed from the mating type locus is discarded (Rine *et al.,* 1981a). It had earlier been shown that the information at *HML* and *HMR* remains intact after mating type interconversion (Harashima *et al.,* 1974). The cassette substitution process thus is a unidirectional transfer of information from *HML* or *HMR* to *MAT*. A plausible mechanism for such a process involves invasion of the duplex DNA cassette at *MAT* with a single strand from the cassette at *HML* or *HMR,* followed by appropriate splicing and resynthesis (see, for example, Klar *et al.,* 1980). More recent work, however, indicates that mating type interconversion is initiated by a double-stranded break at the mating type locus (Strathern *et al.,* 1982).

The movement of information from the storage loci to the mating type locus can be demonstrated by the following two examples of transfer, the first of which was crucial in giving rise to the cassette model, the second being a test of the model:

1. Mutations of *MAT*α and *MAT***a** are corrected ("healed") by mating type interconversion: for example, *HO HML*α *mat*α1⁻ (or *mat*α2⁻) *HMR***a** strains switch efficiently to *HO HML*α *MAT*α *HMR***a.**

2. The mating type locus is mutated ("wounded") by mating type interconversion in strains with defects in *HML* or *HMR:* for example, *HO hml*α⁻ *MAT*α *HMR***a** strains switch efficiently to *HO hml*α⁻ *mat*α⁻ *HMR***a.**

A physical confirmation of the cassette model has come from analysis of cloned *MAT*α, *MAT***a,** *HML*α, and *HMR***a** DNA segments (Hicks *et al.,* 1979; Nasmyth and Tatchell, 1980; Strathern *et al.,* 1980; Nasmyth *et al.,* 1981b). These studies show that *MAT*α and *HML*α share a unique sequence of 747 basepairs that is not present in *MAT***a** and *HMR***a,** and that *MAT***a** and *HMR***a** share a unique sequence of 642 basepairs that is not present at *MAT*α and *HML*α.

A key aspect of controlling yeast cell type by genetic cassettes is that only the cassette at *MAT* is expressed; those at *HML* and *HMR* are not. A clue as to why these latter cassettes are silent comes from studies of mutations occurring in any of four *SIR* (Silent Information Regulator) genes, which allow expression of the ordinarily silent cassettes (Fig. 4) (Rine *et al.,* 1979; Klar *et al.,* 1979; Haber and George, 1979; Rine, 1979). The *SIR* gene products thus act as negative regulators of expression of cassettes at *HML* and *HMR*. We do not yet know whether the *SIR* gene products act only at *HML* and *HMR;* at this point, we know only that *sir⁻* mutants do not have any phenotypes other than allowing expression of *HML* and *HMR*. The *SIR* gene products have been recently found to turn off the storage cassettes by blocking RNA synthesis from these cassettes (Klar *et al.,* 1981a; Nasmyth *et al.,* 1981a). How they exert this control may be particularly intriguing. Transcription of the cassettes appears to be initiated from within the cassettes several hundred basepairs from where the *SIR* gene products

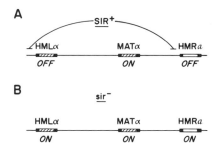

FIG. 4. Inhibition of expression of cassettes at *HML* and *HMR* by the *SIR* gene products. (A) Cassettes at *HML* and *HMR* are not expressed due to action of *SIR* gene products near *HML* and *HMR* in wild-type (*SIR*$^+$) strains. (B) Cassettes at *HML* and *HMR* are expressed in mutants defective in any of the four *SIR* genes.

have been proposed to act. One way for this to occur would be for the *SIR* gene products to control chromatin structure, for example, by causing condensation of the genetic neighborhood around *HML* and *HMR*. Tests of this hypothesis are underway in a number of laboratories.

IV. Control of Mating Type Interconversion

Mating type interconversion is controlled at many different levels. Several of these controls have been identified by cell lineage studies in which changes of cell type are observed during the growth of a clone of *HO* cells (Hicks and Herskowitz, 1976; Strathern and Herskowitz, 1979). Two aspects of yeast have allowed us to perform cell lineage studies: (1) Because yeast cells grow by budding, it is straightforward to distinguish mother and daughter cells after each cell division. These cells can be separated by micromanipulation and tested for their mating type, and in some cases then allowed to undergo further cell divisions. (2) α and **a** cells are easily distinguished from each other by determining their response to α-factor: α cells are not affected, whereas **a** cells become arrested in the G$_1$ phase of the cell cycle and subsequently exhibit a characteristic cell morphology.

For cell lineage studies performed in the continuous presence of α-factor, **a** cells are analogous to terminally differentiated cells, because they are unable to continue cell division in the presence of α-factor (other analogies are discussed below). Our earliest cell lineage studies (Hicks and Herskowitz, 1976) were of this sort and yielded the following results (see Fig. 5). Beginning with an α *HO* spore, cell division always produced two α cells (denoted as "S" and its first daughter "D1"). The S cell at this stage [the two-cell stage; S(2)] often gave rise

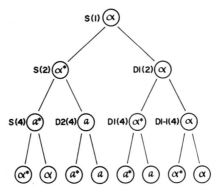

FIG. 5. Switching pattern of a yeast cell of genotype *HO HMLα MATα HMR* a. Mother and daughter cells are separated by micromanipulation (as described in the text, with mother cells drawn to the left and daughter cells to the right). **a** and α cells are distinguished by their response to α-factor. S, spore cell; D1, the spore's first daughter; D2, the spore's second daughter; D1-1, the first daughter of D1. Numbers in parentheses indicate the stage (1-cell, 2-cell, 4-cell). Cells with an asterisk are experienced cells. A lineage is shown in which S(2), S(4), and D1(4) have given rise to switched cells. Reprinted from Rine *et al.* (1981a) with permission.

to two **a** cells in its next cell division. Its daughter, D1(2), never gave rise to **a** cells in its first cell division. However, at its next division, D1 [D1(4)] often yielded two **a** cells. These early cell lineage studies revealed two surprising findings: (1) Cells in a clone differed in their ability to switch mating types: S(2) and D1(4) were competent to switch, whereas S(1) and D1(2) were not. (2) Products of any given cell division were always of the same mating type: either both remained α, or both had switched to **a.** These studies indicated that only cells that had undergone one cell division cycle were competent to switch. Subsequent analysis (Strathern and Herskowitz, 1979) showed that this one-generation delay was not a general requirement for all cells. In fact, cells were observed to switch as often as each cell division cycle. Additional cell lineages demonstrate these points. For example, the S cell in Fig. 5 switched from α to **a** to α in successive cell division cycles. In other words, the S(4) cell—which had just switched to **a**—does not require another cell division before switching again. From these types of studies, we formulated two rules of switching: (1) First, as noted above, the products of any cell division are always of the same mating type. (2) Second, there are two types of cells in a clone that differ in their ability to switch mating type: Cells that have undergone at least one cell division cycle (and become "experienced" cells) are competent to switch; cells that have not yet undergone at least one cell division cycle ("inexperienced" cells) are not competent to switch. A quantitative analysis showed that experienced cells switch in 73% of their cell divisions and that inexperienced cells switched in fewer than 0.1% of their cell division. Furthermore, the switching frequencies from α to **a** and from **a** to α were identical.

The pattern of switching thus reveals several types of control of the switching process:

1. Because cells of changed mating type always occur in pairs, the switching event—the genetic rearrangement leading to cassette substitution—must occur before the mating type locus is duplicated during S. Cells then have the remainder of the cell division cycle (until the next G_1) to remove the old mating apparatus and to synthesize the new mating apparatus. (The conclusion that the genetic change occurs before the mating type locus is duplicated is derived also from observations of switching in *MATa/MATa* and *MATα/MATα* cells; Hicks *et al.*, 1977b.)

2. Cells differ in their competence to switch mating types: at each cell division there is an asymmetric segregation of potential for mating type interconversion. A yeast clone by definition thus contains a lineage of experienced and inexperienced cells (Fig. 6A). Whether all experienced cells are competent to switch (to produce cell lineages shown in Fig. 6B) is unknown (see Strathern and Herskowitz, 1979; Rine *et al.*, 1981a, for discussion). We do not yet know the basis for this asymmetric division of switching potential. Studies on mitotic dis-

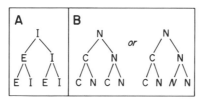

FIG. 6. Cell lineages for experienced and inexperienced cells and for competent and noncompetent cells. The initial cell is analogous to a yeast spore cell (see Fig. 5). Mothers are drawn to the left, and daughters to the right at each cell division. (A) I, Inexperienced cells (cells that have not undergone at least one cell division cycle); E, experienced cells (cells that have undergone at least one cell division cycle). Each cell division, by definition, produces one E cell and one I cell. (B) N, Noncompetent cells (cells that are not competent to switch mating types in their next cell division); C, competent cells (cells that are competent to switch mating types in their next cell division). If *all* experienced cells are competent to switch, the lineage on the left is obtained. If not all experienced cells are competent to switch (such as the *N* cell at the four-cell stage), the lineage on the right is obtained. Whether all experienced cells are competent is not known.

tribution of DNA strands do not provide an explanation consistent with the switching pattern (Williamson and Fennell, 1981). Because mother cells are initially larger than daughter cells (Hartwell and Unger, 1977), perhaps the mother cells accumulate a product necessary for mating type interconversion that is limiting in inexperienced cells.

3. Because competent cells switch to the opposite mating type in greater than 50% of their cell divisions, it is clear that the heterologous cassette is chosen preferentially for substitution. The molecular basis for this "directionality" of switching is not yet understood, but does not result simply from monitoring the heterology of the cassette. This conclusion comes from a comparison of switching by HO $MAT\alpha$ cells that have either the standard library of silent cassettes ($HML\alpha$ HMR **a**) or a library with **a** and α cassettes in reverse positions (HML**a** $HMR\alpha$) (Rine et al., 1981a). In the standard set-up ($HML\alpha$ HMR **a**), experienced α cells switch to **a** at the usual high frequency [in this analysis, 86% switching by the S(2) cells]. In contrast, experienced α cells that are HML**a** $HMR\alpha$ switch to **a** in only 5% of their cell divisions. Efficient switching to **a** thus requires more than simply an **a** cassette present in the genome. Recent work indicates that strains that are $MAT\alpha$ preferentially mobilize the cassette at HMR and that strains that are MAT**a** preferentially mobilize the cassette from HML (Klar et al., 1982). One way for such a discrimination to occur would be for a product of the mating type locus, for example, $\alpha 2$ product, to prevent transposition of the cassette at HML or to stimulate transposition of the cassette at HMR.

Although the molecular bases for the switching pattern are not understood, several perturbations of the switching pattern and of the switching process have recently been observed. In particular, the switching pattern by one sir^- mutant exhibits three aberrations (Klar et al., 1981b): (1) The cassettes at MAT and HML or HMR no longer behave properly in the cassette substitution process—often the cassette at MAT donates its information to HML or HMR and thereby replaces the cassettes residing at these loci. The state of expression of MAT and the silent cassette loci or the presence of the SIR gene products per se thus determine the nature of the genetic rearrangement event. (2) Cells of changed mating type do not always occur in pairs. (3) Inexperienced cells are able to switch mating types. Whether these behaviors of sir^- mutants reflect alterations of the normal process or superimposing of an unnatural pathway of switching remains to be determined.

One additional level of control of the switching process is known: switching occurs in **a** and α cells but not in **a**/α cells. Because switching occurs in **a/a** and α/α cells, the block in **a**/α cells is not due to diploidy per se. Rather, it is due to the functions of the mating type locus—the same functions of *MAT* (**a**1 and α2) that are required to inhibit mating and to stimulate sporulation are also necessary to turn off mating type interconversion (Strathern *et al.*, 1979). The basis for the inhibition of switching has recently been determined and is rather simple: the *HO* gene product is not made in **a**/α cells. We have recently cloned the *HO* gene and used it to probe for the production of *HO* RNA in cells active for switching or unable to switch and find that **a**/α cells fail to produce the RNA corresponding to the *HO* gene (Jensen *et al.*, 1982). Yeast cells therefore turn off the *HO* gene after it has yielded the final product of mating type interconversion, an **a**/α diploid.

V. Analogies to Processes Occurring in Development of Higher Eukaryotes

The pattern of switching by yeast *HO* cells has certain analogies with cell lineages observed in development of higher eukaryotes. To demonstrate these analogies, let us consider the switching pattern of an *HO MAT*α cell with the standard cassettes at *HML* and *HMR* (*HML*α and *HMR* **a**). Such a cell produces a lineage in which the first daughters (D1, D1-1, D1-1-1, etc.) form a stem cell line—these cells are always like their parent cell in being α, in being unable to switch mating types in their next cell division, and in acquiring ability to switch mating types after their next cell division (Fig. 7A). The **a** cells produced in such a lineage can switch back to α in subsequent cell divisions. However, if the genome contains only silent **a** cassettes (*HML***a** *HMR***a**), the **a** cells cannot switch back to **a** (Fig. 7B). In this

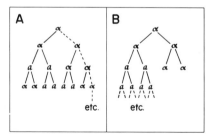

Fig. 7. Analogies of yeast cell lineages to stem cell lineages. The initial cell is a *MAT*α *HO* spore. Lineages are drawn as in Fig. 5. (A) Cell lineage for a cell that has the standard constitution of cassettes at *HML* and *HMR* (*HML*α *HMR***a**). Dotted lines indicate that the first daughters form a stem cell line. (B) Cell lineages for a cell that has only silent **a** cassettes at *HML* and *HMR* (*HML***a***HMR***a**). In this case, cells that switch to **a** cannot switch back to α and thus undergo an irreversible "differentiation."

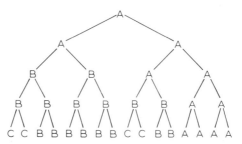

Fig. 8. Production of multiple cell types by sequential cassette insertion. A, B, and C are different cell types determined by the presence of the corresponding cassette at the genomic "playback locus". A cells program the insertion of a B cassette, and B cells program the insertion of a C cassette. The rules for yeast switching (see Fig. 5) have been used to produce this particular cell lineage. Reprinted from Herskowitz *et al.* (1980) with permission.

case, these **a** cells are analogous to stably differentiated cells. (As noted earlier, in the presence of α factor, these **a** cells are like terminally differentiated cells incapable of further cell division.)

The yeast genome contains a library with two silent cassettes, allowing a yeast cell to switch between two different cell types. A genome with more than two such cassettes would of course allow a cell to switch to a corresponding number of different cell types. For example, if the genome contained silent cassettes $A, B, C \ldots Z$, it could switch from a cell of type A to a cell of type B by removing an A cassette from a "playback locus" (analogous to the yeast mating type locus) and replacing it with a B cassette. We have seen that the cassette substitution process in yeast exhibits directionality—the cassette at MAT is preferentially replaced by a heterologous cassette. Similarly, an A cassette at the playback locus could program its own removal by a B cassette, and the B cassette could program its removal by a C cassette, etc. Such a process of sequential cassette insertion could therefore generate a sequential appearance of cell types within a clone (Fig. 8; discussed further in Strathern and Herskowitz, 1979; Herskowitz *et al.*, 1980).

VI. Concluding Comments

The control of cell type determination in yeast provides an example of two important gene control processes: First, it shows that the mating type locus is the cellular master regulatory locus that determines cell type. Studies of the molecular mechanisms by which the products of the mating type locus act promise to reveal much about the way in which eukaryotic genes are regulated. Second, these studies show how such a master regulatory locus is itself controlled—in this case by the position of the genetic cassette in the genome. Genetic studies of sex determination in *Drosophila* and nematodes are revealing other master organismal regulatory loci (Baker and Ridge, 1980; Hodgkin, 1980). Do they code for analogs of $\alpha 1$, $\alpha 2$, and $a1$? How is their expression controlled?

ACKNOWLEDGMENTS

I gratefully acknowledge the people in my laboratory for their contributions to this work: Jim Hicks, Jeff Strathern, Peter Kushner, Buff Blair, Jasper Rine, George Sprague, Jr., Rob Jensen, and Janet Kurjan. I also thank Casaendra Young for preparation of this manuscript. Work from my laboratory has been supported by Research Grants and a Research Career Development Award from the National Institutes of Health.

REFERENCES

Baker, B. S., and Ridge, K. A. (1980). *Genetics* **94**, 383–423.
Haber, J. E., and George, J. P. (1979). *Genetics* **93**, 13–35.
Harashima, S., Nogi, Y., and Oshima, Y. (1974). *Genetics* **77**, 639–650.
Hartwell, L. H., and Unger, M. W. (1977). *J. Cell Biol.* **75**, 422–435.
Herskowitz, I., and Oshima, Y. (1981). *In* "Molecular Biology of the Yeast *Saccharomyces:* Life Cycle and Inheritance" (J. N. Strathern, E. W. Jones, and J. R. Broach, eds.), pp. 181–209. Cold Spring Harbor Lab., Cold Spring Harbor, New York.
Herskowitz, I., Blair, L., Forbes, D., Hicks, J., Kassir, Y., Kushner, P., Rine, J., Sprague, G., Jr., and Strathern, J. (1980). *In* "The Molecular Genetics of Development" (W. Loomis and T. Leighton, eds.), pp. 79–118. Academic Press, New York.
Hicks, J. B., and Herskowitz, I. (1976). *Genetics* **83**, 245–258.
Hicks, J. B., Strathern, J. N., and Herskowitz, I. (1977a). *In* "DNA Insertion Elements, Plasmids, and Episomes" (A. I. Bukhari, J. Shapiro, and S. Adhya, eds.), pp. 457–462. Cold Spring Harbor Lab., Cold Spring Harbor, New York.
Hicks, J. B., Strathern, J. N., and Herskowitz, I. (1977b). *Genetics* **85**, 395–405.
Hicks, J., Strathern, J., and Klar, A. (1979). *Nature (London)* **282**, 478–483.
Hodgkin, J. (1980). *Genetics* **96**, 649–664.
Jensen, R., Sprague, G., Jr., and Herskowitz, I. (1982). *Proc. Natl. Acad. Sci. U.S.A.,* in press.
Klar, A. J. S., Fogel, S., and MacLeod, K. (1979). *Genetics* **93**, 37–50.
Klar, A. J. S., McIndoo, J., Strathern, J. N., and Hicks, J. B. (1980). *Cell* **22**, 291–298.
Klar, A. J. S., Strathern, J. N., Broach, J. B., and Hicks, J. B. (1981a). *Nature (London)* **289**, 239–244.
Klar, A. J. S., Strathern, J. N., and Hicks, J. B. (1981b). *Cell* **25**, 517–524.
Klar, A. J. S., Hicks, J. B., and Strathern, J. N. (1982). *Cell* **28**, 551–561.
Kurjan, J., and Herskowitz, I. (1982). *Cell,* in press.
MacKay, V. L., and Manney, T. R. (1974). *Genetics* **76**, 273–288.
Nasmyth, K., and Tatchell, K. (1980). *Cell* **17**, 753–764.
Nasmyth, K. A., Tatchell, K., Hall, B. D., Astell, C., and Smith, M. (1981a). *Nature (London)* **289**, 244–250.
Nasmyth, K. A., Tatchell, K., Hall, B. D., Astell, C., and Smith, M. (1981b). *Cold Spring Harbor Symp. Quant. Biol.* **45**, 961–981.
Rine, J. D. (1979). Ph.D. thesis, University of Oregon, Eugene, Orgeon.
Rine, J., Strathern, J. N., Hicks, J. B., and Herskowitz, I. (1979). *Genetics* **93**, 877–901.

Rine, J., Jensen, R., Hagen, D., Blair, L., and Herskowitz, I. (1981a). *Cold Spring Harbor Symp. Quant. Biol.* **45,** 951–960.

Rine, J., Sprague, G. F., Jr., and Herskowitz, I. (1981b). *Mol. Cell. Biol.* **1,** 958–960.

Sprague, G. F., Jr., and Herskowitz, I. (1981). *J. Mol. Biol.* **153,** 305–321.

Sprague, G. F., Jr., Rine, J., and Herskowitz, I. (1981). *J. Mol. Biol.* **153,** 323–335.

Sprague, G. F., Jr., Jensen, R., and Herskowitz, I. (1982). *Cell,* in press.

Strathern, J. N., and Herskowitz, I. (1979). *Cell* **17,** 371–381.

Strathern, J. N., Blair, L. C., and Herskowitz, I. (1979). *Proc. Natl. Acad. Sci. U.S.A.* **76,** 3425–3429.

Strathern, J. N., Spatola, E., McGill, C., and Hicks, J. B. (1980). *Proc. Natl. Acad. Sci. U.S.A.* **77,** 2839–2843.

Strathern, J. N., Hicks, J. B., and Herskowitz, I. (1981). *J. Mol. Biol.* **147,** 357–372.

Williamson, D. H., and Fennell, D. J. (1981). *In* "Molecular Genetics in Yeast" (D. von Wettstein, J. Friis, M. Kielland-Brandt, and A. Stenderup, eds.), pp. 89–102. Munksgaard, Copenhagen.

CHAPTER 2

IMMUNOGLOBULIN GENE REARRANGEMENT AND EXPRESSION DURING LYMPHOCYTE DEVELOPMENT

Rolf Joho,* Carol Nottenburg,† Robert L. Coffman,‡ and Irving L. Weissman†

* INSTITUTE OF PATHOLOGY
DIVISION OF EXPERIMENTAL PATHOLOGY
UNIVERSITY HOSPITAL
ZURICH, SWITZERLAND

† LABORATORY OF EXPERIMENTAL ONCOLOGY
DEPARTMENT OF PATHOLOGY
STANFORD UNIVERSITY
STANFORD, CALIFORNIA

‡ DNAX RESEARCH INSTITUTE
PALO ALTO, CALIFORNIA

*CURRENT TOPICS IN
DEVELOPMENTAL BIOLOGY, VOL. 18*

I. Introduction

Higher animals possess a very elaborate system of defense mechanisms—the immune system—that allows the organism to detect and inactivate invading parasites such as viruses, bacteria, fungi, protozoae, etc., and to counteract the sometimes deleterious effects of foreign substances such as toxins, cell surface molecules, etc. The immune system must therefore be able to recognize and respond to non-self molecules while preventing such responses to self molecules, and to encode and express the information which allows the immune system to recognize and distinguish between a virtually unlimited number of different foreign determinants (antigens). Both of these properties of the immune system provide *unique* challenges in terms of the developmental biology of such a recognition system, and therefore we shall concentrate this article on the recent advances in the molecular genetics, including diversification and expression, of antigen-recognition molecules (mainly antibodies) of the immune system within the context of the differentiation of receptor-bearing cells (lymphocytes).

When an animal encounters a foreign molecule—an antigen—it can mount an immune response. Such an immune response can be divided into two parts: a humoral and a cellular response. The humoral immune response is mediated by B lymphocytes that recognize unique antigens and differentiate into antibody-secreting plasma cells. These antibodies are mainly used to combat free-floating antigens, e.g., the extracellular phase of viral and bacterial infections. The B-cell antigen receptor is well understood. It is an antibody molecule embedded in the membrane. An individual B cell and its clonal progeny have the same antibody receptors and thus the same antigen-binding specificity. The receptors of other B cell clones are different. When an individual B cell encounters its antigen the cell is triggered into division to form expanded clones of B cells, some of which differentiate into plasma cells secreting antibodies of the same antigen-binding specificity. This antigen-dependent differentiation from B cells to plasma cells is preceded by antigen-independent differentiation steps that lead to the generation and expression of antigen-specific B-cell surface receptors. It is during this antigen-independent phase of B lymphocyte differentiation when the antigen-binding specificity is determined. Thus, the origin of antibody diversity can be studied by following cellular differentiation from an uncommitted pluripotent hematopoietic stem cell to a B lymphocyte displaying a cell surface receptor specific for a certain antigen. Following antigenic stimulation a large proportion of the clonal progeny of a particular B cell undergoes further maturation to memory B cells (rather than terminal differentiation to plasma cells). Memory B cells carry on their surface receptor immunoglobulins with the same or slightly altered antigen-binding specificity, but a different *class* of antibody. These memory B cells can be restimulated by antigen to produce plasma cells and more memory B cells. Each of the different *classes* of antibodies serves particular and different *functions,* and a central problem in the developmental biology of lymphocytes is the process by which a particular lineage of B cells can undergo a *switch* in the *class* of antibody it expresses while retaining the same antigen-binding specificity. Thus antigen-dependent B-cell differentiation involves two apparently unique events in developmental biology—the alteration of antigen-binding receptor specificity (probably by a *mutational* process), and the switch of the function of an antigen-binding receptor (by a *recombinational* process).

The cellular immune response is controlled and largely mediated by thymus-derived T lymphocytes. Immunocompetent T lymphocytes are effector cells of various functions (T helper cells, T suppressor cells, T killer cells, and T cells which are responsible for some types of inflammatory responses, etc.). The cellular immune response plays an important role during the intracellular phase of a viral infection, and against fungi, parasites, and tumor cells. Thus T lymphocytes focus their attention on infected cells and their cell-surface antigens, rather than free-floating antigens. The T lymphocytes possess a receptor system which has a complex specificity—the corecognition of antigens and the cells which they infect (or to which they are attached). Little is known about the molecular nature of antigen-specific T-cell receptors.

With this brief outline, it is clear that lymphocytes have a complicated life history, which utilizes a number of novel molecular genetic events to provide the needed flexibility to generate functionally appropriate and highly specific immune responses. While much of the information for the kinds of molecular–genetic events has been discovered by the fine analyses of *malignant* clones of lymphocytes, we have chosen to study the events from the perspective of developmental biologists following events in the ontogeny of normal B cells. Thus we have chosen to analyze the nature and distribution of inherited antibody genes by probing the germline (sperm), and to study developmentally regulated changes in these antibody genes by probing different stages in the differentiation of normal B lymphocytes.

II. Origin of Antibody Diversity

A. STRUCTURE AND FUNCTIONS OF ANTIBODY MOLECULES

1. General

An antibody molecule consists of the same number of light and heavy chains. (Kabat *et al.*, 1979) For most antibody types a pair of identical light chains and a different pair of identical heavy chains form a tetramer with several globular domains (Fig. 1). Antibody molecules have a dual function which is reflected in their structure. The two tips of the Y-shaped molecule bind the ligands (antigen) and represent the receptor part of the antibody. The effector part of the molecule represented by the stem of the Y structure consists of globular domains made up by the carboxy-terminal halves of the heavy chains. There are two types of light chains, lambda (λ) and kappa (κ), each about 220 amino acids in length. The carboxy-terminal halves of the light chains are identical, and either of the λ or κ type. Because this part of the light chain is identical for different antibody molecules of the same type it is called the light chain constant region (C_κ and C_λ). The amino-terminal half generally varies in its amino acid sequence for light chains of different antibody molecules. It is therefore called the variable region of the antibody (V_κ or V_λ). In the mouse, most light chains (95%) are of the κ type (Hood *et al.*, 1967). Contrary to the two types of light chains (κ and λ) there are eight types of heavy chains in mice: $\alpha, \gamma1, \gamma2a, \gamma2b, \gamma3, \delta, \epsilon,$ and μ. The heavy chain is about twice as long as the light chain. The amino-terminal quarter of the heavy chain varies in differ-

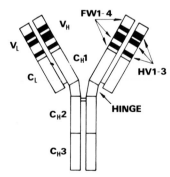

FIG. 1. Structure of the antibody molecule. V_L, C_L represent the variable and constant region part of the light chain. C_H1, C_H2, C_H3, and hinge denote the heavy chain region domains. V_L and V_H are structured into framework (FW 1–4) and hypervariable (HV 1–3) regions.

ent antibody molecules, whereas the remaining carboxy-terminal part is constant for a given type of heavy chain. Like the light chain the heavy chain also consists of a variable region (V_H) and a constant region (C_H). There are eight types of C_H regions C_α, $C_{\gamma 1}$, $C_{\gamma 2a}$, $C_{\gamma 2b}$, $C_{\gamma 3}$, C_δ, C_ϵ, and C_μ, corresponding to the eight types of heavy chains in the mouse. The two C_H regions of a heavy chain pair are always identical and they determine the class or isotype of the antibody. It is mainly the C_H region of the antibody molecule that determines its effector function.

2. Immunoglobulins as Receptors

Antibody molecules or immunoglobulins (Ig) can serve as cell surface receptor molecules (Vitetta *et al.*, 1971; Raff *et al.*, 1973; Julius and Herzenberg, 1974; Pernis *et al.*, 1974; Salsano *et al.*, 1974; Fu *et al.*, 1975). There are mainly two Ig isotypes, IgM and IgD (containing μ and δ heavy chains, respectively) that are present on the membrane of most B lymphocytes. These B cells display many thousands of IgM and IgD cell surface receptor molecules that can recognize antigen, the V_H regions of both μ and δ chains are identical to each other on a single cell (and differ from the V_H regions on any other cell), and the V_L regions on a particular cell are identical to each other. We will explain later how Ig molecules of two different isotypes (IgM and IgD) can contain the same V_H regions. Thus, a particular V_H–V_L combination is not only a marker for that particular immunoglobulin, but also for a particular B cell (Julius *et al.*, 1976). When such a B cell binds its cognate antigen the cell will start to proliferate, and a subset differentiates into antibody-secreting plasma cells (Melchers and Andersson, 1974). This secreted circulating serum immunoglobulin has the same antigen-binding specificity as the membrane IgM and IgD. Thus immunoglobulin receptors on B cells serve to screen the surrounding antigenic environment, and, when appropriately stimulated by antigen (and helper T cells), are triggered to activate their genetic programs for cellular proliferation (to produce clones) as well as for cellular differentiation to plasma cells. This type of precise cell-surface receptor control of proliferation and differentiation was first observed on lymphocytes and now serves as one of the most-studied models in developmental biology.

3. Immunoglobulins as Effectors

During differentiation the IgM- and IgD-producing B cell can switch to the production of immunoglobulins of different isotypes, for instance in mouse, IgG_1, IgG_{2a}, IgG_{2b}, IgG_3, IgA, and IgE (containing

$\gamma 1, \gamma 2a, \gamma 2b, \gamma, \alpha$, and ϵ heavy chains, respectively) (Pernis *et al.*, 1976). Although these immunoglobulins have different C_H regions they maintain the same antigen-binding specificity as the original IgM and IgD antibodies. The basis for this phenomenon—called heavy chain isotype switch—is the fact that the same V_H region can be expressed with different C_H regions during lymphocyte development. During this entire process the light chain remains the same. Therefore, the V region domains (V_H and V_L) that determine the antigen-binding specificity remain basically unaltered, although minor alterations of receptor specificity can occur via somatic mutation and selection.

4. Genetics of Immunoglobulins

The genetic regions that encode the various V_H and C_H regions are located on chromosome twelve of the mouse (Hengartner *et al.*, 1978). Although the loci coding for the different C_H regions are tightly linked, genetic recombination studies have indicated that loci coding for V_H regions are separated from the loci coding for C_H. The κ light chain genes have been mapped to chromosome six (Hengartner *et al.*, 1978) and the λ light chain genes to chromosome sixteen (D'Eustachio *et al.*, 1981) of the mouse. In the mouse there is probably only one gene coding for C_κ (Joho *et al.*, 1980) whereas there are probably four different C_λ genes coding for three nonallelic types of lambda chains (Azuma *et al.*, 1980; Blomberg *et al.*, 1981; Miller *et al.*, 1981). A fourth type of λ chain has not been found and its corresponding gene does not appear to be functional (Blomberg and Tonegawa, 1982).

As early as 1965 Dreyer and Bennett (1965) proposed that the genes coding for the variable and the constant parts of antibody molecules are inherited separately in the genome. They based their proposal on the argument that the C genes could not be repeated many times in the genome because of the conserved nature of their gene products. A family of multiple C genes should have led to divergence during the evolution of a species. However, all C gene products of the same type were identical with the exception of allelic differences within a species. On the other hand if there were multiple V region genes they had to be separated from a unique C gene. This idea was corroborated by the evidence of recombination taking place between V and C genes. This led Dreyer and Bennett to propose the "two genes–one polypeptide" hypothesis. It was almost 11 years later when Hozumi and Tonegawa (1976) provided biochemical evidence that immunoglobulin V and C genes are encoded separately in the germ line of the mouse. These workers showed that in embryonic DNA the genes coding for V_λ and C_λ are separated by a piece of DNA of unknown length. In DNA from a λ

producing myeloma the V_λ and C_λ genes were brought into close proximity in order to allow the transcription and expression of a functional light chain.

B. HYPOTHESES

The variable region portion of the antibody molecule determines its antigen-binding specificity. The variable region of the light and heavy chain can be divided into four framework parts that are relatively constant from one antibody to the next (Figs. 2 and 5) (Kabat *et al.*, 1979). In between these framework parts there are three short segments whose amino acid sequence varies highly from one molecule to the next (even of the same type). These hypervariable regions of an associated pair of heavy and light chains are believed to form the antigen-binding site. The hypervariable regions have therefore also been called complementarity determining regions (CDR) (Kabat, 1978).

To explain the origin of antibody diversity means to describe the origin and expression of the antibody V region genes. Over the last two decades there were two schools of thought that explained the origin of V region genes with two quite different hypotheses: (1) the germ line hypothesis and (2) the various aspects of a somatic diversification hypothesis.

The germ line hypothesis argued that antibody diversity is entirely encoded in the germ line (Hood *et al.*, 1975). One has to postulate a great number of different V genes. Combinatorial association of a particular V_H region with any V_L region will amplify the information stored in the genome. Hence a thousand V_H genes and a thousand V_L genes could possibly code for 10^6 different antigen-binding V region pairs. Since genetic evidence and more recently DNA hybridization experiments (gene counting) have favored a single or only a few constant region genes this germ line hypothesis would also imply separate inheritance of V and C region genes.

The somatic variation hypotheses on the other hand are of several kinds. One form envisaged a unique V gene for kappa, lambda, and heavy chain genes, respectively. This unique V region gene would be somatically diversified during B-cell differentiation, for instance by introduction of point mutations (Brenner and Milstein, 1966; Weigert *et al.*, 1970). Hypervariable regions might be hot spots for such mutations. Soon it became clear that this form of a somatic mutation hypothesis was untenable because the variable region amino acid sequences of proteins of independently arising myelomas showed identical "mutations" at the same positions. Because it was very difficult to understand how a single V gene could repeatedly give rise to the same mutated gene product a modified hypothesis was developed in which a family of related gene products (myeloma proteins) was encoded by the same germ line gene. It was unclear, however, exactly how many different families existed, and how many germ line genes one had to propose. But it was clearly more than one.

A second type of somatic diversification hypothesis envisaged unequal crossing over between a limited number of V region genes to be a mechanism by which germ line information could be amplified (Edelman and Gally, 1967). A more elaborate type of gene interaction hypothesis postulated independent inheritance of germ line "minigenes" coding for only the framework and/or the hypervariable regions (Wu and Kabat, 1970; Kabat *et al.*, 1978; Kindt and Capra, 1978). According to this concept there would in the germ line be no fully assembled V genes. During early embryogenesis and/or during B-cell differentiation preexisting DNA segments coding for the three hypervariable regions would be inserted into a preexisting framework structure (Wu and Kabat, 1970) or assembled in conjunction with independently located framework segments (Kabat *et al.*, 1978). This last mechanism would allow generation of diversity by combinatorial assembly and permutation from relatively few germ line segments. Although the hypotheses described are quite different from one another it became clear over the last few years that they all contribute to the generation of antibody diversity with the possible exception of unequal crossing over between V genes.

C. MULTIPLE V GENES AND SINGLE C GENES

1. Multiple V Genes in the Germ Line

It was quite difficult to determine the exact number of V genes until recombinant DNA technology became available and was used to study the immune system. Several groups of investigators characterized immunoglobulin gene segments in genomic DNA using Southern blot type of experiments (Seidman *et al.*, 1978; Kemp *et al.*, 1979; Cory and Adams, 1980; Davis *et al.*, 1980a; Joho *et al.*, 1980; Rabbitts *et al.*, 1980b). As an example, sperm (germ line), embryo, or myeloma DNA was digested with several different restriction endonucleases and the resulting DNA fragments separated according to molecular weight by electrophoresis through agarose. The DNA fragments were transferred and bound to nitrocellulose filter paper and subsequently hybridized to a radioactively labeled DNA probe specific for a certain V gene sequence. Different band patterns were obtained when radioactive DNA probes with different sequence specificities were used. Multiple bands were detected in all instances when V_κ or V_H gene probes were used whereas only a simple pattern of two bands was observed with a V_λ probe (Brack *et al.*, 1978). Because a band corresponds to a DNA fragment bearing one or more V genes the number of bands detected in such an assay is in direct correlation with the number of V genes cross-hybridizing with the probe used and represents a minimum estimate for the number of V genes present. In order to determine the total number of V genes we would have to know the total number of different V gene probes that yield distinct nonoverlapping band patterns. The probes used so far correspond to several subgroups of myeloma proteins. A subgroup is a family of proteins with very similar V region sequences. The members of one subgroup are closely related to each other and distinctly different from the members of other subgroups. DNA probes representing sequences from several subgroups do not cross-hybridize between subgroups and therefore each probe yields a different band pattern in Southern blot type of experiments (Valbuena *et al.*, 1978). The total number of V genes seems therefore to be determined by the number of subgroups multiplied by their average content of germ line V genes (number of bands). A Southern blot experiment reveals about 5 to 20 bands for any given V region probe. The total number of subgroups probably does not exceed 30 to 50 in case of mouse kappa chains and is much less for the heavy chains. The total number of mouse V_κ genes should be between 100 to 500 and the V_H genes around 100. However, not all genes need to be functional. Several groups of investigators have sequenced V_κ and V_H genes belonging to different multigene families. Some of the genes analyzed contain termination codons and deletions when compared to their functional counterparts. These pseudogenes can not encode functional V regions (Givol *et al.*, 1981; Huang *et al.*, 1981; Joho *et al.*, 1982). The lambda light chain system of the mouse is quite different. There are four nonallelic types of lambda constant region genes, $C_{\lambda 1}$, $C_{\lambda 2}$, $C_{\lambda 3}$, and $C_{\lambda 4}$ (Blomberg *et al.*, 1981). There are at least two V_λ genes, $V_{\lambda 1}$ and $V_{\lambda 2}$, that are expressed with the corresponding $C_{\lambda 1}$ and $C_{\lambda 3}$, and with $C_{\lambda 2}$, respectively, to give rise to three different types of λ chains. The $C_{\lambda 4}$ gene appears to be nonfunctional and probably represents a pseudogene that is no longer used (Blomberg and Tonegawa, 1982). Thus, the variability of lambda chains in the mouse is very restricted. Mouse immunoglobulins use for the most part kappa as their light chain. In only 4 to 5% of all cases is the light chain of the lambda type. The preferential use of the kappa chain is probably necessary to generate enough diversity by combinatorial association with the heavy chains.

Use of the lambda chain may lead to a very restricted antibody repertoire.

2. C Genes are Single Genes in the Germ Line

DNA hybridization studies of many investigators have indicated that the constant region genes are present only once or a few times in the mouse genome. More recent data involving Southern blot type of experiments and direct gene cloning demonstrate that the various types of constant region genes are present only once per mouse haploid genome. Only one mouse C_κ gene could be located on a very short DNA restriction fragment (Joho *et al.*, 1980). For the C_κ gene to be present more than once a DNA region of about 25 kb (kilobases) would have to be repeated in the genome so that the many restriction endonuclease cleavage sites were conserved. Four different C_λ genes have been cloned and mapped in the genome by restriction endonuclease analysis (Blomberg *et al.*, 1981). Amino acid sequence data from myeloma proteins account for three of the four types of lambda constant region sequences. Also, the constant region genes coding for the various heavy chains are single genes. Southern blot type experiments and gene cloning have revealed the order and a direct physical linkage between the various C_H genes (Honjo and Kataoka, 1978; Cory and Adams, 1980; Cory *et al.*, 1980b; Rabbitts *et al.*, 1980a; Honjo *et al.*, 1981).

3. Two Genes One Polypeptide

The fact that only one of multiple V genes in the germ line will be expressed with a unique C gene can only be reconciled by a mechanism of gene expression in which two separate genes (V and C) give rise to a single polypeptide chain. It had been known that the V and C parts of the kappa light chain are encoded on the same mRNA (Milstein *et al.*, 1974). Therefore joining of the V_κ and C_κ part during gene expression had to occur at a pretranslational level. Hozumi and Tonegawa (1976) showed for the first time that V and C genes separately encoded in embryo DNA (on two different DNA restriction fragments) were brought to close proximity in the genome of a lambda-producing plasma cell. Later it was shown by many groups that this mechanism of V and C gene rearrangement is generally operative for κ, λ, and H chains at the DNA level during lymphocyte differentiation (Brack *et al.*, 1978; Bernard *et al.*, 1978; Seidman and Leder, 1978; Early *et al.*, 1979). As stated previously such a mechanism had been postulated much earlier by Dreyer and Bennett (1965).

D. STRUCTURE AND EXPRESSION OF LIGHT CHAIN GENES

1. Organization of the V_L Genes

With the advent of recombinant DNA technology it became possible to isolate and study single genes. From amino acid sequence analysis the region of the light chain extends from amino acid position 1 to 108 and is followed by the constant region (Kabat *et al.*, 1979). Cloning and sequence analysis of V_κ and V_λ genes revealed a surprising feature of the V_L gene (Bernard *et al.*, 1978; Tonegawa *et al.*, 1978; Seidman *et al.*, 1978, 1979). Instead of coding for an amino acid sequence up to position 108 (the end of the V_κ region) or 110 (the end of the V_λ region) the germ line V_κ and V_λ genes coded only for a V region up to position 95 and 97, respectively. This coincides approximately with the end of the third hypervariable region of the light chain. The fourth framework portion of the V region is not encoded by the germ line V gene but instead by one of four separate subgenic elements called J, for joining segments (Figs. 2 and 3).

When an immunoglobulin light chain is synthesized it carries a hydrophobic leader sequence at its amino terminus (Burstein and Schechter, 1977, 1978). This leader sequence of about 20 amino acids is cleaved off during the maturation process of the polypeptide. The analysis of the V_L genes revealed that the main part of the leader is encoded by a separate coding sequence preceding the V gene by an intervening sequence of about 130 to 140 nucleotides in most cases (93 nucleotides for $V_{\lambda 1}$). In this respect Ig genes are split into coding and intervening sequences like most genes of eukaryotic organisms.

The first V_L genes cloned were isolated from embryo DNA. When it was clear that the V_L genes were not fully assembled in embryonic DNA it became necessary to clone and analyze true germ line genes, in

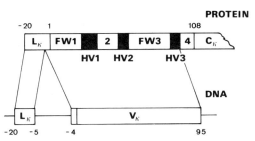

FIG. 2. Structure of the V_κ gene. A short intervening sequence interrupts the DNA coding for the hydrophobic leader (L_κ) (between amino acids −5 and −4). The coding sequence for the variable region (V_κ) stops short of FW4 (at amino acid 95).

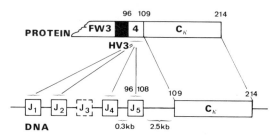

FIG. 3. Structure of the C_κ gene. Four functional J_κ gene segments coding for FW4 (amino acids 96 through 108) precede the C_κ coding sequence (amino acids 109 through 214).

order to test the minigene interaction hypothesis that assembly of V regions from minigenes occurred during early embryogenesis. Our Southern blot analysis of mouse sperm DNA and subsequent cloning and sequencing of sperm V_κ and V_H genes demonstrated that germ line Ig genes are not composed of separate segments but are built as the embryonic ones (Early *et al.*, 1980a; Joho *et al.*, 1980; Gershenfeld *et al.*, 1981).

2. Organization of the C_L Genes

Cloning and sequence analysis of the C_κ and the C_λ genes revealed the J regions coding for the fourth framework. About 1250 nucleotides upstream of the $C_{\lambda 1}$ gene there is a short stretch of 39 nucleotides coding exactly for the fourth framework region of the lambda V region (Bernard *et al.*, 1978; Brack *et al.*, 1978). This is called the $J_{\lambda 1}$ gene segment because it joins with the $V_{\lambda 1}$ gene to form a complete $V_{\lambda 1}$ region gene in a lambda-producing plasma cell. The C_κ gene is structurally very similar. Between 2500 and 4000 nucleotides upstream of the single C_κ gene there are five short J_κ DNA segments ($J_{\kappa 1}-J_{\kappa 5}$) of 39 nucleotides each (Fig. 3). Four of the five J_κ gene segments code for all known fourth framework regions of kappa chains (Max *et al.*, 1979; Sakano *et al.*, 1979b). The fifth J_κ segment ($J_{\kappa 3}$) has alterations at several positions of conserved amino acids and has probably lost the sequence involved in correct RNA splicing. This J_κ segment is not utilized and has never been found in any of the kappa chains sequenced. These five short DNA segments are separated by about 300 base pairs of DNA not coding for any amino acid sequence found in immunoglobulins.

3. Expression of Light Chain Genes

Cloning and sequence analysis of rearranged expressed light chain genes have mainly used DNA from the only clonal plasma cell populations readily available in large amounts—myelomas. In a λ1 producing myeloma the single $V_{\lambda 1}$ gene is joined to the $J_{\lambda 1}$ gene segment in such a way that translation of the complete $V_{\lambda 1}$ region gene becomes possible (Bernard *et al.*, 1978; Brack *et al.*, 1978). The large 1250 base pair intervening sequence between the $J_{\lambda 1}$ and the $C_{\lambda 1}$ gene is spliced out during λ mRNA processing (Rabbitts, 1978; Schibler *et al.*, 1978). A complete functional lambda light chain gene therefore contains two nontranslated intervening sequences: a short one of 93 base pairs separating the coding sequence of the hydrophobic leader sequence from the main coding sequence of the V region and a much larger one separating the $V_{\lambda 1}$ region part from the $C_{\lambda 1}$ region coding sequence. Expression of kappa light chain genes uses the same principle. The difference is that any one of the perhaps 300 different V_κ genes can join with one of the four functional J_κ gene segments. This combinatorial joining may lead to a fourfold amplification of the stored V_κ gene information of the germ line (Fig. 4).

4. Diversity by Intracodonal V–J Joining

Germ line and embryonic V_κ genes end at a position corresponding to amino acid 95, which is a highly conserved proline residue in mouse

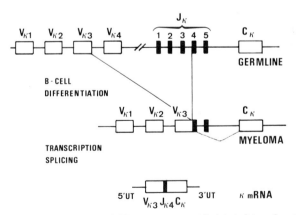

FIG. 4. Light chain expression. A V_κ gene segment is jointed to a functional J_κ gene segment during B-cell differentiation by DNA translocation. Transcription and subsequent RNA splicing yields mature light chain mRNA.

kappa chains. The beginning of the J_κ genes corresponds to amino acid 96. The exact point of V–J joining may not always be the same (Max *et al.*, 1979; Sakano *et al.*, 1979b). In some cases it is between the third nucleotide of codon 95 of the V_κ gene and the first nucleotide of codon 96 of the J_κ gene. In other cases V–J joining takes place between one nucleotide to the right of codon 95 of the V_κ gene and the second nucleotide of codon 96 of the J_κ gene. There are examples of joining between the second or third nucleotide to the right of codon 95 in the V_κ gene and the last nucleotide of codon 96 or the first nucleotide of codon 97 of the J_κ gene, respectively. The essential requirement to form a functional V_κ region gene is to fuse the V_κ gene and the J_κ gene in a correct reading frame. The J_κ gene segments contain stop codons in a different reading frame. Therefore out of phase joining leads to a prematurely terminated V region fragment. However, this intracodonal V–J joining can result in different codons for amino acid 96 depending on the precise point of joining. Since amino acid 96 is part of the third hypervariable region further antibody diversity may be introduced. It seems that slippage of V–J joining can only occur to the right of codon 95 because all κ chains have a conserved proline residue at this position (Weigert *et al.*, 1978, 1980; Rudikoff *et al.*, 1980). This amino acid may be necessary to guarantee the structural integrity of the light chain. Should V–J joining occur inside codon 95 it may lead to a nonfunctional V_κ gene and would therefore not be observed.

E. STRUCTURE AND EXPRESSION OF HEAVY CHAIN GENES

1. *Organization of V_H Genes*

Although the V_H genes are structured much like the V_L genes there is one very important difference. Cloning and DNA sequence analysis of V_H genes of mouse sperm DNA showed that the V_H coding sequence ends after the third framework region (Early *et al.*, 1980a; Sakano *et al.*, 1980). The following DNA sequence codes neither for the third hypervariable region nor for the fourth framework region. A short intervening sequence of about 80 base pairs separates the coding sequence of a hydrophobic leader from the main part of the V_H region coding sequence. The V_H gene is already assembled containing hypervariable regions 1 and 2 inside framework segments 1, 2, and 3 (Fig. 5) (Bernard and Gough, 1980; Early *et al.*, 1980a; Sakano *et al.*, 1980).

2. *Organization and Expression of the C_H Locus*

The C_H region is fairly complex containing eight different C_H genes coding for the constant region parts of the various heavy chain isotypes.

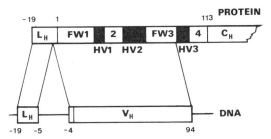

FIG. 5. Structure of the V_H gene. A short intervening sequence interrupts the coding sequence for the hydrophobic leader (L_H). The coding sequence for the variable region (V_H) stops short of HV3 (at amino acid 94).

During B lymphocyte differentiation the μ chain is the first heavy chain to be expressed. It is only during subsequent stages of lymphocyte development that other heavy chain isotypes (like $\gamma 1$, $\gamma 2a$, $\gamma 2b$, etc.) are expressed. Analysis of cloned germ line C_H genes demonstrated four different J_H gene segments to be present about 8000 base pairs upstream of the C_μ coding region (Newell *et al.*, 1980; Sakano *et al.*, 1980; Gough and Bernard, 1981). As in the case of the $J_{\lambda 1}$ and the four J_κ genes, the four J_H genes can code for amino acid sequences corresponding to the fourth framework of the V_H region. A DNA segment coding for the third hypervariable region was not present in contiguity with any of the four J_H segments. This missing DNA segment was called the D segment because it would code for a diversity determining region in the complete V_H gene (Early *et al.*, 1980a). Analysis of a functional rearranged V_H gene from antibody-producing tissue showed the germ line V_H gene segment to be joined to a D DNA segment and to be followed by one of the four J_H gene segments (Bernard and Gough, 1980; Early *et al.*, 1980a; Sakano *et al.*, 1980). The exact number and location of the D segments are not fully known yet. At least 14 different D segments have been found in mouse DNA. One D segment is located about 700 base pairs upstream of the J_H gene farthest away from the C_μ gene (Sakano *et al.*, 1981). Eleven D segments have been found to cluster in a 60-kb-long DNA region (Kurosawa *et al.*, 1981; Kurosawa and Tonegawa, 1982). Activation of a complete V_H region gene requires therefore at least two joining events, one joining a V_H gene segment with a D segment (V–D joining), and one joining this D segment to one of the four J_H gene segments (D–J joining). Combinatorial assembly of a complete V_H region gene from a V_H gene segment, a D segment and a J_H segment can lead to an even greater amplification of germ line information than during maturation of the light chain genes (Fig. 6).

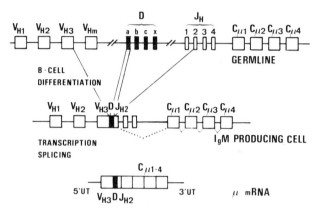

FIG. 6. Heavy chain expression. A V_H gene segment is joined to a D gene segment and a J_H gene segment during B-cell differentiation by two events of DNA translocation (V_H–D and D–J_H joining). Transcription and RNA splicing yields mature heavy chain mRNA.

3. *Diversity by Intracodonal V_H–D–H_H Joining*

Intracodonal V–J joining as described for the light chain system is also operating during V_H–D and D–J_H joining. This may introduce diversity at either end of the third hypervariable region. Comparative amino acid sequence analysis of many different myeloma and hybridoma heavy chains suggests greater "slippage" during V_H–D–J_H joining than during V_L–J_L joining (Rao *et al.*, 1979; Sakano *et al.*, 1980; Schilling *et al.*, 1980).

F. MECHANISM OF V_L–J_L AND V_H–D–J_H JOINING

Several mechanisms can be envisaged to account for Ig gene rearrangements and the precise joining of the V_L with J_L and V_H with D and J_H, respectively. The relative location and orientation of the V genes to the corresponding C gene is not known. It is generally assumed (although not proven) that the V_κ gene cluster is in the same orientation upstream at an unknown distance from the single C_κ gene. The organization of the V_H gene cluster and the C_H genes is similar, yet on a different chromosome. Southern blot type of experiments on myeloma cell DNA have provided evidence that during the process of V_L–J_L and V_H–D–J_H joining the DNA between the V and J regions to be joined may be deleted (Seidman *et al.*, 1980; Sakano *et al.*, 1981). If D segments are situated between the V_H cluster and the J_H–C_H gene locus V_H–D–J_H joining may occur as a two-step process with deletion of the corresponding pieces of intervening DNA. It has been shown in myeloma cells that V genes downstream of the one to be expressed are deleted from the genomic DNA. Also J genes upstream of the one joined to a V gene appear to be deleted. A mechanism of unequal sister chromatid exchange has also been proposed and could account for gene translocations but would result in retention of the intervening sequences in duplicate on the nonexpressed chromosome, albeit on differing cells depending on sister chromatid exchange or homologous crossing-over, and whether pre- or post-S phase (Van Ness *et al.*, 1982).

Comparison of DNA sequences 3′ to the V genes and 5′ to the J genes led to an interesting observation (Early *et al.*, 1980a; Sakano *et al.*, 1980). A highly conserved palindromic sequence of seven nucleotides (consensus sequence CACAGTG) is present after all known V_κ, V_λ, and V_H genes. This heptamer is followed by a nonconserved DNA sequence of either about 11 or 22 nucleotides in length to be followed again by a highly conserved sequence of 9 or 10 nucleotides (consensus sequence ACAAAAACC). For all V_κ genes studied the nonconserved spacer DNA is about 11 nucleotides long whereas for the V_λ and V_H genes it is about 22 base pairs long. This structure—heptamer–spacer–decamer—is present in an inverted fashion preceding each J gene segment (Fig. 7). Upon close inspection an interesting feature emerges. An 11 base pair spacer is present following each V_κ gene, however, all four J_κ gene segments are preceded by a 22 base pair spacer. The $V_{\lambda 1}$ gene is followed by a 22 base pair spacer and the corresponding $J_{\lambda 1}$ gene preceded by an 11 base pair spacer. It seems that during V–J joining two recognition sequences—one with a 11 base

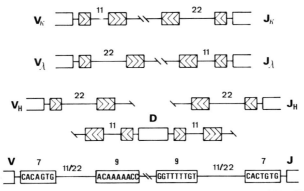

FIG. 7. Presumptive recognition sequences involved in V_L–J_L and V_H–D–J_H joining. The hatched boxes represent the conserved heptameric and decameric recognition sequence which is shown as a consensus sequence in the lower part of the figure. The nonconserved spacer is drawn as a line and its approximate length in base pairs is indicated (11 or 22).

pair spacer, and one with a 22 base pair spacer—are required. It is noteworthy that 11 and 22 base pairs correspond approximately to one or two turns, respectively, in a DNA double helix. The presumptive recognition sequence of V_H and J_H genes both contain a 22 base pair spacer. It was therefore predicted that the D DNA segments should be flanked by the same inverted recognition sequence containing an 11 base pair spacer on either side. Recent cloning and sequence analysis of D DNA segments have confirmed this prediction (Early *et al.*, 1982; Kurosawa *et al.*, 1981; Sakano *et al.*, 1981). This finding supports the notion that the structure—heptamer–spacer–decamer—following each V and D gene segment and preceding in an inverted fashion each D and J gene segment is of crucial importance in the process of immuno-globulin gene rearrangement. Analysis of human kappa light chain genes has demonstrated that this highly conserved recognition sequence is present in human and mouse (Bentley and Rabbitts, 1980; Hieter *et al.*, 1980). Also this finding strengthens the importance of the recognition sequence discussed.

G. Somatic Variation

Early amino acid sequence studies of lambda light chains have demonstrated the occurrence of somatic variants in an immune response although their contribution to antibody diversity remained unclear. Twelve out of 18 sequenced $\lambda 1$ chains proved to be identical and were thought to represent the product of the germ line gene (Weigert *et al.*, 1970). The remaining six $\lambda 1$ chains had one to three amino acid differences in the V region. DNA–RNA hybridization (gene counting) and later Southern blot analysis and gene cloning implied only one $C_{\lambda 1}$ gene in the genome (Tonegawa, 1976). The variant $\lambda 1$ type chains were apparently formed by a somatic process presumably creating point mutations. Recent evidence by several groups indicates that antibody variants may be a normal part of an immune response. To test this hypothesis we cloned a kappa light chain gene from the germ line (Gershenfeld *et al.*, 1981). This gene is of the $V_\kappa 24$ subgroup and is expressed in a normal immune response to phosphorylcholine. This gene is expressed in the phosphorylcholine-binding myelomas M167 and M511. The cloned germ line gene, however, encoded neither the M167 nor the M511 amino acid sequence. When we sequenced a cDNA clone representing the V_κ region of M167 we found that it differed from the $V_\kappa 24$ germ line gene by four bases encoding two amino acid differences and two silent base change. We also compared the published amino acid sequence of M511 and noted four different amino acid residues that can be explained by five base changes in the $V_\kappa 24$ germ line gene. Since by

Southern blot analysis, we were able to demonstrate that neither an M167 nor an M511 germ line gene exists, we concluded that the M167 and M511 sequences arose by a somatic mechanism. Selsing and Storb (1981) independently isolated and sequenced the identical $V_\kappa 24$ gene from a different BALB/c substrain which had diverged from our own BALB/c line at least 30 years ago and reached the same conclusion. Several groups analyzing different immunoglobulin genes found similar results, all implying somatic diversification of germ line genes presumably by point mutations (Bothwell *et al.*, 1981a; Crews *et al.*, 1981; Pech *et al.*, 1981).

In a different approach to the same problem immunoglobulin proteins from hybridomas created from spleen cells of immunized mice showed a pattern of amino acid substitutions consistant with this concept of somatic mutations (Gearhart *et al.*, 1981). The various heavy and light chains from antibodies with known antigen-binding properties fall into distinct groups with very similar sequences. It seems likely that there is one germ line gene coding for the representatives of one such group. Inspection of the sequences of the first 40 amino acids reveals somatic variants in a substantial percentage of the chains analyzed but only in cells expressing heavy chains other than μ (Gearhart *et al.*, 1981). If the variants occur throughout the entire V region we predict that many immunoglobulin molecules—perhaps the majority—to be somatic variants of their germ line genes. These somatic amino acid substitutions are not confined to the hypervariable regions but occur in the framework as well. We do not understand the precise significance yet for the generation of antibody diversity, however, it may be of great importance.

H. GENERATION OF DIVERSITY

As we have discussed on the preceding pages with a single exception all of the hypotheses originally proposed are at least partially correct. In the germ line of the mouse there are a few hundred V_κ and V_H genes (as proposed by the germ line hypothesis). This is the raw material of genetic information which is amplified by a mechanism of gene interaction. The minigene hypothesis originally proposed by Kabat (1978) is supported in part by the finding of the D DNA segments which are minigenes for the third hypervariable region of the heavy chains, and the various J gene segments which represent independently inherited fourth framework region genes. However, cloning and sequence analysis of germ line V_H and V_κ genes has demonstrated that hypervariable regions 1 and 2 (and 3 for V_κ) and framework regions 1, 2, and 3 are already assembled in the germ line and therefore the entire minigene hypothesis cannot be supported. The only type of gene interaction for which no evidence has been found up to now is the concept of unequal crossing over between different germ line V genes. However, it cannot be excluded yet. Somatic variation is an additional mechanism by which antibody diversity may be introduced.

It is possible to calculate the approximate number of different antibody molecules that can be generated in an immune response of the mouse. If we assume about 300 functional V_κ gene segments and four J_κ gene segments, there are 1200 possible V_κ–J_κ joining products. If intracodonal recombination can generate a minimum of three different amino acids at position 96 there are at least 3600 different V_κ region genes. We do not know of course whether all 3600 are also functionally different from one another. The heavy chain genes can be modulated through introduction of the D DNA segment to generate a greater V_H region repertoire. If 100 functional V_H gene segments combine with four J_H gene segments and perhaps any one of 10 different D gene segments (the actual number of D segments is not known) a total of 4000 different V_H region genes can be generated. "Slippage" during the process of V_H–D and D–J_H joining introduces differences at both junctions points. If we allow for only three different possibilities at each junction point (which is probably an underestimate) we end up with almost 40,000 different V_H region genes. It has been a long standing dogma with little evidence to support it that any light chain can combine with any heavy chain to form an antibody molecule. If this were true for the majority of such combinations then combinatorial association of 3600 V_κ regions with about 40,000 V_H regions might generate about 1.5×10^8 different antibody molecules. Even if only 1% of these molecules is functionally different and active there are still more than one million different immunoglobulins. The aforementioned somatic variation process introducing amino acid substitutions may increase the number of functionally different antibody molecules by a factor yet to be determined. It is important to note that many non-IgM myelomas show somatic variants, and so somatic variation may be an important component of specificity in the class-switched cells. A further property of immunoglobulin molecules operating at the receptor level is the phenomenon of multispecificity. Although an antibody molecule is generally highly specific for its antigen it nevertheless has the capacity to bind to some apparently unrelated antigens. This multispecificity may—at a reduced affinity—further enlarge the universe of possible antigenic determinants that can be recognized by the immune system.

III. B-Cell Development and Maturation

A. ORIGIN OF B LYMPHOCYTES

The B-cell lineage is a descendant from the pluripotent hematopoietic stem cell which also gives rise to the other major hematopoietic lineages. Several discrete cell types committed to the B lineage can be defined on the basis of surface phenotype, function, and, in a few cases, morphology (Fig. 8).

1. Pre-B Cells

The term "pre-B" has been used to denote cells that are committed to the B lineage but do not yet express surface immunoglobulins (sIg). Until very recently however, they were poorly defined because they express none of the allo- or xenoantigenic markers commonly used to classify other lymphoid cell types. Recently, we have described several rat monoclonal antibodies which have enabled us to define two types of pre-B cell (Coffman and Weissman, 1981a,b). The monoclonal antibody RA3-2C2 recognizes an antigen expressed on B cells and about 20% of sIg⁻ cells in the bone marrow. The 2C2⁺ sIg⁻ fraction of marrow contains all of the B-cell precursors found in whole marrow and can be divided into two subpopulations on the basis of cell size. The large 2C2⁺ sIg⁻ cells give rise to B cells in long-term *in vivo* assays, but not in short-term, *in vitro* assays. The small 2C2⁺ sIg⁻ cells have the morphology of typical small lymphocytes and many can give rise to sIg⁺ B cells in 48 hours *in vitro*. Further evidence that these cells represent two different cell types comes from the observation that small pre-B cells express the ThB antigen, as do B cells and plasma cells, but large pre-B cells do not (Coffman *et al.*, 1982). This difference, as well as the

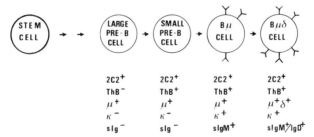

FIG. 8. Differentiation along the B cell lineage. Several pre-B and B cell types can be distinguished according to the presence or absence of intracellular or membrane-bound differentiation markers (antigens).

different rates at which B cells arise from these two cells suggest that large pre-B cells are precursors of small pre-B cells. The pattern of Ig gene organization in these two cells confirms this interpretation (Table I).

2. Virgin B Cells

B cells bearing only IgM on their surface are the first to appear during embryonic life and are probably the first sIg$^+$ cells to arise during adult B-cell generation in the bone marrow as well (Kearney and Abney, 1978). Although no direct lineage experiment has been done, most current evidence favors the hypothesis that IgM$^+$ IgD$^-$ B cells gradually express δ chains and nearly all B cells outside the bone marrow are IgM$^+$ IgD$^+$. It is still unclear if IgM$^+$ IgD$^+$ B cells arise from their precursors in an antigen-independent fashion—and therefore rightfully belong to the class of *virgin* B cells—or if their maturation is antigen-dependent. In the latter case we might provisionally call these mature B cells, signifying a *maturational* change following antigen insufficient to trigger the clonal amplification and differentiation we associate with the development of memory B cells and plasma cells. In several experimental systems, virtually all antigen-specific B cells are IgM$^+$ IgD$^+$ in the absence of deliberate challenge with antigen (Coffman and Cohn, 1977; Zan-bar *et al.*, 1977b; Gronowicz *et al.*, 1979) and in another system the transition from IgM$^+$ IgD$^-$ to IgM$^+$ IgD$^+$ precursors in nonimmunized animals has been shown to be caused by antigen-nonspecific factors (Layton *et al.*, 1981). It is still possible that these IgM$^+$ IgD$^+$ B cells could have arisen via stimulation by a cross-reacting antigen, or via maturation after stimulation by helper T cells responding to different antigens but recognizing cross-reacting immunoglobulin markers. Nevertheless, in the absence of studies in antigen-free mice, one is led to the conclusion that the coexpression of μ and δ on B cells may not require antigenic stimulation. It is therefore possible that most peripheral virgin B cells are IgM$^+$ IgD$^+$ and only a minority, the remainder, are IgM$^+$ IgD$^+$. Both IgM and IgD on the surface of a B cell have the same antigen binding specificity (Goding and Layton, 1976; Coffman and Cohn, 1977) and the same V_H regions (Maki *et al.*, 1981). The major functional difference between IgM$^+$ IgD$^-$ and IgM$^+$ IgD$^+$ B cells is their response to antigen. Cells bearing both μ and δ chains usually respond to antigen by proliferating and differentiating into plasma cells and memory B cells. Newly formed IgM$^+$ IgD$^-$ cells are far more likely than IgM$^+$ IgD$^+$ cells to be tolerized by an encounter with antigen (Metcalf and Klinman, 1976; Cambier *et al.*,

1976), although they, too, can give rise to IgM plasma cells (Coffman and Cohn, 1977).

3. Memory B Cells

Memory B cells are generated from virgin B cells by the net effect of antigenic stimuli and differ from virgin B cells in two important ways. They respond more rapidly to a subsequent challenge of the same antigen and the majority express an sIg isotype other than IgM (Coffman and Cohn, 1977; Zan-bar et al., 1977a). Most memory cells that express an IgG subclass will give rise predominantly to plasma cells of the same isotype. Memory cells appear to be heterogeneous with respect to surface δ and there is good evidence that $IgD^+ IgG^+$ cells mature into $IgD^- IgG^+$ memory cells (Herzenberg et al., 1980).

B. IMMUNOGLOBULIN GENE REARRANGEMENTS DURING B-CELL DIFFERENTIATION

Translocation of a V gene segment from its germ line context to a position immediately 5′ to a J gene segment results in an alteration of the restriction map of the J and C genes. In clonal plasmacytoma tumors, this generates one or two non-germ line H and L gene-bearing restriction fragments which are easily detected by Southern blotting. In normal cell populations, however, hundreds of different rearrangements may exist, each yielding a different restriction map. One must therefore observe rearrangement by the disappearance of the germ line restriction fragment rather than by the appearance of a non-germ like fragment. By measuring the band intensity on autoradiograms of Southern blots it is possible to make a quantitative estimate of the extent of H or L chain rearrangement in DNA from purified cells at different stages of development (Joho and Weissman, 1980; Coleclough et al., 1981; Nottenburg and Weissman, 1981).

Pre-B Cells

Immunoglobulin gene rearrangement has been thought to take place during the early stages of B-cell differentiation, certainly prior to the display of both H and L chains on sIg^+ cells. Until very recently, however, it was not known at which stage in differentiation these rearrangements occur. The recently developed monoclonal antibodies that can be used in the definition and isolation of pre-B cells now make it possible to study the rearrangement process as it occurs during early B cell development (Coffman and Weissman, 1981a).

DNA preparations from large and small pre-B cells ($RA3-2C2^+$,

TABLE I

Immunoglobulin Gene Reorganization during
B Cell Differentiation[a]

| | Fraction of germ line restriction fragment remaining when probed with | |
Cells	J_H	$J_\kappa - C_\kappa$
Sperm	1.00	1.00
Large pre-B	<0.1 (0.16 max)	0.99 (0.95–1.03)
Small pre-B	<0.1 (0.14 max)	0.65 (0.52–0.73)
B cells	<0.1	0.33

[a] Large and small pre-B cells, and B cells were analyzed for the extent of their heavy and light chain gene rearrangements (see text).

sIg⁻ bone marrow cells) were cut with appropriate restriction endonucleases, run on agarose gels, transferred to nitrocellulose filters, and probed with DNA clones containing the J_H or $J_\kappa - C_\kappa$ genes (Coffman and Weissman, 1982). As an internal standard, filters were simultaneously probed for part or all of the C_μ gene which, in each case, is on a restriction fragment which is not altered by V–J joining. The intensity of the J_H or $J_\kappa - C_\kappa$ bands was compared to the intensity of the C_μ internal standard band in each DNA sample. The results of this analyses are shown in Table I. The J_H/C_μ and $J_\kappa - C_\kappa/C_\mu$ ratios of sperm are set equal to 1 and a decrease in that ratio is a measure of the extent of loss of the germ line fragment. Pre-B cells of both stages have almost totally lost the germ line J_H fragment. J_H bands in these lanes are very light and difficult to quantitate accurately, but certainly contain an average of less than 10% of the J_H genes present in the same amount of sperm DNA. Most, if not all, of this J_H comes from nonlymphoid contaminants which account for 5–15% of the pre-B fractions. It appears, therefore, that rearrangement at the J_H locus occurs very early in the B-cell lineage, either at the time of expression of the RA3-2C2 determinant or perhaps prior to it in another, as yet undefined, pre-B cell stage.

Rearrangement at the J_κ locus appears to be a significantly later event. Large pre-B cells have the same amount of $J_\kappa - C_\kappa$ as sperm. Small, more mature pre-B cells show a significant degree of rearrangement but only about half as much as an κ^+ B cells. Unlike H chain rearrangements, κ rearrangement in κ expressing B cells is not complete and a majority of cells retains one germ line gene (Joho and Weissman, 1980; Coleclough *et al.*, 1981). These results suggest that the translocation of new DNA to a position immediately 5′ to a J_κ gene occurs within the stage defined phenotypically as small pre-B cells. Thus it is possible, for the first time, to isolate mammalian cells that are actively rearranging and deleting specific portions of their genome as an essential step in differentiation. The observation that heavy chain rearrangement precedes light chain rearrangement has also been made in Abelson leukemia virus-induced pre-B cell tumors (Alt *et al.*, 1981). Most of these tumors have only heavy chain gene rearrangements and none has only light chain gene rearrangements. Analysis of hybridoma DNA derived from fetal or neonatal liver cells led to similar conclusions (Maki *et al.*, 1980a; Perry *et al.*, 1981).

The apparent asynchrony in H and L rearrangement during differentiation is reflected at the level of Ig synthesis as well. Biosynthetic labeling experiments with cells purified on the fluorescence activated cell sorter indicate that both large and small pre-B cells synthesize significant amounts of heavy chain but little, if any, κ light chain (Coffman and Weissman, 1982). It is quite possible that gene reorganization acts as an "activator" of Ig gene expression and that transcription begins as soon as a complete H or L gene is formed.

C. ALLELIC EXCLUSION

In mammalian cells at a genetic locus both alleles are expressed. There are only two known exceptions to this general rule. In cells of XX genotypes one of two X chromosomes is inactivated and its genes remain silent and in immunoglobulin-producing cells only one of the two alleles is expressed (Pernis *et al.*, 1965). Although maternally and paternally coded immunoglobulin molecules are found in the serum, an individual lymphocyte clone expresses only one or the other allele but not both. Study of this phenomenon of allelic exclusion with myelomas is very difficult because of the aneuploid nature of myeloma cells. In some κ-producing myelomas immunoglobulin gene rearrangement had taken place only on one chromosome (Seidman and Leder, 1978). Comparative Southern blot analysis between embryonic (nonrearranged) and myeloma DNA revealed two C_κ bearing bands in case of the myeloma DNA, one of which was identical to the one found in embryo or sperm DNA, and a second new band bearing the rearranged and expressed V_κ and C_κ genes. In other myelomas a germ line C_κ arrangement could no longer be detected but only the rearranged form (Hozumi and Tonegawa, 1976; Rabbitts and Forster, 1978; Steinmetz and Zachau, 1980). This presumably reflects loss of the homologous C_κ gene-bearing chromosome. A third group of myelomas showed two different forms of C_κ gene rearrangements. One DNA restriction fragment carried a productively rearranged $V_\kappa–J_\kappa–C_\kappa$ gene which corresponds to the expressed κ chain gene. A second new type of DNA fragment revealed upon cloning and sequence analysis an improperly rearranged V_κ or C_κ gene. This abortive rearrangement can be of several kinds. A gene can have undergone V–J joining in an out of phase reading frame (Altenburger *et al.*, 1980; Max *et al.*, 1980). This would lead to a prematurely terminated V_κ region product. In another type of abortive rearrangement V_κ genes have apparently been translocated and jointed to other locations than a J_κ gene, like to the intervening sequence between the J_κ gene cluster and the C_κ gene (Choi *et al.*, 1980; Schnell *et al.*, 1980; Seidman and Leder, 1980). Aberrant rearrangement of a V_λ gene has also been reported (Bothwell *et al.*, 1981b). The fact that the myeloma cells are highly aneuploid and malignant makes a reasonable interpretation of these experiments virtually impossible since these aberrant rearrangements may merely reflect the neoplastic phenotypes of tumor cells and not be significant for normal B lymphocytes. It was therefore necessary to study immunoglobulin gene rearrangements in normal cells.

Our first such study was to isolate κ bearing normal B lymphocytes from a BALB/c mouse spleen using highly specific rabbit anti-mouse κ antibodies and the fluorescence-activated cell sorter (Joho and Weissman, 1980). An analysis of the intensity of the $J_\kappa–C_\kappa$-containing segments from these cells on Southern blots revealed approximately 35 to 40% of the C_κ gene to be in the germ line context, consistent with the conclusion that most kappa expressing B cells have translocated genetic material 5' to their J regions on one of two chromosomes only. Thus, for the kappa locus, the major contribution to allelic exclusion is via limited translocation, resulting in only one of two chromosomes containing a $V_\kappa–J_\kappa–C_\kappa$ in place as an adequate transcriptional unit. The degree to which the other 10 to 15% of alterations in the genome 5' to the J_κ region occurred in appropriate or inappropriate contexts is not possible to determine by whole genomic analysis. Coleclough *et al.* (1981) extended their myeloma analysis to B cells, and conclude that 25 to 35% of the kappa chromosome remains in the germ line context, and proposed a stochastic probability model for V gene rearrangements on the kappa chromosome, implying that unsuccessful rearrangement on one chromosome does not prevent an attempt at successful rearrangement on the homologous chromosome.

Allelic markers do exist for the heavy chain chromosome in the mouse. Heavy chain allelic markers have been found for $\mu, \delta, \gamma, \alpha,$ and ϵ isotypes. We have demonstrated restriction fragment length polymorphism around the $\mu, \delta, \gamma1,$ and α C_H regions (Nottenburg and

Weissman, 1981, and unpublished results). We decided to study the correlation of the expression of a particular allotype with the arrangement of the heavy chain chromosome around the region 5′ to the J_H (similar to our κ study) in normal B lymphocytes. DNA was isolated from parents and F_1 sperm and IgM^+ IgD^+ B cells of F_1 mice expressing one parental allotype. Whole genomic Southern blots were analyzed with C_μ probes to define the context of the two parental BALB/c and the C57/Bl) heavy chain chromosomes (Nottenburg and Weissman, 1981). Greater than 90%, and probably greater than 95% of both the expressed and the unexpressed heavy chain chromosomes show rearrangements in the J_H region in B lymphocytes expressing only one parental BALB/c heavy chain allele. In exactly the same cells, almost all of which are simultaneously expressing κ light chains, a substantial portion of the $J_\kappa - C_\kappa$ region remains in the germ line context. Thus the process of J region translocations proceeds somewhat differently on the heavy and the kappa chain chromosome, at least quantitatively. Furthermore, J_H region translocations cannot be the limiting factor for formation of an expressed heavy chain allele, as both chromosomes show equivalent loss of germ line context $J_H - C_\mu$ sequences in cells that express only one of two chromosomes' allele. How, then, can a particular B cell control the expression of one of two heavy chain alleles? A preliminary answer comes from a DNA sequence analysis of these regions in normal B lymphocytes. We prepared a genomic library from FACS sorted BALB/c IgM^+ IgD^+B cells and cloned the rearranged C_μ genes (Early et al., 1982). Four of these clones containing C_μ sequences have been isolated and their DNA sequence established (Early et al., 1982). Two of the clones contained precise $V_H - D - J_H$ junctions in the correct reading frame, and two others did not. One contained a precise $D - J_H$ junction without a V_H gene. This clone provided a D sequence fragment and its 5′ flanking sequence in the germ line context for the subsequent isolation and analysis of other D region subgenic elements. The other clone contained a $V_H - D - J_H$ junction leading to a reading frame which contains a termination codon within the D region and one immediately 3′ to the J_H gene segment. Thus, although a rearrangement has occurred, it should not give rise to a functional protein. This result implies that allelic exclusion may also result from a rearrangement if a complete V_H region and a transcriptionally active and translatable sequence do not result.

Why does there appear to be such a difference between gene rearrangement frequencies in the heavy chain and the light chain chromosome? We believe that it is probably due to the requirement for more extensive genetic alterations to occur on the heavy chain then the kappa chain chromosome. It is well known that heavy chain chromosomes must undergo at least two gene rearrangements to form a V_H region, $D-J_H$ rearrangements, and V_H-D rearrangements. In addition, Kurosawa *et al.* (1981) have proposed that D regions themselves undergo extensive recombinational alteration prior to their participation in either $D-J_H$ or V_H-D joining, although alteration of germ line D segments to B cell (or myeloma) D segments may also involve a base insertion reaction (D. Baltimore, personal communication). Thus the enzymatic mechanisms for heavy chain rearrangements are more extensive. It shall be most interesting to determine whether the processes of heavy chain chromosome and kappa chain chromosome rearrangements are different in kind or only differ quantitatively. Qualitative differences would imply differences in the enzymes mediating such changes, or the substrates upon which these enzymes act (for example, a multicomponent enzyme may contain a site-specific subunit, and there could be kappa and H site-specific proteins which fit into such a multiprotein complex necessary for successful rearrangement). A quantitative difference could be accomplished with the same enzyme system, if the H chain chromosome contains many more attachment sites than the light chain chromosome or sites with a higher binding constant, or if the H chain chromosome is open to enzyme action while the light chain chromosome is closed (examples might include chromosomal protein arrangements, or the state of methylation of H and L chromosomes during this developmental process). The small pre-B cell population, which appears to include cells in the process of rearranging their kappa genes, should be the logical cell type with which to ask these questions.

The aforementioned experiments make it clear however that myelomas are not the most valid model system to study the phenomenon of allelic exclusion. Since these tumor cells are aneuploid, it is not surprising that one cannot follow the fate of a nonexpressed gene (silent allele) upon which there is no further selective pressure.

In summary, two levels of gene rearrangements have been shown to be predominant mechanisms for mouse H chain and kappa chain allelic exclusion, respectively. For kappa chains, $V_\kappa-J_\kappa$ joining on one of two chromosomes is the predominant mechanism for allelic exclusion, whereas for H chains, inappropriate or incomplete rearrangements to J_H occurs on the nonexpressed chromosome. Nevertheless, it is possible that other mechanisms contribute to nonexpression of an immunoglobulin gene, as must occur in a minority of cases for kappa light chains; other possible mechanisms include later levels of regulation: appropriate $V_\kappa-J_\kappa$ and/or V_H-D-J_H joining on both chromosomes with specific V_H-V_L association defects, such that no complete Ig molecule can be constructed; and the possibility that the appearance of cell-surface immunoglobulin acts as a signal to terminate genetic rearrangements. It is also possible that double appropriate and double inappropriate rearrangements occur with a significant frequency, but that such cells are at a selective disadvantage *in vivo*. Such a possibility would predict significant wastage of B cells at the latest stages of their maturation in the bone marrow. In fact, estimates of B cell (as well as T cell) production far exceed the rate of their appearance in the peripheral lymphocyte pool (Scollay *et al.*, 1980).

D. PLASMA CELL MATURATION

1. Membrane and Secreted Form of IgM

After an antigenic stimulus a virgin B lymphocyte starts to mature into IgM-secreting plasma cells (Melchers and Andersson, 1974). The V region parts of the membrane and the secreted form of IgM and therefore its antigen-binding specificity are identical. However, the carboxy-terminus of the two types of μ chains differ from one another (Kehry *et al.*, 1980; Singer *et al.*, 1980; Sidman, 1981). The membrane-bound μ chain (μ_m) has an extremely hydrophobic stretch of amino acids that is not present in the μ chain of the secreted IgM (μ_s). Several groups have shown that two distinct forms of μ mRNA of different lengths can be detected (Alt *et al.*, 1980; Early *et al.*, 1980b; Rogers *et al.*, 1980). The longer (2.7 kb) μ_m mRNA serves as a template for the synthesis of the membrane form of μ in a cell-free protein-synthesizing system. The slightly shorter form (2.4 kb) directs the synthesis of the μ_s chain of the secreted IgM. Southern blotting and gene cloning have revealed only a single C_μ gene in the genome (Early *et al.*, 1980b). Analysis of the coding regions of the C_μ gene by sequencing and R loop mapping has shown that the gene coding for the secreted μ_s chain consists of four separated coding regions corresponding to the four structural constant region domains of the IgM molecule (Calame *et al.*, 1980; Gough *et al.*, 1980). The C_μ gene coding for the membrane form is identical for the first, second, and third coding region. The fourth coding region is shortened and an additional two small coding regions 1850 base pairs downstream are used to code for the carboxy-terminus of the μ_m chain. These coding sequences carry the information for the extremely hydrophobic terminus. It has been well documented that processing of large precursor RNA molecules into mature mRNA involves RNA splicing (Rabbitts, 1978; Schibler *et al.*, 1978). The switch of the membrane IgM to the secreted IgM during

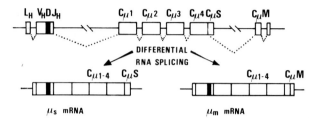

FIG. 9. Secreted and membrane-bound IgM. Depending on the mechanism of RNA splicing an IgM-producing cell can synthesize the secreted and/or the membrane-bound form of IgM.

B-cell maturation involves generation of two different mRNAs from the same precursor by a differential RNA splicing mechanism (Fig. 9).

IgM bound at the membrane is in a monomeric form (one pair of μ_m chains associated with one pair of light chains). The secreted form of IgM is a pentameric molecule consisting of five monomeric IgM molecules interconnected through disulfide bridges with five molecules of a third type of polypeptide, the J chain. J chains and the corresponding mRNAs cannot be detected in surface IgM-bearing B cells but only in IgM-secreting plasma cells (Mather *et al.*, 1981). Thus, induction of J chain synthesis after an antigenic stimulus seems to be coregulated when a B cell matures into an IgM-secreting plasma cell.

2. *Simultaneous Expression of IgM and IgD*

The majority of splenic B lymphocytes express IgM and IgD simultaneously at the cell surface (Pernis *et al.*, 1974; Salsano *et al.*, 1974; Fu *et al.*, 1975). That this is not simply a phase in B-cell maturation when residual long-lived μ_m mRNA is coexpressed with newly synthesized δ mRNA has been established in studies with a mouse tumor cell line (BCL1), that can be grown *in vivo* and *in vitro* and continues to synthesize both isotypes (Strober *et al.*, 1980). The C_μ and C_δ genes are closely linked and there are no J_H genes in between. Cloning of DNA of μ and δ producing cells showed V_H–D–J_H joining at the J_H locus, however, no rearrangement could be detected around the C_δ gene (Liu *et al.*, 1980; Tucker *et al.*, 1980; Moore *et al.*, 1981). This supports the concept of coexpression of IgM and IgD by a mechanism of differential RNA splicing from a large RNA precursor molecule encompassing the entire V_H–D–J_H–C_μ–C_δ region (Fig. 10). Splicing of the complete V_H region RNA to the C_μ coding part leads to a μ mRNA. Depending on a yet different splicing event this μ mRNA can code for the membrane or the secreted form of the chain (Alt *et al.*, 1980; Early *et al.*, 1980b;

Rogers *et al.*, 1980). A δ mRNA can be produced from the same precursor by deleting the transcript region of the C_μ gene and splicing the V_H-D-J_H region transcript directly to the C_δ region transcript. Modulation of splicing at the 3' end of the C_δ gene allows the production of two types of δ mRNAs analogous to the membrane and secreted form of the μ chain (Dildrop and Beyreuther, 1981).

E. HEAVY CHAIN SWITCH

Most virgin B lymphocytes displaying IgM and IgD molecules at the cell surface not only develop into IgM-producing plasma cells but may also differentiate upon antigenic stimulation into plasma cells secreting antibodies of different isotypes such as IgG_1, IgG_{2a}, IgA, IgE, etc. (Coffman and Cohn, 1977; Zan-bar *et al.*, 1977a). The antigen-binding specificity of the various isotypes is identical or only slightly altered in immunoglobulin molecules secreted from progeny of the same clone. This phenomenon of "heavy chain switch" (the expression of the same V_H region with more than one C_H region) was puzzling until the structure of the C_H region was elucidated. The structure of the C_H region was deduced by two independent and complementary approaches. Most recently cloning of large overlapping pieces of mouse DNA has allowed a direct physical linkage of the C_H gene complex (Liu *et al.*, 1980; Tucker *et al.*, 1980; Honjo *et al.*, 1981; Moore *et al.*, 1981; Nishida *et al.*, 1981; Roeder *et al.*, 1981). These experiments have demonstrated a gene order to be correct that had been proposed previously by a more indirect approach (Honjo and Kataoka, 1978). The phenomenon of heavy chain switch and of V and C region translocation through a mechanism of DNA deletion (in studies with myelomas) has led to the concept of several subsequent steps of DNA deletions bringing into close proximity the V_H gene and the C_H gene to be expressed. Since μ is the first isotype to be synthesized V_H-D-J_H joining activates transcription and expression of a μ chain gene (Fig. 10). A second translocation of the complete heavy chain V region gene into close proximity with, i.e., the $C_{\gamma 1}$ gene activates transcription of the gene (Kataoka *et al.*, 1980). Heavy chain genes located between J_H and $C_{\gamma 1}$ would be deleted. The experimental strategy was therefore to count the number of C_H genes of all possible isotypes in myeloma tissue synthesizing a particular heavy chain isotype. The absence of a certain C_H gene would map this one between the V_H-D-J_H and the C_H being expressed. The presence of a C_H gene other than the one being expressed would map the former downstream (on the 3' side) of the expressed one. As soon as enough DNA probes for the various C_H genes became available experiments performed by many groups using myeloma cells revealed a

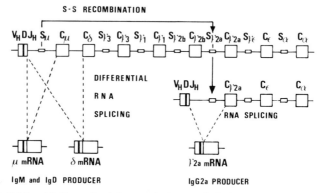

FIG. 10. IgM and IgD synthesis/heavy chain switch. Differential RNA splicing allows a cell to simultaneously produce μ and δ chains with the same V_H region. A DNA translocation event between the S_μ and the $S_{\gamma 2a}$ sequences enables a IgM-producing cell to switch to the synthesis of IgG_{2a}.

consistent picture of the gene order that could later be confirmed more precisely by direct physical linkage. Cloning and sequence analysis of the expressed α chain gene of an IgA-producing myeloma and the comparison to the C_α gene in the germ line has demonstrated such a second translocation event (Davis *et al.*, 1980a). An intact V_H region gene (V_H-D-J_H) including 5 kb of its 3' flanking sequence (part of the sequence between J_H and C_μ) has been translocated to a position about 7 kb 5' of the C_α gene. The germ line C_α gene does not have any preceding J_H genes. The only four J_H genes known are 5' to the C_μ gene. The second translocation event occurs through deletion of DNA between a point 5 kb to the right of J_H and at some distance upstream of the C_α to be expressed. The points of deletion are not precisely fixed but seem to occur inside tandemly repeated regions of DNA the so-called S (switch) regions (Davis *et al.*, 1980b; Dunnick *et al.*, 1980; Takahashi *et al.*, 1980; Kataoka *et al.*, 1981; Nikaido *et al.*, 1981; Obata *et al.*, 1981). All C_H genes with the exception of C_δ have such S sequences upstream of the coding region. Because the C_μ gene is the C_H gene most 5' and the only one preceded by J_H genes joining of V_H-D-J_H leads to the activation and production of the μ chain. During subsequent steps of B-cell maturation the complete V_H region gene including part of its 3' flanking sequence is rearranged close to the C_H gene to be expressed. This event may not require the same precision as V_L-J_L or V_H-D-J_H joining because the regions of recombination, the S sequences, are part of the large intervening sequence of the precursor RNA to the mature heavy chain mRNA. Such a mechanism of heavy chain switching would allow any given clone of B cell to produce only one isotype at any given time. Switching to a new isotype would abolish the synthesis of the previous one. Thus precursors of plasma cells secreting a certain isotype could switch several times and express isotypes whose genes are located downstream of the one currently expressed. This model implies undirectional (irreversible) switching because the genes of the previously expressed isotypes are thought to be deleted. Most experimental evidence is in agreement with a switch in the direction $\mu \rightarrow \delta \rightarrow \gamma3 \rightarrow \gamma1 \rightarrow \gamma2b \rightarrow \gamma2a \rightarrow \alpha$ (Neuberger and Rajewsky, 1981). However, heavy chain switch in the reverse direction ($\gamma2a \rightarrow \gamma2b \rightarrow \gamma1$) has been reported (Radbruch et al., 1980). A small percentage of $\gamma1$ producing myeloma cells (X63) have the capacity to synthesize $\gamma2b$. The cloned $\gamma2b$ producer contains a small population of cells expressing $\gamma2a$. This is in accord with the proposed class switch $\gamma1 \rightarrow \gamma2b \rightarrow \gamma2a$ and subsequently to α. It is difficult to understand how a $\gamma2b$ producing cell can switch back to $\gamma1$ if the $\gamma1$ gene has been deleted. Because these experiments were done with a continuously growing line of myeloma cells the stable reversible class switch cannot be explained by translation of long-lived mRNA for the two isotypes in this study. Three to four copies of chromosome 12 are present in the myeloma cells used. Reversion of class switch might involve activation of one of the homologous chromosomes, i.e., by unequal crossing-over between a nonrearranged C_H gene and the expressed $V_H - D - J_H - C_H$ gene of the second chromosome. Such a somatic crossing-over might lead to a reversible class switch expressing the same V_H region. Because myelomas may contain several copies of chromosome 12 such an event may preferentially occur in aneuploid plasma cells and its significance for normal B-cell maturation remains to be evaluated. Obata et al. (1981) analyzed the rearranged and expressed $\gamma1$ gene in an IgG$_1$-producing myeloma (MC101). They found α chain specific switch region sequences (S_α) on the 5' side of the $S_{\gamma1} - C_{\gamma1}$ region sequences and preceded by a $V_H J_H - S_\mu$ sequence. The authors explained their finding with a sister-chromatid exchange model. Unequal crossing-over between sister chromatids and subsequent cell division could produce one cell carrying a chromosome bearing a deletion in the C_H region and a second cell carrying a chromosome with a partially duplicated C_H region. This second cell type could undergo several steps of class switching and apparently reverse the direction by utilizing the second set of C_H genes.

There is, however, another possible interpretation. DNA deletion as a function of the class switch might only occur during terminal differentiation to plasma cells, much as has been shown occurred in the development of a rat IgD myeloma (Moore et al., 1981). B cells expressing IgG, IgA, and/or IgE isotypes may not have deleted their C_μ genes, In this view coexpression of a particular V_H gene with both C_μ and the other C_H, e.g., C_α gene would require a special mechanism, e.g. (1) very long transcripts, or (2) copy-insertion of $V_H-D-J_H-C_\mu-S_\mu$ to the S_α site prior to deletion upon terminal differentiation. In fact, we have preliminary evidence that IgA$^+$ Peyers patch cells maintain C_μ genes intact (Nottenburg, 1981), although studies on clonal IgA$^+$ B-cell populations to identify the status of the expressed V_H genes are not yet possible.

IV. Immunoglobulin Genes in T Lymphocytes

A. Idiotypic Determinants Common to B and T Cells

Thymus-derived lymphocytes (T cells) play an important function in cell-mediated immunity. Like B cells that recognize antigens via surface receptors, T cells can also recognize antigenic determinants. Contrary to B cells where the antigen receptor is well known (membrane Ig) the T cell receptor has not yet been identified and characterized (Warner, 1974; Rajewsky and Eichmann, 1977).

Analysis of T lymphocytes with antiidiotypic sera has indicated that antigenic determinants of immunoglobulin variable regions are present at the cell surface although these findings have been seriously debated (Binz and Wigzell, 1977; Marchalonis *et al.*, 1980). At first this indicated V_H genes to be expressed and probably be involved in a T-cell-mediated immune response. Such an interpretation is no longer easily tenable because of the fact that a complete V_H region gene consists of three gene segments (V_H, D, and J_H). This makes it possible that a common idiotypic determinant present on T cells is coded for by only one of these gene segments. Thus, it is conceivable that, for example, a D gene segment by itself or, e.g., in conjunction with a hitherto unidentified gene segment, is used to code for the T-cell receptor structure. Expression of such a D gene segment might lead to an antigenic determinant on the T cell surface that can also be found on a B cell, although a complete V_H gene is not expressed. A short stretch of a polypeptide (i.e., coded by D or J_H) might be the only common gene product between B and T cells. Of course, the preparation and specification of antiidiotypic antibodies are fraught with potential errors and artifacts. An *antiidiotypic* antibody must be demonstrated to react with the variable region of a particular immunoglobulin, and not to antigens bound by the immunoglobulin, nor to determinants specified by constant region structures on the immunoglobulin, nor to highly cross-reactive determinants such as carbohydrate side chains; otherwise the idiotypic antibody cannot be taken as a potential marker for a particular V region gene product. Another caution is required. Idiotypic determinants on T and B cells may result from the expression of two nonidentical genes which are phylogenetically related, but which are not the product of the same gene in contemporary organisms. A specific example of this would be our finding of a monoclonal antibody detecting a specific amino acid sequence in the V_κ region of the mouse myeloma T15 and all mouse Thy-1 molecules (Pillemer and Weissman, 1981).

It is possible, in this regard, that putative V_T and V_H (or V_L) genes exist which share idiotypic determinants, but which diverged (by gene duplication) early in vertebrate (or late prevertebrate) evolution. In this case separate V_T and V_H genes could exist which are still genetically linked (to C_H allotypic determinants) if the duplication event did not lead to an interchromosomal translocation.

B. IMMUNOGLOBULIN GENE EXPRESSION IN T CELLS

As soon as RNA and DNA probes specific for immunoglobulin genes were available several groups investigated transcriptional activity of Ig genes in T cells and T lymphomas. In normal thymocytes, some T lymphomas and even in myeloid tumor cell lines, RNA-bearing C_μ sequences could be detected (Kemp et al., 1980a,b). No such C_μ sequences were found in erythroleukemia, mastocytoma, and sarcoma cell lines. Three distinct species of RNA-bearing C_μ sequences can be detected, however, all are of a different size than the μ mRNAs found in B lymphomas and plasmacytomas. It is not known whether V_H sequences are present on the C_μ-bearing RNA molecules or whether sequences specific for T cells, but not shared with B cell-specific mRNA, are present. Contrary to earlier reports (Storb et al., 1976) RNA carrying C_κ or C_λ sequences could not be detected in tissues other than of B cell origin. Attempts to identify a protein with antigenic determinants specific for the μ chain were not successful (Walker and Harris, 1980). The function of this C_μ-bearing RNA is not known. It is certainly surprising that such an RNA was found in nonlymphoid (myeloid) cells and it raises the possibility that the C_μ sequence bearing RNA might be present in many hematopoietic cells even though they may not further differentiate along the lymphoid pathway.

C. IMMUNOGLOBULIN GENE REARRANGEMENTS IN T CELLS

Analysis of J_H–C_μ region rearrangement led to ambiguous results. In some C_μ RNA-bearing T lymphomas the J_H locus was rearranged whereas in others no J_H locus rearrangements could be detected (Cory et al., 1980a; Forster et al., 1980; Kronenberg et al., 1980; Cayre et al.,

1981; Kurosawa *et al.*, 1981). With the advent of functional T cell clones it became possible to study Ig gene translocations in normal cells of known functions rather than in malignant T cells whose functional activity was obscure. The important finding of these experiments is the fact that not all functional T cell clones exhibit J_H-C_μ region translocations (Kronenberg *et al.*, 1980; Kurosawa *et al.*, 1981). Cloning and sequencing of the rearranged J_H-C_μ region revealed $D-J_H$ joining, however, no V_H gene could be detected. This indicates that V_H genes are not used in conjunction with D and J_H gene segments in T cells. If V_H genes were used to code for the T-cell receptor they would have to be translocated to another yet unidentified set of J_H genes and/or the presumptive T-cell constant region gene (C_T). Since some functional T cell clones do not show any J_H-C_μ region rearrangements, this indicates that the J_H-C_μ locus is not used to express the genes for the T-cell receptor. Rearrangement of the J_H-C_μ locus and transcription of the C_μ gene may demonstrate the common ontogenetic origin of B and T cells, and may occur at a relatively early stage of lymphocyte differentiation. Similar experiments with C_κ probes did not reveal any rearrangements in the $J_\kappa-C_\kappa$ locus in all the T cell lines studied. From the experiments described it is clear that our knowledge of T-cell function at the level of DNA is still in its infancy.

V. Evolution of Immunoglobulin Genes and Their Relatives

A. EVOLUTION OF IMMUNOGLOBULINS

Immunoglobulin molecules are built of several domain-like structures of about 110 amino acid residues each (Hood *et al.*, 1975). Light chains consist of two such domains corresponding to the variable and the constant part. Heavy chains consist of four or five domains depending on the isotype. The various heavy chain constant region domains show considerable homology to one another, to constant region domains of different isotypes and of light chains. There is also significant, albeit less homology to variable region domains of heavy and light chains. These findings demonstrate an evolutionary relationship of all immunoglobulin molecules and imply a common primordial immunoglobulin gene corresponding to such a domain.

During evolution several rounds of duplications of a primordial immunoglobulin domain gene might have provided the raw material of genes upon which evolution has built today's immune system. Some of the duplicated and linked genes must have evolved into the C_H locus. Another set of duplicated primordial genes evolved into the cluster of V_L or V_H genes. The fact that kappa, lambda, and heavy chains are encoded on three different chromosomes implies that the duplication events leading to these loci must have occurred at an early time point in evolution and prior to the formation of multiple V_H, V_L, and C_H genes.

The organization of immunoglobulin genes into several multigene families not unique to the immune system seems to be a general principle used by nature throughout evolution to organize genes of similar structures and function. There are other gene systems that contain multiple identical or very similar genes, i.e., histones and ribosomal genes. Even genes that were usually considered to be single genes turned out to be organized in sets of related genes, i.e., globins, interferons. Thus, gene duplication and further divergence of the various genes of a multigene family seem to be very potent tools of nature during evolution to increase the gene pool and therefore the genetic versatility of the organism (Hood et al., 1975).

B. RELATIVES OF IMMUNOGLOBULINS

In recent years amino acid sequences of several cell surface molecules have become available. These molecules are important either as cellular differentiation markers or as surface molecules involved in recognition phenomena similar to immunoglobulin molecules. Comparative amino acid sequence analysis has revealed significant homology of these molecules to the immunoglobulin domain. Molecules encoded by the major histocompatibility complex of the mouse (H-2) and of man (HLA) are folded in a domain-like structure and are associated with a light chain (β_2-microglobulin) (Orr et al., 1979; Rothbard et al., 1980; Coligan et al., 1981). This structure is reminiscent of the antibody molecule consisting of a light and a heavy chain. Both chains, β_2-microglobulin (β_2M) and H-2, show homology to the immunoglobulin domain. β_2M is of similar size (MW 11,500) like an immunoglobulin domain. H-2 and HLA molecules are larger (MW 45,000) but one domain shows homology to the immunoglobulin domain. These findings point to a common evolutionary origin of immunoglobulins, H-2, HLA, and β_2-microglobulin. It is interesting that all of these molecules consist of separately encoded light and heavy chains, are membrane bound, and play a crucial function in recognition and cell–cell communication.

Thy-1 is a glycoprotein present on some lymphoid (T cells) and brain cells. This differentiation antigen shows extensive sequence homology to immunoglobulin domains and is almost of the same size (105 amino acids) (Campell et al., 1979), and, as we have noted, still shows some V_L idiotypic determinant (Pillemer and Weissman, 1981).

This is another example of a cell surface molecule that is presumably involved in some kind of recognition process and seems to have the same evolutionary origin as immunoglobulins, H-2, HLA, and β_2-microglobulin. Of particular interest in this regard is the report that Thy-1 molecules are concentrated at the synaptosomal regions of neurons, a region involved in the transport and salvage of the neurotransmitter acetylcholine. If the Thy-1 molecule is involved in some interaction with acetylcholine, then its relationship to a choline- (phosphorylcholine, acetylcholine) binding V region may indicate an interesting and important conservation of cellular receptor systems.

Today we have very few clues to understand precisely the origin, evolution, and function of all these related genes. It is of course very tempting to think that a primordial gene system was coding for cell-surface receptor and ligand molecules necessary for cellular interaction during the development of metazoae. Duplications and subsequent divergent evolution of such a system may have led to several different subsystems involved in cellular differentiation, communication, and recognition.

VI. Summary

The immune system is able to cope with a virtually unlimited repertoire of different antigenic determinants. Several mechanisms are utilized to amplify the genetic information and to increase the versatility of the immune system. Combinatorial association of a heavy and a light chain during the process of antibody formation theoretically allows p × q different antibodies to be formed from p heavy chains and q light chains although it is not clear what fraction of such combinations will be functionally active. The light and heavy chain variable region genes are inherited in a discontiguous fashion as "minigenes." Two such genes segments (V_L and J_L) form a complete light chain variable region gene. The heavy chain variable region gene is formed by three independently inherited gene segments (V_H, D, and J_H). Combinatorial assembly of a particular V_H and V_L gene with a J_H or J_L and a D segment, respectively, leads to great amplification of the V region information stored in the germ line. Immunoglobulin gene rearrangements during B lymphocyte differentiation activates expression of a particular immunoglobulin gene in an antigen-independent process.

Combinatorial assembly of genes from gene segments and of antibody molecules from light and heavy chains is not the only source of antibody diversity. Introduction of nucleotide changes along the expressed V genes creates immunoglobulin molecules that are somatic variants from their germ line genes. The extent of diversity generated by such a process of somatic diversification is not known but may be substantial.

During the antigen-dependent phase of lymphocyte maturation antibody molecules of different isotypes with the same antigen-binding specificity are produced in progenies of the same virgin B lymphocyte. This process of heavy chain switch is mediated by another form of immunoglobulin gene rearrangements. An intact, functionally assembled V_H gene is translocated from a position next to one C_H gene to the new C_H gene to be expressed. This process allows transcription of the same V_H region gene with several different C_H genes.

Immunoglobulin molecules consist of multiple, homologous domains each about 110 amino acid residues in length. It is likely that a primordial immunoglobulin domain gene existed at some point in evolution. This gene must have been duplicated several times and the resulting copies were organized in three multigene families (kappa, lambda, and heavy chains) located on three different chromosomes. In the mouse there are at least another three, superficially unrelated gene products that show significant homology to the immunoglobulin domain. Molecules encoded in the major histocompatibility complex (H-2) are folded into domains with homology to the immunoglobulin domain. These H-2 molecules are associated with β_2-microglobulin like antibody molecules consisting of light and heavy chains. Also β_2-microglobulin is homologous to the immunoglobulin domain. Thy-1 is a differentiation marker present on some lymphoid cells and in the brain. This molecule is of almost the same length as an immunoglobulin domain and related to it. All of these related proteins probably have a common ancestor in evolution. They are located at the cell membrane and are of crucial importance in recognition and in cell–cell interactions.

REFERENCES

Alt, F. W., Bothwell, A. L. M., Knapp, M., Siden, E., Mather, E., Koshland, M., and Baltimore, D. (1980). *Cell* **20**, 293–301.

Alt, F., Rosenberg, N., Lewis, S., Thomas, E., and Baltimore, D. (1981). *Cell* **27**, 381–390.

Altenburger, W., Steinmetz, M., and Zachau, H. G. (1980). *Nature (London)* **287**, 603–607.

Azuma, T., Steiner, L. A., and Eisen, H. N. (1980). *Proc. Natl. Acad. Sci. U.S.A.* **78**, 569–573.

Bentley, D. L., and Rabbitts, T. H. (1980). *Nature (London)* **288**, 730–733.

Bernard, O., and Gough, N. M. (1980). *Proc. Natl. Acad. Sci. U.S.A.* **77**, 3630–3634.

Bernard, O., Hozumi, N., and Tonegawa, S. (1978). *Cell* **15**, 1133–1144.

Binz, H., and Wigzell, H. (1977). *Contemp. Top. Immunobiol.* **7**, 113–177.

Blomberg, B., and Tonegawa, S. (1982). *Proc. Natl. Acad. Sci. U.S.A.* **79**, 530–533.

Blomberg, B., Traunecker, A., Eisen, H., and Tonegawa, S. (1982). *Proc. Natl. Acad. Sci. U.S.A.* **78,** 3765–3769.

Bothwell, A. L. M., Paskind, M., Reth, M., Imanishi-Kari, T., Rajewsky, K., and Baltimore, D. (1981a). *Cell* **24,** 625–637.

Bothwell, A. L. M., Paskind, M., Schwartz, R. C., Sonenshein, G. E., Gefter, M. L., and Baltimore, D. (1981b). *Nature (London)* **290,** 65–67.

Brack, C., Hirama, M., Lenhard-Schuller, R., and Tonegawa, S. (1978). *Cell* **15,** 1–14.

Brenner, S., and Milstein, C. (1966). *Nature (London)* **211,** 242–243.

Burstein, Y., and Schechter, I. (1977). *Proc. Natl. Acad. Sci. U.S.A.* **74,** 716–720.

Burstein, Y., and Schechter, I. (1978). *Biochemistry* **17,** 2392–2400.

Calame, K., Rogers, J., Early, P., Davis, M., Livant, D., Wall, R., and Hood, L. (1980). *Nature (London)* **284,** 452–455.

Cambler, J. C., Kettman, J. R., Vitetta, E. S., and Uhr, J. W. (1976). *J. Exp. Med.* **144,** 293–297.

Campbell, D. G., Williams, A. F., Bayley, P. M., and Reid, K. B. M. (1979). *Nature (London)* **282,** 341–342.

Cayre, Y., Palldino, M. A., Marcu, K. B., and Stavnezer, J. (1981). *Proc. Natl. Acad. Sci. U.S.A.* **78,** 3814–3818.

Choi, E., Kuehl, M., and Wall, R. (1980). *Nature (London)* **286,** 776–779.

Coffman, R. L., and Cohn, M. (1977). *J. Immunol.* **118,** 1806–1815.

Coffman, R. L., and Weissman, I. L. (1981a). *J. Exp. Med.* **153,** 269–279.

Coffman, R. L., and Weissman, I. L. (1981b). *Nature (London)* **289,** 681–683.

Coffman, R. L., and Weissman, I. L. (1982). In preparation.

Coleclough, C., Perry, R. P., Karjalainen, K., and Weigert, M. (1981). *Nature (London)* **290,** 372–378.

Coligan, J. E., Kindt, T. J., Kehara, H., Martinko, J., and Nathenson, S. G. (1981). *Nature (London)* **291,** 35–39.

Cory, S., and Adams, J. M. (1980). *Cell* **19,** 37–51.

Cory, S., Adams, J. M., and Kemp, D. J. (1980a). *Proc. Natl. Acad. Sci. U.S.A.* **77,** 4943–4947.

Cory, S., Jackson, J., and Adams, J. M. (1980b). *Nature (London)* **285,** 450–456.

Crews, S., Griffin, J., Huang, H., Calame, K., and Hood, L. (1981). *Cell* **25,** 59–66.

Davis, M. M., Calame, K., Early, P. W., Livant, D. L., Joho, R., Weissman, I. L., and Hood, L. (1980a). *Nature (London)* **283,** 733–739.

Davis, M. M., Kim, S. K., and Hood, L. E. (1980b). *Science* **209,** 1360–1365.

D'Eustachio, R., Bothwell, A. L. M., Takaro, T. K., Baltimore, D., and Ruddle, F. H. (1981). *J. Exp. Med.* **153,** 793–800.

Dildrop, R., and Beyreuther, K. (1981). *Nature (London)* **292,** 61–63.

Dreyer, W. J., and Bennett, J. C. (1965). *Proc. Natl. Acad. Sci. U.S.A.* **54,** 864–869.

Dunnick, W., Rabbitts, T. H., and Milstein, C. (1980). *Nature (London)* **286,** 669–675.

Early, P. W., Davis, M. M., Kaback, D. B., Davidson, N., and Hood, L. (1979). *Proc. Natl. Acad. Sci. U.S.A.* **76,** 857–861.

Early, P., Huang, H., Davis, M., Calame, K., and Hood, L. (1980a). *Cell* **19,** 981–992.

Early, P., Rogers, J., Davis, M., Calame, K., Bond, M., Wall, R., and Hood, L. (1980b). *Cell* **20,** 313–319.

Early, P., Nottenburg, C., Weissman, I. L., and Hood, L. (1982). *Mol. Cell. Biol.* **2,** 829–836.

Edelman, G. M., and Gally, J. A. (1967). *Proc. Natl. Acad. Sci. U.S.A.* **57,** 353–358.

Forster, A., Hobart, M., Hengartner, H., and Rabbitts, T. H. (1980). *Nature (London)* **286,** 897–899.

Fu, S. M., Winchester, R. J., and Kunkel, H. G. (1975). *J. Immunol.* **114**, 250–252.

Gearhart, P. J., Johnson, N. D., Douglas, R., and Hood, L. (1981). *Nature (London)* **291**, 29–34.

Gershenfeld, H. K., Tsukamoto, A., Weissman, J. L., and Joho, R. (1981). *Proc. Natl. Acad. Sci. U.S.A.* **78**, 7674–7678.

Givol, D., Zakut, R., Effron, K., Rechavi, G., Ram, D., and Cohen, J. B. (1981). *Nature (London)* **292**, 426–430.

Goding, J. W., and Layton, J. E. (1976). *J. Exp. Med.* **144**, 852–857.

Gough, N. M., and Bernard, O. (1981). *Proc. Natl. Acad. Sci. U.S.A.* **78**, 509–513.

Gough, N. M., Kemp, D. J., Tyler, B. M., Adams, J. M., and Cory, S. (1980). *Proc. Natl. Acad. Sci. U.S.A.* **77**, 554–558.

Gronowicz, E. S., Doss, C., Assisi, F., Vitetta, E. S., Coffman, R. L., and Strober, S. (1979). *J. Immunol.* **123**, 2049–2056.

Hengartner, H., Meo, T., and Müller, E. (1978). *Proc. Natl. Acad. Sci. U.S.A.* **75**, 4494–4498.

Herzenberg, L. A., Black, S. J., Tokuhisa, T., and Herzenberg, L. A. (1980). *J. Exp. Med.* **151**, 1071–1087.

Hieter, P. A., Max, E. E., Seidman, J. G., Maizel, J. V., and Leder, P. (1980). *Cell* **22**, 197–207.

Honjo, T., and Kataoka, T. (1978). *Proc. Natl. Acad. Sci. U.S.A.* **75**, 2140–2144.

Honjo, T., Nakai, S., Nishida, Y., Kataoka, T., Yamiwaki-Kataoka, Y., Takahashi, N., Obata, M., Shimizu, A., Yaoita, Y., Nikaido, T., and Ishida, N. (1981). *Immunol. Rev.* **59**, 33–67.

Hood, L., Gray, W. R., Sanders, B. G., and Dreyer, W. J. (1967). *Cold Spring Harbor Symp. Quant. Biol.* **32**, 133–146.

Hood, L., Campbell, J. H., and Elgin, S. C. R. (1975). *Annu. Rev. Genet.* **9**, 305–353.

Hozumi, N., and Tonegawa, S. (1976). *Proc. Natl. Acad. Sci. U.S.A.* **73**, 3628–3632.

Huang, H., Crews, S., and Hood, L. (1981). *J. Mol. Appl. Genet.* **1**, 93–102.

Joho, R., and Weissman, I. L. (1980). *Nature (London)* **284**, 179–181.

Joho, R., Weissman, I. L., Early, P., Cole, J., and Hood, L. (1980). *Proc. Natl. Acad. Sci. U.S.A.* **77**, 1106–1110.

Joho, R., Gershenfeld, H., and Weissman, I. L. (1982). In preparation.

Julius, M. H., and Herzenberg, L. A. (1974). *J. Exp. Med.* **140**, 904–920.

Julius, M. H., Janaway, C. A., and Herzenberg, L. A. (1976). *Eur. J. Immunol.* **6**, 288–292.

Kabat, E. A. (1978). *Adv. Protein Chem.* **32**, 1–75.

Kabat, E. A., Wu, T. T., and Bilofsky, H. (1978). *Proc. Natl. Acad. Sci. U.S.A.* **75**, 2429–2433.

Kabat, E. A., Wu, T. T., and Bilofsky, H. (1979). "Sequences of Immunoglobulin Chains."

Kataoka, T., Kawakami, T., Takahashi, N., and Honjo, T. (1980). *Proc. Natl. Acad. Sci. U.S.A.* **77**, 919–923.

Kataoka, T., Miyata, T., and Honjo, T. (1981). *Cell* **23**, 357–368.

Kearney, J. F., and Abney, E. R. (1978). *Contemp. Top. Immunobiol.* **8**, 245–265.

Kehry, M., Ewald, S., Douglas, R., Sibley, C., Raschke, W., Fabrough, D., and Hood, L. (1980). *Cell* **21**, 393–406.

Kemp, D. J., Cory, S., and Adams, J. M. (1979). *Proc. Natl. Acad. Sci. U.S.A.* **76**, 4627–4631.

Kemp, D. J., Harris, A. W., Cory, S., and Adams, J. M. (1980a). *Proc. Natl. Acad. Sci. U.S.A.* **77**, 2876–2880.

Kemp, D. J., Wilson, A., Harris, A. W., and Shortman, K. (1980b). *Nature (London)* **286,** 168–170.

Kindt, T. J., and Capra, J. D. (1978). *Immunogenetics* **6,** 309–321.

Kronenberg, M., Davis, M. M., Early, P. W., Hood, L. E., and Watson, J. D. (1980). *J. Exp. Med.* **152,** 1745–1761.

Kurosawa, Y., and Tonegawa, S. (1982). *J. Exp. Med.* **155,** 201–218.

Kurosawa, Y., von Boehmer, H., Haas, W., Sakano, H., Traunecker, A., and Tonegawa, S. (1981). *Nature (London)* **290,** 565–570.

Layton, J. E., Baker, J., Bartlett, P. F., and Shortman, K. (1981). *J. Immunol.* **126,** 1227–1233.

Liu, C., Tucker, P. W., Mushinski, J. F., and Blattner, F. R. (1980). *Science* **209,** 1348–1353.

Maki, R., Kearny, J., Paige, C., and Tonegawa, S. (1980a). *Science* **209,** 1366–1369.

Maki, R., Traunecker, A., Sakano, H., Roeder, W., and Tonegawa, S. (1980b). *Proc. Natl. Acad. Sci. U.S.A.* **77,** 2138–2142.

Maki, R., Roeder, W., Traunecker, A., Sidman, C., Wabl, M., Raschke, W., and Tonegawa, S. (1981). *Cell* **24,** 353–365.

Marchalonis, J. J., Warr, G. W., Rodwell, J. D., and Karush, F. (1980). *Proc. Natl. Acad. Sci. U.S.A.* **77,** 3625–3629.

Mather, E. L., Alt, F. W., Bothwell, A. L. M., Baltimore, D., and Koshland, M. E. (1981). *Cell* **23,** 369–378.

Max, E. E., Seidman, J. G., and Leder, P. (1979). *Proc. Natl. Acad. Sci. U.S.A.* **76,** 3450–3454.

Max, E. E., Seidman, J. G., Miller, H., and Leder, P. (1980). *Cell* **21,** 793–799.

Melchers, F., and Andersson, J. (1974). *Eur. J. Immunol.* **4,** 181–188.

Metcalf, E. S., and Klinman, N. R. (1976). *J. Exp. Med.* **143,** 1327–1340.

Miller, J., Bothwell, A., and Storb, U. (1981). *Proc. Natl. Acad. Sci. U.S.A.* **78,** 3829–3833.

Milstein, C., Brownlee, G. G., Cartwright, E. M., Jarvis, J. M., and Proudfoot, N. J. (1974). *Nature (London)* **252,** 354–359.

Moore, K. W., Rogers, J., Hunkapiller, T., Early, P., Nottenburg, C., Weissman, I., Bazin, H., Wall, R., and Hood, L. E. (1981). *Proc. Natl. Acad. Sci. U.S.A.* **78,** 1800–1804.

Neuberger, M. S., and Rajewsky, K. (1981). *Proc. Natl. Acad. Sci. U.S.A.* **78,** 1138–1142.

Newell, N., Richards, J. E., Tucker, P. W., and Blattner, F. R. (1980). *Science* **209,** 1128–1132.

Nikaido, T., Nakai, S., and Honjo, T. (1981). *Nature (London)* **292,** 845–848.

Nishida, Y., Kataoka, T., Ishida, N., Nakai, S., Kishimoto, T., Böttcher, I., and Honjo, T. (1981). *Proc. Natl. Acad. Sci. U.S.A.* **78,** 1581–1585.

Nottenburg, C. (1981). Ph.D. dissertation, Dept. of Genetics, Stanford University.

Nottenburg, C., and Weissman, I. L. (1981). *Proc. Natl. Acad. Sci. U.S.A.* **78,** 484–488.

Obata, M., Kataoka, T., Nakai, S., Yamagishi, H., Takahashi, N., Yamawaki-Kataoka, Y., Nikaido, T., Shimizu, A., and Honjo, T. (1981). *Proc. Natl. Acad. Sci. U.S.A.* **78,** 2437–2441.

Orr, H. T., Lancet, D., Robb, R. J., Lopez de Castro, J. A., and Strominger, J. L. (1979). *Nature (London)* **282,** 266–270.

Pech, M., Höchtl, J., Schnell, H., and Zachau, H. G. (1981). *Nature (London)* **291,** 668–670.

Pernis, B., Chiappino, G., Kelus, A. S., and Gell, P. G. H. (1965). *J. Exp. Med.* **122,** 853–875.

Pernis, B., Brouet, J. C., and Seligmann, M. (1974). *Eur. J. Immunol.* **4,** 776–778.

Pernis, B., Forni, L., and Luzzati, A. L. (1976). *Cold Spring Harbor Symp. Quant. Biol.* **41**, 175–183.

Perry, R. P., Kelley, D. E., Coleclough, C., and Kearney, J. F. (1981). *Proc. Natl. Acad. Sci. U.S.A.* **78**, 247–251.

Pillemer, E., and Weissman, I. L. (1981). *J. Exp. Med.* **153**, 1068–1079.

Rabbitts, T. H. (1978). *Nature (London)* **275**, 291–296.

Rabbitts, T. H., and Forster, A. (1978). *Cell* **13**, 319–327.

Rabbitts, T. H., Forster, A., Dunnick, W., and Bentley, D. L. (1980a). *Nature (London)* **283**, 351–356.

Rabbitts, T. H., Matthyssens, G., and Hamlyn, P. H. (1980b). *Nature (London)* **284**, 238–243.

Radbruch, A., Liesegang, B., and Rajewsky, K. (1980). *Proc. Natl. Acad. Sci. U.S.A.* **77**, 2909–2913.

Raff, M. C., Feldmann, M., and de Petris, S. (1973). *J. Exp. Med.* **137**, 1024–1030.

Rajewsky, K., and Eichmann, K. (1977). *Contemp. Top. Immunobiol.* **7**, 69–112.

Rao, D. N., Rudikoff, S., Krutzsch, H., and Potter, M. (1979). *Proc. Natl. Acad. Sci. U.S.A.* **76**, 2890–2894.

Roeder, W., Maki, R., Traunecker, A., and Tonegawa, S. (1981). *Proc. Natl. Acad. Sci. U.S.A.* **78**, 474–478.

Rogers, J., Early, P., Carter, C., Calame, K., Bond, M., Hood, L., and Wall, R. (1980). *Cell* **20**, 303–312.

Rothbard, B. J., Hopp, T. P., Edelman, G. M., and Cunningham, B. A. (1980). *Proc. Natl. Acad. Sci. U.S.A.* **77**, 4239–4243.

Rudikoff, S., Rao, D. N., Glaudemans, C. P. J., and Potter, M. (1980). *Proc. Natl. Acad. Sci. U.S.A.* **77**, 4270–4274.

Sakano, H., Hüppi, K., Heinrich, G., and Tonegawa, S. (1979). *Nature (London)* **280**, 288–294.

Sakano, H., Maki, R., Kurosawa, Y., Roeder, W., and Tonegawa, S. (1980). *Nature (London)* **286**, 676–683.

Sakano, H., Kurosawa, Y., Weigert, M., and Tonegawa, S. (1981). *Nature (London)* **290**, 562–565.

Salsano, F., Frøland, S. S., Natvig, J. B., and Michaelsen, T. E. (1974). *Scand. J. Immunol.* **3**, 841–846.

Schibler, U., Marcu, K. B., and Perry, R. P. (1978). *Cell* **15**, 1495–1509.

Schilling, J., Clevinger, B., Davie, J. M., and Hood, L. (1980). *Nature (London)* **283**, 35–40.

Schnell, H., Steinmetz, M., Zachau, H. G., and Schechter, I. (1980). *Nature (London)* **286**, 170–173.

Scollay, R. G., Butcher, E. C., and Weissman, I. L. (1980). *Eur. J. Immunol.* **10**, 210–218.

Seidman, J. G., and Leder, P. (1978). *Nature (London)* **276**, 790–795.

Seidman, J. G., and Leder, P. (1980). *Nature (London)* **286**, 779–783.

Seidman, J. G., Leder, A., Edgell, M. H., Polsky, F., Tilghman, S. M., Tiemeier, D. C., and Leder, P. (1978). *Proc. Natl. Acad. Sci. U.S.A.* **75**, 3881–3885.

Seidman, J. G., Max, E. E., and Leder, P. (1979). *Nature (London)* **280**, 370–375.

Seidman, J. G., Nau, M. M., Norman, B., Kwan, S. P., Scharff, M., and Leder, P. (1980). *Proc. Natl. Acad. Sci. U.S.A.* **77**, 6022–6026.

Selsing, E., and Storb, U. (1981). *Cell* **25**, 47–58.

Sidman, C. (1981). *Cell* **23**, 379–389.

Singer, P. A., Singer, H. H., and Williamson, A. R. (1980). *Nature (London)* **285**, 294–300.

Steinmetz, M., and Zachau, H. G. (1980). *Nucleic Acids Res.* **8**, 1693–1707.

Storb, U., Hager, L., Putnam, D., Buck, L., Farin, F., and Clagett, J. (1976). *Proc. Natl. Acad. Sci. U.S.A.* **73**, 2467–2471.

Strober, S., Gronowicz, E. S., Knapp, M. R., Slavin, S., Vitetta, E. S., Warnke, R. A., Kotzin, B., and Schröder, J. (1980). *Immunol. Rev.* **48**, 169–195.

Takahashi, N. T., Kataoka, T., and Honjo, T. (1980). *Gene* **11**, 117–127.

Tonegawa, S. (1976). *Proc. Natl. Acad. Sci. U.S.A.* **73**, 203–207.

Tonegawa, S., Maxam, A. L., Tizard, R., Bernard, O., and Gilbert, W. (1978). *Proc. Natl. Acad. Sci. U.S.A.* **75**, 1485–1489.

Tucker, P. W., Liu, C., Mushinski, J. F., and Blattner, F. R. (1980). *Science* **209**, 1353–1360.

Valbuena, O., Marcu, K. B., Weigert, M., and Perry, R. P. (1978). *Nature (London)* **276**, 780–784.

Van Ness, B. G., Coleclough, C., Perry, R. P., and Weigert, M. (1982). *Proc. Natl. Acad. Sci. U.S.A.* **79**, 262–266.

Vitetta, E. S., Baur, S., and Uhr, J. W. (1971). *J. Exp. Med.* **134**, 242–264.

Walker, I. D., and Harris, A. W. (1980). *Nature (London)* **288**, 290–293.

Warner, N. L. (1974). *Adv. Immunol.* **19**, 67–216.

Weigert, M., Cesari, I. M., Yonkovich, S. J., and Cohn, M. (1970). *Nature(London)* **228**, 1045–1047.

Weigert, M., Gatmaitan, L., Loh, E., Schilling, J., and Hood, L. (1978). *Nature (London)* **276**, 785–790.

Weigert, M., Perry, R., Kelley, D., Hunkapiller, T., Schilling, J., and Hood, L. (1980). *Nature (London)* **283**, 497–499.

Wu, T. T., and Kabat, E. A. (1970). *J. Exp. Med.* **132**, 211–250.

Yaoita, Y., and Honjo, T. (1980). *Nature (London)* **286**, 850–853.

Zan-Bar, I., Strober, S., and Vitetta, E. S. (1977a). *J. Exp. Med.* **145**, 1188–1205.

Zan-Bar, I., Vitetta, E. S., and Strober, S. (1977b). *J. Exp. Med.* **145**, 1206–1215.

CHAPTER 3

TRANSCRIPTION BY RNA POLYMERASE III

Gennaro Ciliberto, Luisa Castagnoli, and Riccardo Cortese

EUROPEAN MOLECULAR BIOLOGY LABORATORY
HEIDELBERG, FEDERAL REPUBLIC OF GERMANY

I. Introduction

Well-established mechanisms of regulation of gene expression occur at the level of transcription (Darnell, 1979). It is therefore very important to clarify the molecular details of the interaction between the RNA polymerases and the DNA template.

A. RNA POLYMERASES

The best characterized RNA polymerases are those of prokaryotic organisms. In *Escherichia coli* a single RNA polymerase is responsible for all transcription (Chamberlin, 1976) and the level of transcription depends on specific sequences on the gene (the transcriptional signals) and on specific factors capable of binding to the DNA (repressors, activators) (Pribnow, 1979; Rosenberg and Court, 1979). In *E. coli,* superimposed upon gene specific regulation mechanisms there are also

59

more general regulatory phenomena involving many different genes. A well-known example of these general mechanisms is the "stringent" control (Gallant, 1979), whereby transcription of stable RNAs, such as rRNA and tRNA, is regulated independently and antithetically to that of unstable RNAs, i.e., mRNA.

In eukaryotes stable and unstable RNAs are transcribed by different RNA polymerases (Roeder, 1976; Paule, 1981). RNA polymerase I is specialized in the transcription of 5.8 S, 18 S, and 28 S rRNA genes; RNA polymerase II is responsible for transcription of mRNAs and of most small nuclear RNAs (U_1, U_2, U_3, U_4, U_5, U_6) (Zieve, 1981); tRNA, 5 S RNA, and other types of small nuclear and cytoplasmic RNAs (K, L, M, 4.5 S RNA) are transcribed by RNA polymerase III (Weinmann and Roeder, 1974; Zieve, 1981). This enzyme also transcribes two small RNAs encoded by the genome of adenovirus 2 (VAI and VAII RNAs) (Weinmann *et al.*, 1976) and two similar RNAs encoded by the genome of Epstein–Barr virus (EBER I and EBER II) (Rosa *et al.*, 1981) (Table I).

Biochemical and genetic evidence (Ingles *et al.*, 1976) supports the existence of these different RNA polymerases in all eukaryotes from yeast to man. It is reasonable to expect that genes transcribed by the same RNA polymerase will have some common structural features with which they interact with the same transcriptional machinery.

TABLE I

TRANSCRIPTIONAL PRODUCTS OF RNA POLYMERASES

RNA polymerase	Transcriptional product
RNA polymerase I	18 S rRNA
	23 S rRNA
	5.8 S rRNA
RNA polymerase II	mRNA
	U_1, U_2, U_3, U_4
	U_5, U_6
RNA polymerase III	K, L, M small RNAs
	4.5 S RNA
	5 S RNA
	tRNA
	VA I and VA II of adenovirus 2
	EBER I and EBER II of Epstein–Barr virus

B. RNA POLYMERASE III

RNA polymerase III has been well characterized in yeast (Schultz and Hall, 1976), *Xenopus laevis* (Sklar *et al.*, 1975), mouse plasmacytoma cells (Sklar and Roeder, 1976), uninfected and adenovirus 2 infected human KB cells (Jaehning *et al.*, 1977), *Bombyx mori* (Sklar *et al.*, 1976a), and *Drosophila* (Gundelfinger *et al.*, 1980). The enzyme is apparently composed of 10 (Sklar *et al.*, 1976b) or 11 (Gundelfinger *et al.*, 1980) subunits with a total molecular weight of about 650,000. There are some differences in the structure and the biochemical properties of RNA polymerase III enzymes from the various sources, however, there is no species specificity in transcription: tRNA and 5 S RNA genes from various sources and VA RNA genes are correctly transcribed by *X. laevis,* murine, human and *Drosophila* RNA polymerase III transcriptional systems (Weil *et al.*, 1979; Cortese *et al.*, 1978; Dingermann *et al.*, 1981).

Purified preparations of active RNA polymerase III are incapable of accurately transcribing cloned 5 S RNA or tRNA genes (Ng *et al.*, 1979). Precise initiation and termination require the addition of other proteic factors which do not copurify with the polymerase. So far it has been possible to establish the requirement for at least two different factors to obtain accurate transcription of tRNA and VA RNA genes (Segall *et al.*, 1980). In addition to these a third factor is essential for transcription of 5 S RNA genes. As knowledge progresses it appears probable that the RNA polymerase III molecule acquires its capacity to correctly transcribe through the activity of other proteins.

It is not clear at the present time to what extent RNA polymerase III transcription is regulated. Many molecules of tRNA and 5 S RNA are synthesized in every cell; therefore, by and large, RNA polymerase III transcription must be of the "constitutive" type. There are a few cases, however, in which regulation at the level of transcription does occur: the differential transcription of tRNA genes in the posterior silk gland of *B. mori* (Sprague *et al.*, 1977), and the switch from oocyte to somatic-type 5 S RNA gene transcription in *X. laevis* (Wegnez *et al.*, 1972; Ford and Southern, 1973).

II. Transcription of 5 S RNA Genes

A. GENE STRUCTURE

5 S RNA is a molecule of 120 ± 4 nucleotides present in every eukaryotic organism and associated with the large subunit of ribosomes (Erdman, 1981; Tschudi and Pirrotta, 1981). Its sequence is

rather conserved, and in all cases it can be rearranged in a similar secondary structure (Garrett *et al.*, 1981). Despite the advanced knowledge about its structure, little is known about its function.

A common feature of 5 S RNA genes in different organisms is that they are clustered (Pardue *et al.*, 1973; Johnson *et al.*, 1974; Wimber and Steffensen, 1970; Prensky *et al.*, 1973). The number of genes present per aploid genome is 140 in yeast (Long and Dawid, 1980) and 3×10^5 in *Notophtalmus viridescens* (Pukkila, 1975). The former is one of the lowest, the latter one of the highest number of 5 S RNA genes in eukaryotic cells. In no instance have introns been found. In *X. laevis* (Jacq *et al.*, 1977) and in *X. borealis* (Korn and Brown, 1978) within each oocyte-type 5 S DNA repeat unit, in addition to the normal 5 S RNA gene, a partial (80% homologous) copy of the gene has been found which is called a "pseudogene" and constitutes a duplication of the first 101 nucleotides of the coding region. Gene products from the pseudogene are not observed in the cells of *X. laevis* (Jacq *et al.*, 1977), but a cloned pseudogene, when microinjected in the nucleus of *Xenopus* oocytes, is capable of promoting transcription (Miller and Melton, 1981). The function, if any, of these pseudogenes is not known. The existence of pseudogenes has been known for some time for many other genes (Lauer *et al.*, 1980; Lacy and Maniatis, 1980; Jahn *et al.*, 1980; Nishioka *et al.*, 1980; Vanin *et al.*, 1980; Heilig *et al.*, 1980; Bentley and Rabbitts, 1980).

5 S RNA genes, like all eukaryotic DNA, are wound around histone octamers. However, unlike the majority of DNA sequences (Cremisi *et al.*, 1976; Prunell and Kornberg, 1977), 5 S RNA genes have a nonrandom disposition of nucleosomal particles along their DNA sequence. Louis *et al.* (1980) have reported that in the case of 5 S RNA genes of *Drosophila*, nucleosomal particles assume only two alternative positions with respect to those genes. Somewhat similar results were obtained by Gottesfeld and Bloomer (1980) in the study of *X. laevis* 5 S RNA genes. This nonrandom distribution of nucleosomes along the DNA, sometimes referred to as "phasing," is the object of interesting studies in a variety of systems and there are some indications that it may be related to gene activity. Louis *et al.* (1980) suggest a relationship between the two alternative positions found and the transcriptional activity of the 5 S RNA genes: the region where transcription starts and that constituting the promoter are linker DNA and nucleosomal DNA, respectively, in one phase and vice versa in the other. In general, however, the matter of nucleosomal phasing along 5 S RNA genes is far from settled, due to some complications in the experimental protocol (Dingwell *et al.*, 1981) and to at least one discordant result (Baer and Kornberg, 1979).

B. TRANSCRIPTIONAL SIGNALS

1. *Transcriptional Systems*

Two systems have been used to study the transcription of 5 S RNA genes: *in vivo* microinjection into the nucleus of *Xenopus* oocytes (Brown and Gurdon, 1977, 1978) and *in vitro* cell extracts (Birken-meier *et al.*, 1978; Weil *et al.*, 1979; Ng *et al.*, 1979). In both systems, a faithful and efficient transcription has been obtained irrespective of whether a cluster of 10 or more genes or single genes were used as template.

2. *The Internal Control Region*

Our view of the interaction between RNA polymerase and genes has, until now, been based on the *E. coli* transcriptional system. A combination of biochemical and genetic studies in the last 10 years has led to the conclusion that there are specific sequences, distinct from the coding region and located in the 5' flanking DNA, which function as transcriptional signals. Though there are differences among the various genes in the number and the function of these sequences (boxes), in most cases it was possible to identify sites called *promoters* whose sequences are rather conserved, to which RNA polymerase binds and from which it initiates transcription. In certain cases regulatory sites specific for particular genes have been identified. These may be found upstream and/or downstream to the promoter, and are the target of regulatory proteins such as activators or repressors. On the other end (3' end) of the coding region of a gene, specific sequences have the function of terminating transcription. This picture is logically satisfactory because it contains all the elements which are needed to explain how a gene is transcribed and also leads to a distinction between coding sequence and transcriptional (promotion and termination) signals. Recent studies with purified genes of eukaryotic organisms have led to a similar conclusion in the case of RNA polymerase II transcription (Wasylyk *et al.*, 1980; Grosschedl and Birnstiel, 1980a,b; Benoist and Chambon, 1981; Mathis and Chambon, 1981; Faye *et al.*, 1981; Dierks *et al.*, 1981; Gruss *et al.*, 1981; Guarente and Ptashne, 1981; Struhl, 1981). Here, regions important for promotion of transcription were identified in the 5' flanking sequence and in some cases termination signals were identified in the 3' flanking region (Hentschel and Birnstiel, 1981).

It was therefore a surprise when it was reported that purified 5 S DNA could still specifically promote transcription by RNA polymerase III even when all the specific natural sequences of the 5' flanking region had been substituted with *E. coli* plasmid DNA sequences

(Sakonju *et al.*, 1980). D. D. Brown and his co-workers in a series of experiments have established that the promoter of the somatic 5 S RNA gene of *X. borealis* resides in a sequence within the coding region (Sakonju *et al.*, 1980; Bogenhagen *et al.*, 1980). These authors could delete *in vitro* up to 50 nucleotides from the 5′ side or up to 40 nucleotides from the 3′ side of the coding region and still obtain specific and efficient transcription. The combination of these two results leads to the conclusion that the 5 S RNA coding sequence from nucleotide + 50 to nucleotide + 83 contains all the information necessary and sufficient for promotion of transcription.

In an independent study Engelke *et al.* (1980) have shown that *X. laevis* egg extracts are able to promote specific transcription of the 5 S RNA genes only if supplemented with a proteic factor (MW 37,000) present in abundant quantity in the *Xenopus* oocytes. The purified cofactor binds to the 5 S RNA gene (Engelke *et al.*, 1980) and acts as an activator of transcription. Footprint analysis of the DNA sequences which come in contact with the protein shows that they correspond approximately to the 30-bp internal promoter region identified by Brown and co-workers. Moreover, the first 20 nucleotides of the internal control region could be deleted without affecting the binding to the cofactor (Sakonju *et al.*, 1981). It appears then that the 3′ half of the control region is the site which directs the binding of the cofactor, whereas an intact 30-bp sequence is required for transcription.

2. *Importance of the Flanking Regions*

Another important signal for correct transcription is the termination signal. Termination of 5 S RNA gene transcription occurs at a stretch of four or five T residues located immediately after the coding sequence of all 5 S RNA genes so far sequenced (Brown and Brown, 1976; Korn and Brown, 1978). This signal seems to be sufficient, although there are cases where a certain degree of readthrough occurs (Miller and Melton, 1981; Bogenhagen and Brown, 1981) suggesting that the sequence surrounding the stretch of Ts may affect the efficiency of the termination event (Bogenhagen and Brown, 1981).

A precise role of the 5′ flanking sequence has not been established. It does seem to participate in the interaction with the transcriptional apparatus: DNA carrying only the 5′ flanking sequence inhibits transcription from an intact gene (Wormington *et al.*, 1981). Furthermore, deletions of part of the 5′ flanking region up to but not including the wild-type initiation nucleotide cause abnormal initiation (Sakonju *et al.*, 1980).

C. REGULATION

In the genome of *X. laevis* and other amphibians there are two main classes of 5 S RNA genes: oocyte-type (O-T) and somatic-type (S-T) (Wegnez *et al.*, 1972; Ford and Southern, 1973). The coding regions of these two types of genes show only a few differences (positions 30, 53, 55, and 79) but their 5' flanking regions share little homology (Wormington *et al.*, 1981). The S-T 5 S RNA genes are present in about 800 copies per haploid genome (Peterson *et al.*, 1980) and are expressed both in oocytes and in somatic cells; the O-T 5 S RNA genes are more abundant (about 24,000) (Brown and Fedoroff, 1978) and their expression is restricted to the oocytes. There must obviously be a mechanism for this regulation.

Recent experiments have provided some insight into the understanding of the mechanism of this regulation. Transcription of 5 S RNA genes is specifically inhibited *in vitro* by the presence of 5 S RNA molecules (Pelham and Brown, 1980). This inhibition appears to be caused by the binding of 5 S RNA to the activator protein (see above) which has been shown to be essential for the expression of the gene. In this way the gene product inhibits its own transcription. 5 S RNA could be either a competitive or an allosteric inhibitor of the binding reaction between the activator factor and the internal control region of the 5 S RNA gene. The secondary structure of the 5 S RNA (Garrett *et al.*, 1981) immediately suggests that the simpler hypothesis of a competitive inhibition is more probable. Even though the 5 S RNA forms a complicated series of stems and loops, the region from nucleotides 50 to 83 is present on the same side of the molecule, constituting an RNA region structurally analogous to the corresponding DNA sequence as shown in Fig. 1. The number of 5 S RNA molecules transcribed is therefore determined by the number of free activator molecules present in the cell. A massive synthesis of the activator could be responsible for the high level of 5 S RNA gene expression during oogenesis.

During embryonic development, however, O-T genes are switched off despite the presence of activator molecules. Moreover, somatic cell extracts of *X. laevis* contain a protein antigenically related to the oocyte activator cofactor (Honda and Roeder, 1980; Pelham *et al.*, 1981). The mechanism responsible for this repression is still not clear. Even though the O-T genes are not expressed *in vivo* in somatic cells, a purified oocyte-type gene is efficiently transcribed in *in vitro* systems prepared from somatic cell cultures of *X. laevis* (Pelham *et al.*, 1981). It is possible that the information necessary for repression in somatic cells resides in sequences not present in the cloned gene, or that the

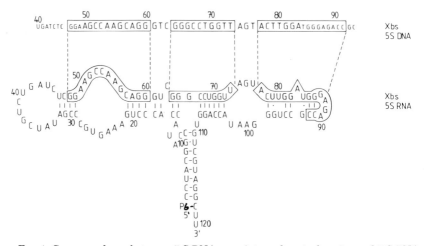

FIG. 1. Correspondence between 5 S RNA gene internal control region and 5 S RNA. The sequence shown is that of *X. borealis* somatic 5 S RNA, but equivalent structures can be obtained with 5 S RNA from every organism. Obviously, in this diagram we have not taken into account possible tertiary interactions. Boxed nucleotides in the 5 S DNA correspond to regions protected by the 5 S DNA specific activator protein.

repression mechanism is effective only at the level of chromatin. Recent studies point toward this last interpretation. Korn and Gurdon (1981) have investigated the negative control of the O-T genes in somatic cells. These authors have microinjected intact nuclei of somatic cells into mature oocytes. This change of environment *did not,* in general, "activate" the O-T genes contained in the transplanted somatic nuclei; if, however, prior to microinjection, these nuclei were pretreated with a relatively high concentration of NaCl, then, following transplantation, the O-T genes were turned on. Similar results were obtained in D. D. Brown's laboratory with a different experimental approach. It was demonstrated that chromatin purified from somatic cells direct *in vitro* transcription of S-T, but not of O-T 5 S RNA genes. If, however, the chromatin was pretreated with 0.6 *M* NaCl, O-T 5 S RNA was synthesized. The authors speculate that in the chromatin of somatic cells the O-T genes are not accessible to the transcriptional cofactors, but salt treatment results in exposure of these genes to the transcriptional apparatus. It is well known that at this concentration of NaCl histone H1 molecules are detached from chromatin (Thoma *et al.*, 1979; Strätling, 1979). These molecules are responsible for the higher order folding of the chromatin structure (Strätling, 1979; McGee and Felsenfeld, 1980); it is possible therefore that a selective compaction of the chromatin at the level of the O-T genes is responsible for the differential expression of the two gene families.

III. Transcription of tRNA Genes

A. GENE STRUCTURE

The vast literature on tRNA structure and function enables us not to review here the knowledge available on this thoroughly studied molecule (for review see Singhal and Fallis, 1979).

In every cell there are roughly as many tRNA species as codons. There is a considerable degree of heterogeneity in the distribution of the relative abundances of the various species in different cells and tissues and there is a reasonably good correlation between species abundance and codon usage (Garel, 1974, 1976). A precise estimate of the total amount of tRNA molecules in eukaryotic cells is available only for yeast (2×10^6 tRNA molecules/cell) (Waldron and Lacroute, 1975). The number of tRNA genes is of the order of 400 in yeast (Schweizer et al., 1969), 680 in Drosophila (Grigliatti et al., 1973), 8000 in X. laevis (Clarkson and Birnstiel, 1973), and 1300 in humans (Hattlen and Attardi, 1971). Since tRNA species are 40–50, each tRNA gene is represented in multiple copies, from 8–10 in yeast to about 180 in Xenopus. Unlike 5 S RNA genes, they show only a moderate degree of clustering (Clarkson and Birnstiel, 1973) and are distributed throughout the genome, either individually or in small clusters.

Also in the case of tRNA genes there is some evidence for nucleosomal "phasing." Wittig and Wittig (1979) have found in the case of tDNA^{Lys}, tDNA^{Phe}, and tDNA^{Met} of chick embryo, that these genes are always found wound around the nucleosome particle and not in the linker region between nucleosomes. The beginning of the coding sequence is positioned generally about 20 bp inside the nucleosome core. Though interesting, it is not yet clear whether this particular arrangement plays any role in the expression of tRNA genes.

Unlike 5 S RNA genes, it was soon discovered that some tRNA genes contain introns that are transcribed and then spliced out (Goodman et al., 1977; Valenzuela et al., 1978). The function, if any, of these introns is even more obscure than the function of introns in mRNA precursors. The introns appear to be present in a limited number of genes, always in the same position between nucleotides 37 and 38, though their length can vary considerably from 14 nucleotides in tDNA^{Tyr} of yeast (Goodman et al., 1977) to 60 nucleotides in tDNA^{Trp} of yeast (Abelson, 1979). More recently, two tRNA genes (tDNA^{Ala} and tDNA^{Ile}) were found in the chloroplast genome Zea mays, contained within a rRNA transcriptional unit, and carrying long introns of 806 and 949 bp, respectively (Koch *et al.*, 1981). It is not known whether these genes are transcribed and whether their transcriptional product is correctly spliced.

B. TRANSCRIPTIONAL SYSTEMS

tRNA genes from a variety of organisms have been purified and characterized (Goodman *et al.*, 1977; Valenzuela *et al.*, 1978; Beckmann *et al.*, 1977; Clarkson and Kurer, 1976; Yen *et al.*, 1977; Cortese *et al.*, 1978; Garber and Gage, 1979; Hagenbüchle *et al.*, 1979; Venegas *et al.*, 1979; Müller and Clarkson, 1980; Hovemann *et al.*, 1980; Mao *et al.*, 1980; Schmidt *et al.*, 1980; Santos and Zasloff, 1981). Transcriptional studies have been done either by microinjection in the nucleus of *X. laevis* oocytes (Kressmann *et al.*, 1978; Cortese *et al.*, 1978, 1980; De Robertis and Olson, 1979; Melton and Cortese, 1979; Telford *et al.*, 1979; Melton *et al.*, 1980a) or in cell-free systems from *X. laevis* germinal vesicles (Ogden *et al.*, 1979; Silverman *et al.*, 1979; Mattoccia *et al.*, 1979) or in tissue culture extracts from a variety of organisms (Weil *et al.*, 1979; Sprague *et al.*, 1980; Manley *et al.*, 1980; Clarkson *et al.*, 1981; Dingermann *et al.*, 1981).

In cell extracts the only observable transcriptional product is not the mature tRNA but a longer RNA molecule with extra nucleotides both at the 5' and at the 3' ends, whereas in experiments done with other systems, such as *in vivo* microinjection or nuclear extracts, in addition to precursor molecules, complete mature tRNAs are also obtained. tRNA transcription invariably starts in the 5' flanking sequence of the genes and terminates at a stretch of Ts in the 3' flanking region. Therefore, all tRNA primary transcripts contain extra nucleotides at both ends. For termination there seems to be a simple rule: RNA polymerase III will transcribe everything up to the nearest stretch of Ts, where it stops. In contrast, for initiation there seems to be no simple rule. In all known cases initiation occurs at a purine variously located between position -10 and -3. It is not clear, however, how this nucleotide is selected: in Fig. 2 there is a list of the cases in which the precise point of initiation has been established. The initiating nucleotide is almost always a purine preceded and followed by a pyrimidine. This is true in 8 of the 10 cases shown in Fig. 2; in the two exceptions (tDNA^{Tyr} Sup4-0 and tDNA^{Met}) the sequence PyPuPy is not present in the 5' flanking region immediately preceding the coding sequence. We can imagine that a purine surrounded by pyrimidines is a preferred initiation site, but initiation of tRNA transcription can still occur at another purine whenever this preferred site is absent.

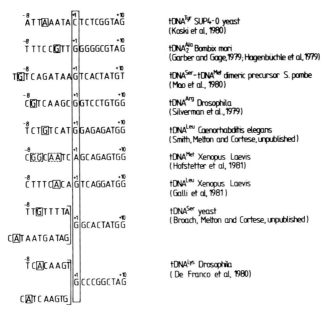

FIG. 2. Initiation of transcription of eukaryotic tRNA genes. Boxed nucleotides are the first nucleotides of the primary transcriptional product. Uncertainty in the case of tDNA^{Met} from *X. laevis* is represented by dashed lines. In the case of tDNA^{Ser} from yeast and of tDNA^{Lys} from *Drosophila,* two genes have an identical coding sequence but different 5′ flanking sequences.

C. MATURATION

Different tRNA genes give rise to different RNA products when microinjected into the nucleus of frog oocytes (Cortese *et al.,* 1978; Melton and Cortese, 1979; De Robertis and Olson, 1979; Melton *et al.,* 1980a; Hofstetter *et al.,* 1981). In some cases the only observable product is mature tRNA, normally processed at the 5′ and at the 3′ ends, with an added CCA terminus and with a normal complement of modified nucleotides. In these cases the lack of detectable precursors is due to the rapidity of the tRNA processing reactions in the oocyte system, as shown also by further studies with mutants altered in some of the maturation steps (see later). However, in many cases, either because of the inefficiency of the maturation enzymes or because of a reason intrinsic to the structure of the transcripts themselves, one or more precursor molecules are observed. In this experimental system it was possible to obtain considerable information on the maturation pathway of tRNA precursors. Accumulating precursor molecules could be sequenced and also could be reinjected into the nucleus or into the cytoplasm of the frog oocytes to study their metabolism further. Further information on the maturation pathway could be obtained from a study of the transcriptional properties of *in vitro* constructed mutant tRNA genes (Castagnoli *et al.*, 1982).

Multiple steps of maturation at the 5' and at the 3' extremities and several nucleoside modifications are needed to obtain a functional tRNA molecule. Two general features emerge: (1) The various steps of the maturation pathway are ordered: precursors which have immature termini contain fewer modified nucleotides, but those present are fully modified. The complete set of modified nucleotides can be detected only after maturation of the termini has occurred. (2) There appears to be a compartmentalization of the various enzymatic activities: splicing and 5' end maturation enzymes are exclusively localized in the nucleus (Melton *et al.*, 1980a; De Robertis *et al.*, 1981; Castagnoli *et al.*, 1982); 3' maturation enzyme(s) including the CCA nucleotidyltransferase are present both in the nucleus and the cytoplasm. With one exception, all modification enzymes studied are localized in the nucleus or, at any rate, they fully modify tRNA precursors before they leave this compartment. The tRNA molecules which appear in the cytoplasm are almost fully mature: the only further modification is the biosynthesis of 2-O-MeG which occurs last and exclusively in this compartment. It is curious that also in prokaryotes the last step in the tRNA maturation pathway is the biosynthesis of 2-O-MeG (Sakano *et al.*, 1974).

Only some of these reactions have been studied in detail. Splicing enzymes from yeast (Peebles *et al.*, 1979; Knapp *et al.*, 1979) and from *X. laevis* (Otsuka *et al.*, 1981) have been purified and it was shown that the endonuclease and ligase activities could be separated. In at least one case it was possible to show that an enzyme responsible for the elimination of the extranucleotides at the 3' end is an endonuclease (Garber and Gage, 1979; Hagenbüchle *et al.*, 1979).

It is still not clear why (in the case of tRNA, as well as in the case of other RNA molecules) the cell goes through such a complicated maturation process. We could hypothesize that the necessity of a maturation pathway or at least of the size reducing nucleolytic steps may simply be a consequence of the mechanism of transcription of these genes. We could understand the reason for the 3' end processing considering that the 3' termini of the primary transcriptional product is determined by the sequence of the termination signal (a stretch of Ts always located a variable number of nucleotides downstream to the coding region). On the other hand, in order to obtain a functional tRNA as adaptor in protein synthesis it is necessary to remove the stretch of Ts which would interfere with the correct structure of the amino acid stem and substitute it with the universally present CCA end (no eukaryotic tRNA gene so far sequenced shows the presence of a codified CCA). Apparently, during evolution, it has been easier to introduce a maturation step rather than evolve a specific termination signal for tRNA genes.

The reason for maturation at the 5' end is less straightforward. It is clear that the initiation step can be very precise in the sense that for any particular tRNA gene all transcripts usually start at the same nucleotide. Why then are the first nucleotide of the primary transcript and of the tRNA not the same? The answer may be found in the necessity to have different promoter sequences for the various tRNA genes. In every cell various tRNA species are present at widely different concentrations. We can imagine that, though homologous to a large extent (see later), the specific sequences constituting the promoter of the various tRNA genes differ. The interaction of the RNA polymerase with the different promoters will therefore generate different transcriptional efficiencies. We postulate that the precise positioning of the RNA polymerase III on a specific promoter determines the site of transcription initiation. Differences in the sequence of the various promoters dictate variations in the exact positioning of the RNA polymerase, thus generating specific initiation points, different for different genes. On the other hand, in order to obtain mature and functional tRNA molecules their sequences must form a cloverleaf structure with a uniform amino acid acceptor stem. In order to adapt all the 5' termini to this requirement a 5' processing reaction is therefore necessary. It is in line with this reasoning that a 5' maturation step is not required in the case of 5 S RNA transcripts; the corresponding genes, though present in many copies, have the same sequence and therefore an identical promoter. If these arguments are correct, there should be a correlation between the structure of the promoter and the initiation of transcription of a tRNA gene. At the present time not enough data are available to attempt to establish this correlation.

D. TRANSCRIPTIONAL SIGNALS

1. The Internal Split Promoter

We have already stated in the previous section that transcription of purified tRNA genes has been mostly studied with X. laevis oocytes either by microinjection or with extracts of isolated nuclei. With several genes it was established that the 5' flanking region, as in the case of 5 S RNA genes, does not contain any information essential for promotion of transcription and could be partly or entirely substituted with plasmid DNA sequences (Telford *et al.*, 1979; Garber and Gage, 1979; De Franco *et al.*, 1980; Sprague *et al.*, 1980; Ciliberto *et al.*, 1982a). The obvious conclusion from these results is that sequences essential for promotion of transcription are located within the coding region.

A considerable wealth of accumulated data has helped in defining the precise nature and boundaries of the internal control region. A rather detailed analysis has been performed with three genes: a tRNA^{Pro} from *Caenorhabditis elegans* (Ciliberto *et al.*, 1982a,b; Ciampi *et al.*, 1982) and a tDNA^{Met} and a tDNA^{Leu} from *X. laevis* (Hofstetter *et al.*, 1981; Galli *et al.*, 1981). The results obtained with these three different genes are very similar and the differences observed may be due to unavoidable differences in the strategy used to construct *in vitro* mutants of the genes.

The general approach to establish the structure of the internal control region was to construct *in vitro* deletion and insertion mutants and, in the case of tDNA^{Pro}, also base pair substitution mutants (Ciampi *et al.*, 1982) which were then tested for their transcriptional activity in the oocyte system. In the case of tRNA^{Pro}, trimming from the 5' or the 3' ends of the coding sequence showed that the two sequences from nucleotide +1 to +8 and from nucleotide +61 to +71 were unimportant. Further insertion and deletion mutants allowed the identification of a central DNA sequence from nucleotide +19 to nucleotide +49 which is not essential; in fact it can be substituted with a segment of DNA of similar length with only a partial impairment of transcription. We must emphasize, however, that at least in the case of tDNA^{Pro} a significant decrease of the transcriptional activity could be observed if single base substitutions were introduced within the segment in question (Ciampi *et al.*, 1982). Our conclusion is therefore that information *important but not essential* for transcription is contained within this region. In a similar set of experiments the essential information for promotion of transcription could be localized in two separated sequences, one from base +9 to base +18, the other from base +50 to base +60. Corresponding essential regions were identified in an identical position in the other two cases examined (Hofstetter *et al.*, 1981; Galli *et al.*, 1981) and involve sequences particularly conserved among the various eukaryotic tRNA genes (Gauss and Sprinzl, 1981). In a study of *in vivo* selected tDNA^{Tyr} mutants of *Saccharomyces cerevisiae* (Koski *et al.*, 1980) the only mutant inactive in directing tRNA synthesis in an *in vitro* system had a single base pair change of the invariable nucleotide at position 56 from C to G; this nucleotide is contained within the second essential region of the three genes discussed above.

How is a tRNA gene recognized by the transcriptional machinery? The peculiar structure of the tRNA molecule, capable of forming stems and loops, has led to the idea that analogous hairpins and loops may be formed at the level of the gene and that this secondary structure of the DNA plays an important role in the gene expression. We think that in the case of tRNA genes it is possible to rule out any involvement of at least three of the potential stems in promotion of transcription. Taking together the results obtained with several deletion mutants in the tRNA[Pro] gene (Ciliberto *et al.*, 1982a,b) we could show that the aa-, the D-, and the T-stems are not essential for transcription because any one of them can be deleted without effect. Moreover, single base pair changes in the coding sequence, which do not affect the potential secondary structure of the gene, do influence dramatically the extent of transcription (Koski *et al.*, 1980; Ciampi *et al.*, 1982). The two essential regions contain truly independent signals for promotion of transcription regardless of the overall tRNA gene sequence within which they are located. To show this we constructed *in vitro* a "hybrid tRNA gene" in which the two essential sites came from two different genes and we showed that this "hybrid gene" was able to direct efficient transcription in the *in vivo* oocyte system.

The sequence of the two essential regions is rather conserved in the various tRNA genes and corresponds to regions of the tRNA molecules characterized by the presence of several invariant or semiinvariant nucleotides (Fig. 3). It is reasonable to imagine that some of these invariant nucleotides were recruited in the course of evolution to constitute a promoter for RNA polymerase III.

The two essential regions are located at a distance of 30–40 nucleotides, depending upon the length of the DNA segment codifying for the extra arm of the corresponding tRNA. In some genes this distance is larger, due to the presence of an intervening sequence. In order to investigate how transcription is affected by the distance between these two essential regions we constructed *in vitro* a series of mutants of the tRNA[Pro] gene, carrying in the middle of the gene insertions from 10 to 200 bp (Ciliberto *et al.*, 1982b). Their transcriptional properties indicate that the distance between the two elements constituting the promoter of the gene is indeed important: the longer the insert, the lower the extent of transcription. There is, however, a threshold effect: with inserts up to 100 base pairs in length there is reduced but still clearly detectable transcription, whereas with longer inserts transcription is completely eliminated. We could imagine that the RNA polymerase III complex has itself a certain degree of physical flexibility, stretching or

FIG. 3. Generalized eukaryotic tRNA secondary structure. Any nucleotide can be found in the positions represented by an empty box. R and Y stand for always a purine and always a pyrimidine, respectively. Hatched regions correspond, at level of DNA, to the two regions essential for transcription.

contracting to adapt itself to the distance between the essential regions; alternatively one can conceive a relatively rigid RNA polymerase III complex and the DNA essential control regions freely moving in the space, occasionally occupying the correct position to interact with the RNA polymerase III complex: the probability of occupying the right position should be inversely proportional to the interposed distance. However, it is not clear why inserts longer than 100 bp inactivate transcription. This is a threshold effect not easily explained with the flexibility hypothesis. We suggest that it may reflect a completely different phenomenon. It is known that when DNA is microinjected in the nucleus of *Xenopus* oocytes it is rapidly wound around nucleosomal particles (Melton *et al.*, 1980b). When a tRNA gene is wound around a histone octamer, the two essential regions, which are about 40 nucleotides apart, will be at two diametrically opposite sides because a full turn of DNA around a nucleosomal particle is about 80 nucleotides. In this conformation their physical distance is more or less equal to the diameter of a nucleosome. RNA polymerase III is sufficiently large to span across the nucleosomes and bind to the two sites across the histone core. When the length of the segment interposed between the two essential regions is lengthened or shortened, the physical distance between them necessarily decreases; we suppose that, while a shorter distance is not optimal, it may still allow a certain degree of transcription. When the interposed sequence becomes so long that the two essential regions cannot be on the same nucleosome, interaction with the same polymerase molecule is impossible and no transcription would occur. This leads to the prediction that introns present in an active tRNA gene should not exceed 80–100 nucleotides and might explain the small size of the tRNA gene introns so far discovered (Abelson, 1979).

2. Role of the 5' Flanking Region

In the case of tRNA genes the 5' flanking sequences are not neutral but contain information relevant, though not essential for transcription. In the case of tDNA^{Lys} from *Drosophila* (De Franco *et al.*, 1980) and in the case of tDNA^{Met} from *X. laevis* (Clarkson *et al.*, 1981) two copies of each of these genes were found, of which only one was actively transcribed *in vitro*. As the coding sequences were identical (tDNA^{Lys}) or nearly identical (only two base differences for tDNA^{Met}) the attention was focused on the 5' flanking regions. By exchanging *in vitro* the 5' flanking sequences of "active" and "inactive" genes it was possible to establish that the 5' flanking region of the inactive gene was responsible for lack of transcription: in other words they had an inhibitory effect on transcription of the downstream coding region. Since RNA polymerase III must interact with the 5' flanking sequence during the process of selection of the initiation point, it may be that the sequence surrounding the first nucleotide influences the efficiency of the initiation process. The inhibitory sequences of tDNA^{Lys} and tDNA^{Met} may then constitute an extreme example of negative influence on the mechanism of selection of the first nucleotide. In the case of tDNA^{Met}, the inhibitory flanking sequence shows a stretch of alternating CG which has led Clarkson *et al.* (1981) to suggest the presence in this region of a DNA helix in the Z conformation.

Have these "incompatible" sequences any role for tRNA gene expression in living organisms? Are genes flanked by such sequences "pseudogenes" inactive in their natural context, or are they inactive only in the particular transcriptional system used? This last hypothesis is likely to be true. One important piece of evidence pointing to this derives from the work of Sprague *et al.* (1980) who studied the properties of the tRNA^{Ala} gene from the posterior gland of *B. mori*. These authors obtained different results using two different transcriptional systems. In the oocyte nuclear extracts they showed that the only region of the gene essential for transcription was located within the coding sequence, whereas the 5' flanking region could be deleted without any decrement in the transcriptional activity of the gene. However, if a homologous extract of *B. mori* posterior gland was used for *in vitro* transcription, the natural 5' flanking sequence was found to be essential. It is therefore possible that the *Drosophila* tDNA^{Lys} and the *X. laevis* tDNA^{Met}, which are inactive in the *Xenopus* system, are active in different transcriptional systems.

A further role of the 5' flanking region is indicated by some recent results obtained in our laboratory. We have removed the coding sequence from a tRNA^{Pro} gene of the nematode *Caenorhabditis elegans* and substituted it with a plasmid DNA sequence of about 100 bp. Upon microinjection of this DNA in the nucleus of frog oocytes, we detected low but significant transcription. A similar series of experiments carried out with a different tRNA gene points to the same conclusion. A tRNA^{Tyr} gene from *E. coli* is scarcely transcribed when microinjected in the *Xenopus* oocytes (Melton and Cortese, 1979). Adjacent to the tDNA^{Tyr} coding region we introduced, by *in vitro* DNA recombination, the 5' flanking region derived from two active eukaryotic tRNA genes (tDNA^{Leu} and tDNA^{Pro}, both from *C. elegans*). This resulted in a fivefold and twofold increase of transcription, respectively. We think that these two pieces of evidence point to the same conclusion, namely, that the 5' flanking sequence of a tRNA gene, at least in the two cases we have examined, contains a weak RNA polymerase III promoter. This weak promoter is considerably less active than the internal promoter when an intact gene is used and can be revealed only if the internal promoter is inactive or removed. Again, the relative strength of these two promoters could be a property of the specific transcriptional system used. It is possible that in cells different from *X. laevis* occytes the 5' flanking promoter plays a more important role in transcription. This conclusion could also be applied to the results of Sprague *et al.* (1980) on the specific requirement of the natural 5' flanking region for transcription in the homologous system. What is a weak promoter in the oocyte may be a strong promoter in the homologous system and vice versa.

3. Termination Signals

In all tRNA genes so far sequenced a stretch of four or more T residues immediately follows the coding region. Every transcript so far sequenced terminates with a stretch of Us coded by this region. Termination can occur at any stretch of Ts, even when it is removed from its natural position adjacent to the coding sequence and placed by *in vitro* recombination at a considerable distance downstream (Ciliberto *et al.,* 1982a). In this case longer transcripts are barely detectable but large amounts of mature tRNA molecules are synthesized. Apparently these longer transcripts are rapidly processed by maturation enzymes. These longer transcripts however are shown to accumulate in the case of mutant tRNA genes which are still transcribed but cannot be processed. A stretch of Ts acts as termination signal even when it is placed in the middle of a tRNA gene, as has been done in a tRNA^{Tyr} from yeast, giving a transcript shorter than a normal tRNA (Koski *et al.,* 1980).

We do not know whether the stretch of Ts is the only possible termination signal. In principle there may be other sequences or structures capable of inducing termination. One such example could be the case reported by Koski *et al.* (1980). Mutations in two nucleotides U_{15} and U_{21} of the coding region of tRNA^{Tyr} of yeast give rise to transcripts shorter than normal and lacking a few nucleotides at the 3' end. However it was not established whether this effect could have been due to abnormal termination or to posttranscriptional processing of the 3' terminal nucleotides.

It appears then that termination of RNA polymerase III transcription is a simpler process than that of RNA polymerase II, which still remains rather obscure, except in the case of the histone genes, where a termination signal has been tentatively identified (Hentschel and Birnstiel, 1981). The structures required for termination of transcription of RNA polymerase III are simpler than those required for termination in *E. coli,* where, in addition to the stretch of T residues, a preceding GC-rich region capable of forming a hairpin loop is required (Rosenberg and Court, 1979).

IV. Other Genes Transcribed by RNA Polymerase III

A. VIRAL-SPECIFIC RNAs

Adenovirus 2 and Epstein–Barr virus-infected cells contain two RNAs of relatively small size, called VA I and VA II for adenovirus 2 (Ohe and Weissman, 1971; Soderlund *et al.,* 1976), and EBER I and EBER II for Epstein–Barr (Lerner *et al.,* 1981). VA I and VA II RNAs are encoded in the viral genome and transcribed *in vivo* by the cellular RNA polymerase III (Soderlund *et al.,* 1976; Weinman *et al.,* 1976). The VA I gene is responsible for the synthesis of two distinct RNA species, a major one of 157 nucleotides (VA IG) and a less abundant one of 160 nucleotides (VA IA) which differs from the more abundant product because its transcription starts three nucleotides upstream (Vennström *et al.*, 1978a). The VA II gene, which is located 98 nucleotides downstream from the VA I gene (Akusjärvi *et al.*, 1980), gives only one transcript of about 140 nucleotides (Mathews and Pettersson, 1978). Both VA I and VA II genes are transcribed in *in vitro* cell-free RNA polymerase III-dependent transcriptional systems, giving rise to the same RNA molecules observed *in vivo* (Weil *et al.*, 1979; Wu, 1980). Both *in vivo* and *in vitro* the VA I RNA gene is significantly more expressed than the VA II RNA gene. Unlike tRNA transcripts, VA I and VA II RNAs are not subjected to any processing or modification reaction (Vennström *et al.*, 1978b).

A detailed investigation of the transcriptional signals for the VA I gene has been reported (Fowlkes and Shenk, 1980; Guilfoyle and Weinmann, 1981). The experimental approach used was to generate subclones containing progressive deletions from the 5' or from the 3' extremities of the gene. Essentially, the results pointed to the presence of an internal promoter spanning the region from nucleotide $+11$ to nucleotide $+72$ (relative to VA IG), containing all the information necessary for promotion of transcription. Within this 60-bp DNA region it is possible to identify sequences showing significant homology with the internal split control region of tRNA genes (see Fig. 4). *In vitro* transcription competition experiments with mixed templates showed that the DNA segment from nucleotide 55 to nucleotide 70 of the coding region of the VA I gene, though unable to direct transcription, was capable of specifically competing for normal transcription of an intact VA I gene. This region therefore seems to be responsible for binding to a factor essential for transcription and present in limiting amounts.

The overall picture emerging is strongly similar to that of tRNA genes. Also in this case there is some evidence that the 5' flanking region may play an as yet undefined role in the process of initiation of transcription. For instance, a deletion of the two bases in position -25 and -26 relative to the VA I (G) starting point eliminates the initiation of transcription of VA IA, without affecting the initiation of transcription of VA IG (Thimmappaya *et al.*, 1979). It is difficult to explain this effect with a simple model: this is yet another example of the complication residing in the mechanism of selection of the initiation point for transcription.

Much less is known about EBER I, a 166 nucleotides RNA, and EBER II a 172 nucleotides RNA, except that they are very similar and contain sequences showing considerable homology to the intragenic control region of tRNA and VA genes (Rosa *et al.*, 1981).

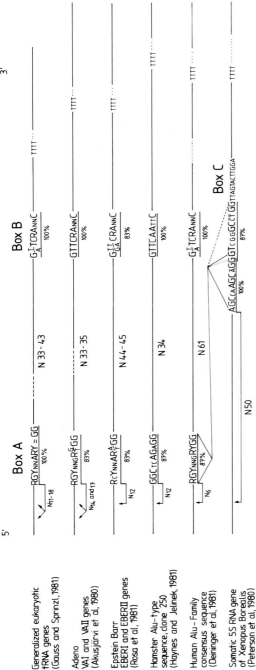

Fig. 4. Elements constituting the genes transcribed by RNA polymerase III. Arrows indicate the site of initiation of transcription. N followed by numbers indicates the number of intervening nucleotides between the indicated regions. tDNA box A and box B are taken as the average consensus sequence. Equivalent boxes in the other genes show a variable degree of homology (indicated as percentage of homology) with the tDNA boxes. To calculate the percentage of homology we have not taken into account positions which can be occupied by any nucleotide. Large and small capital letters indicate nucleotides homologous and nonhomologous to the tDNA consensus sequence, respectively. In the sequences constituting box A and B, N means that any nucleotide can be found at that position; R and Y represent always a purine or a pyrimidine, respectively. In box A of tRNA genes the two dashes indicate the variable presence in this position of none, one, or two nucleotides (Gauss and Sprinzl, 1981). In the internal control region of 5 S RNA genes we show the high homology of the sequence of the first 22 nucleotides with tRNA gene box A (considered as duplicated). Nucleotides indicated with a dash correspond to positions in the tDNA box A where the occasional presence of one or two nucleotides is found. The universally present termination signal is represented by a stretch of T residues.

Very little is known about the function of VA or EBER RNAs. They share with many small RNAs the property of being immunoprecipitable by anti-LA antibodies found in the serum of patients affected by systemic lupus erythematosis (Lerner *et al.*, 1981). Different authors have proposed various possible roles, without experimental support. Among the suggestions one proposes that they may be involved in the splicing of viral messengers (Murray and Holliday, 1979) and another that they are necessary for transport of spliced messages from nucleus to cytoplasm (Mathews, 1980). Recently, Monstein and Philipson (1981) have observed a potential complementarity between a region of the VA I RNA sequence and a region of eukaryotic 18 S rRNA and suggest a role of VA I RNA at the level of translation. This is an attractive hypothesis because it allows the classification of these RNAs in a functional class together with tRNA and 5 S RNA; that is, they are all small RNAs involved in some aspects of protein synthesis, and sharing a common transcriptional mechanism.

B. The Alu Family of Interspersed Repetitive Sequences

In the human genome there is a family of interspersed repetitive sequences, about 300 bp in length, most of which contain a common restriction site for the endonuclease Alu I and for this reason called the "Alu family" of repetitive sequences. There are about 300,000 copies of this sequence per haploid genome (Houck *et al.*, 1979; Rubin *et al.*, 1980; Jelinek *et al.*, 1980; Pan *et al.*, 1981; Jagadeeswaran *et al.*, 1981). They have also been found in the neighborhood of several cloned single copy genes (Duncan *et al.*, 1979). RNA hybridizing to Alu sequences is present in large amounts in the heterogeneous nuclear RNA (hnRNA) (Pan *et al.*, 1981), attached to RNA hybridizing to single copy genes (Fedoroff *et al.*, 1977). Whether Alu sequence RNAs are also contained in cytoplasmic mRNA engaged in protein synthesis is still a controversial question (Pan *et al.*, 1981; Calabretta *et al.*, 1981). The presence of Alu-family RNA in relatively long transcripts suggests that they may be synthesized by RNA polymerase II. However Alu sequence DNA are probably also transcribed by RNA polymerase III. Purified Alu-family clones have been tested in cell-free transcriptional systems and were found to be good templates for RNA polymerase III transcription (Elder *et al.*, 1981; Duncan *et al.*, 1981) and inspection of their sequences shows the presence of sequences homologous to those identified as responsible for promotion of transcription of tRNA genes.

The *in vitro* transcriptional product is homogeneous in length for each cloned DNA and varies from 300 to 600 nucleotides from clone to clone. The 5′ end of the transcriptional products always corresponds to sequences close to the beginning of the Alu-family consensus region; the variability in length of the various transcripts from different Alu-family clones is apparently due to different locations of the termination signals in the adjacent non-Alu-family DNA (Elder *et al.*, 1981).

A very similar phenomenon also occurs in mouse, rat, and hamster, the difference here being that the equivalent of the Alu-family DNA is about half the size found in human DNA, i.e., about 130 nucleotides (Kraiev *et al.*, 1980; Haynes *et al.*, 1981). Examination of the human Alu-family sequence suggests that it might have arisen as a duplication of the 130 ancestral sequence. It is less clear to what extent Alu-family DNA is transcribed *in vivo* by RNA polymerase III. Transcripts about 300 nucleotides in length (7 S RNA) in humans (Weiner, 1980) or about 150 nucleotides (4.5 S RNA) in mouse (Harada and Kato, 1980) and Chinese hamster (Jelinek and Leinwand, 1978) have been found which are homologous to Alu sequence DNA. These transcripts are cytoplasmic small RNAs associated with nucleoprotein particles precipitable by anti-La antibodies (Lerner and Steitz, 1981) found in the serum of patients affected by systemic lupus erythematosis and their function, if any, is unknown.

V. Conclusions

All RNA polymerase III transcribed genes are constructed according to a similar design in which two important elements can be recognized: (1) a region of DNA essential for promotion of transcription and directing initiation of transcription upstream from its 5′ boundary (this could be considered the "promoter" of the gene); (2) a termination signal located at a variable distance downstream from the 3′ boundary of the promoter region. For these reasons in every RNA polymerase III transcribed gene the promoter sequence is always part of the transcript. Furthermore, the overall process of transcription, at least in the *Xenopus* oocyte system, can be influenced by, but does not depend on, the sequences located outside the internal promoter.

The structure of the internal promoter and its relationship with the initiation of transcription are different for tRNA and for 5 S RNA genes. The promoter of tRNA genes is composed of two essential regions (boxes A and B) separated by 30–40 bp and highly conserved in all tRNA genes (Fig. 4). Initiation of transcription occurs 11–18 bp upstream from box A. In contrast, 5 S RNA genes contain an internal promoter sequence 34 nucleotides long and initiation of transcription occurs 50 bp upstream from the 5′ boundary of the control region (Fig. 4). The other Pol III transcribed genes (VA I and II, EBER I and II, Alu-family DNA) are apparently very similar to tRNA genes (Fig. 4).

In the case of adenovirus 2 VA I and VA II an internal promoter could be defined, showing at its boundaries two regions of homology with the box A and B of the tRNA genes. Furthermore, initiation of transcription occurs 12 or 15 nucleotides upstream from the 5' end of the internal promoter. Epstein–Barr EBER I and EBER II genes are very similar to VA I and VA II (Fig. 4). In the consensus sequence of the Alu-family DNA (both human and murine) regions homologous to the tRNA's boxes A and B are always found and in the *in vitro* transcriptional studies it was shown that initiation of transcription occurs 6 to 13 nucleotides upstream from a region showing high homology with tRNA genes's box A (Fig. 4). Recently, support for the importance of these two boxes for *in vitro* transcription of Alu-family DNA is provided by the results of G. Paolella and F. Baralle (personal communication). These authors have studied the transcriptional properties of two contiguous and divergent Alu-family sequences located in front of the human ε-globin gene (Baralle *et al.*, 1980), and discovered that only one of them is transcribed in *in vitro* cytoplasmic extracts from HeLa cells. Inspection of the sequence of the Alu-family member which is not transcribed reveals the absence of box A. Furthermore, several deletion mutants of the "expressed" Alu-family sequence were constructed. Their transcriptional analysis is compatible with the "two boxes hypothesis"; only those subclones containing both box A and box B sequences are able to direct efficient transcription.

We can tentatively classify Pol III transcribed genes in two classes. *Class I* includes tRNA genes, VA I and VA II genes, EBER I and EBER II genes, and the Alu-family of interspersed repetitive sequences. This class would be characterized by an internal split promoter consisting of two components (box A and box B) separated by 30 to 60 nucleotides. In the case of tRNA genes the boundaries of box A and box B have been determined experimentally. From a comparison of the homologous regions of all eukaryotic tRNAs a consensus sequence can be derived which is RGYNNARY-GG for box A and GT/ATCRANNC (for the explanation of these symbols see legend to Fig. 4). Box A and box B-like sequences are found in all the other members of this class, with only limited variation from the tRNA consensus sequence. Within these two boxes the specific importance of each nucleotide will be assessed only by single point mutations. In the case of tDNA^{Tyr} SUP4-O gene of yeast, a mutant in the fourth nucleotide of box B (a C to G transversion) was inactive in transcription, whereas a mutant in the seventh nucleotide of box A (a G to T transversion) resulted in a fivefold increase in transcriptional efficiency (Koski *et al.*, 1980). In this first class initiation of transcription occurs at a short distance from box A.

Class 2 includes only 5 S RNA genes. Here the promoter consists of a 34 bp sequence. So far no internal dissection of this sequence has been performed: therefore we do not know whether it must be considered a continuous structure or if it could be subdivided in essential boxes separated by nonessential nucleotides. In this class initiation of transcription occurs at a longer distance from the 5′ end of the promoter region. An inspection of the sequence of the internal promoter region of 5 S RNA genes shows some interesting features (Fig. 4). Its first 22 bp (nucleotides 50 to 71) appear to be a tandem duplication of the same sequence constituting the tRNA box A. This sequence is followed by a 12 bp sequence showing scarce homology with tRNA, VA, EBER, and ALU sequences. One is tempted to conclude that the 5 S RNA promoter region is also subdivided into two distinct components: the first 22 bp are a duplicated tRNA box A, perhaps equivalent in function, whereas the last 12 nucleotides of the control region may constitute another box, specific for 5 S RNA genes (box C). The biochemical analysis of the transcriptional system gives indirect support to this hypothesis. In order to obtain correct transcription of Pol III genes, the purified RNA polymerase III must be supplemented with several additional cell extract fractions. Two separated fractions are necessary and sufficient for specific transcription of tRNA and VA RNA genes. In addition to these two, a third factor is specifically needed for correct transcription of 5 S RNA genes. It is probable that the tRNA box A region and its duplicated equivalent in the 5 S RNA genes interact with similar components of the transcriptional machinery (and perhaps with the RNA polymerase III itself) whereas the 5 S RNA-specific cofactor interacts with the last 12 nucleotides of the internal promoter region (box C). In a recent study Sakonju *et al.* (1981) have shown that precisely this region is necessary and sufficient to bind the 5 S RNA-specific cofactor. It will be interesting to analyze in detail the interaction between the first and the second half of the 5 S RNA internal promoter and between box A and box B of tRNA genes, in order to establish their respective role in transcription.

ACKNOWLEDGMENTS

This article has been improved by the careful criticism of Dr. Vincenzo Pirrotta. We also thank Prof. Tina Pietropaolo for useful suggestions and Wendy Moses for typing the manuscript.

REFERENCES

Abelson, J. (1979). *Annu. Rev. Biochem.* **48**, 1035–1069.
Akusjärvi, G., Mathews, M. B., Andersson, P., Vennström, B., and Pettersson, U. (1980). *Proc. Natl. Acad. Sci. U.S.A.* **77**, 2424–2428.
Baer, B. W., and Kornberg, R. D. (1979). *J. Biol. Chem.* **254**, 9678–9681.

Baralle, F. E., Shoulders, C. C., Goodbourn, S., Jeffreys, A., and Proudfoot, N. J. (1980). *Nucleic Acids Res.* **8,** 4393–4404.

Beckmann, J. S., Johnson, P. F., and Abelson, J. (1977). *Science* **196,** 205–208.

Benoist, C., and Chambon, P. (1981). *Nature (London)* **290,** 304–310.

Bentley, D., and Rabbitts, T. (1980). *Nature (London)* **288,** 730–733.

Birkenmeier, E. H., Brown, D. D., and Jordan, E. (1978). *Cell* **15,** 1077–1086.

Bogenhagen, D. F., and Brown, D. D. (1981). *Cell* **24,** 261–270.

Bogenhagen, D. F., Sakonju, S., and Brown, D. D. (1980). *Cell* **19,** 27–35.

Bogenhagen, D. F., Wormington, W. M., and Brown, D. D. (1982). *Cell* **28,** 413–421.

Brown, D. D., and Fedoroff, N. V. (1978). *In* "Cell Differentiation and Neoplasia" (G. F. Saunders, ed.), pp. 297–303. Raven, New York.

Brown, D. D., and Gurdon, J. B. (1977). *Proc. Natl. Acad. Sci. U.S.A.* **74,** 2064–2068.

Brown, D. D., and Gurdon, J. B. (1978). *Proc. Natl. Acad Sci. U.S.A.* **75,** 2849–2853.

Brown, R. D., and Brown, D. D. (1976). *J. Mol. Biol.* **102,** 1–14.

Calabretta, B., Robberson, D. L., Maizel, A. L., and Saunders, G. F. (1981). *Proc. Natl. Acad. Sci. U.S.A.* **78,** 6003–6007.

Castagnoli, L., Ciliberto, G., and Cortese, R. (1982). *Nucleic Acids Res.* **10,** 4135–4145.

Chamberlin, M. J. (1976). *In* "RNA Polymerase" (R. Losick and M. Chamberlin, eds.), pp. 17–67. Monograph Series, Cold Spring Harbor Laboratory, Cold Spring Harbor, New York.

Ciampi, M. S., Melton, D. A., and Cortese, R. (1982). *Proc. Natl. Acad. Sci. U.S.A.* **79,** 1388–1392.

Ciliberto, G., Castagnoli, L., Melton, D. A., and Cortese, R. (1982a). *Proc. Natl. Acad. Sci. U.S.A.* **79,** 1195–1199.

Ciliberto, G., Traboni, C., and Cortese, R. (1982b). *Proc. Natl. Acad. Sci. U.S.A.* **79,** 1921–1925.

Ciliberto, G., Raugei, G., Costanzo, F., Dente, L., and Cortese, R. (1983). Submitted.

Clarkson, S. G., and Birnstiel, M. L. (1973). *Cold Spring Harbor Symp. Quant. Biol.* **38,** 451–459.

Clarkson, S. G., and Kurer, U. (1976). *Cell* **8,** 183–195.

Clarkson, S. G., Koski, R. A., Corlet, J., and Hipskind, R. A. (1981). *In* "Developmental Biology using Purified Genes" (D. D. Brown and C. F. Fox, eds.). ICN-UCLA Symposia on Molecular and Cellular Biology, Vol. 23. Academic Press, New York.

Cortese, R., Melton, D. A., Tranquilla, T., and Smith, J. D. (1978). *Nucleic Acids Res.* **5,** 4593–4611.

Cortese, R., Harland, R., and Melton, D. A. (1980). *Proc. Natl. Acad. Sci. U.S.A.* **77,** 4147–4151.

Cremisi, C., Pignatti, P. F., Croissant, D., and Yaniv, M. (1976). *J. Virol.* **17,** 204–211.

Darnell, J. E., Jr. (1979). *Prog. Nucleic Acids Mol. Biol.* **23,** 228–290.

De Franco, D. D., Schmidt, O., and Söll, D. (1980). *Proc. Natl. Acad. Sci. U.S.A.* **77,** 3365–3368.

Dente, L., Fasano, O., Costanzo, F., Traboni, C., Ciliberto, G., and Cortese, R. (1982). *EMBO J.* **1,** 817–820.

De Robertis, E. M., and Olson, M. W. (1979). *Nature (London)* **278,** 137–143.

De Robertis, E. M., Black, P., and Nishikura, K. (1981). *Cell* **23,** 89–93.

Dierks, P., Van Ooyen, A., Mantei, N., and Weissmann, C. (1981). *Proc. Natl. Acad. Sci. U.S.A.* **78,** 1411–1415.

Dingermann, T., Sharp, S., Appel, B., De Franco, D., Manet, S., Heiermann, R., Pongs, O., and Söll, D. (1981). *Nucleic Acids Res.* **9,** 3907–3918.

Dingwall, C., Lomonossoff, G. P., and Laskey, R. A. (1981). *Nucleic Acids Res.* **9,** 2659–2673.

Duncan, C. H., Biro, P. A., Choudary, P. W., Elder, J. T., Wang, R. R. C., Forget, B. G., de Riel, J. K., and Weissman, S. M. (1979). *Proc. Natl. Acad. Sci. U.S.A.* **76**, 5095–5099.

Duncan, C. H., Yagadeeswaran, P., Wang, R. R. C., and Weissman, S. M. (1981). *Gene* **13**, 185–196.

Elder, J. T., Pan, J., Duncan, C. H., and Weissman, S. M. (1981). *Nucleic Acids Res.* **9**, 1171–1190.

Engelke, D. R., Ng, S. Y. N., Shastry, B. S., and Roeder, R. G. (1980). *Cell* **19**, 717–728.

Erdman, V. A. (1981). *Nucleic Acids Res.* **8**, r25–r42.

Faye, G., Leung, D. W., Tatchell, K., Hall, B. D., and Smith, M. (1981). *Proc. Natl. Acad. Sci. U.S.A.* **78**, 2258–2268.

Fedoroff, N., Wellauer, P. K., and Wall, R. (1977). *Cell* **10**, 597–610.

Ford, P. J., and Southern, E. M. (1973). *Nature (London) New Biol.* **241**, 7–12.

Fowlkes, D. M., and Shenk, T. (1980). *Cell* **22**, 405–413.

Gallant, J. A. (1979). *Annu. Rev. Genet.* **13**, 393–415.

Galli, G., Hofstetter, H., and Birnstiel, M. L. (1981). *Nature (London)* **294**, 626–631.

Garber, R. L., and Gage, P. (1979). *Cell* **18**, 817–828.

Garel, J. P. (1974). *J. Theor. Biol.* **43**, 211–225.

Garel, J. P. (1976). *Nature (London)* **260**, 805–806.

Garrett, R. A., Bouthwaite, S., and Noller, H. F. (1981). *Trends Biochem. Sci.* **6**, 137–139.

Gauss, D. H., and Sprinzl, M. (1981). *Nucleic Acids Res.* **9**, r1–r23.

Goodman, H. M., Olson, M. V., and Hall, B. D. (1977). *Proc. Natl. Acad. Sci. U.S.A.* **74**, 5453–5457.

Gottesfeld, J. M., and Bloomer, S. L. (1980). *Cell* **21**, 751–760.

Grigliatti, T. A., White, B. M., Tener, G. M., Kaufman, T. C., Holden, J. J., and Suzukji, D. T. (1973). *Cold Spring Harbor Symp. Quant. Biol.* **38**, 461–474.

Grosschedl, R., and Birnstiel, M. L. (1980a). *Proc. Natl. Acad. Sci. U.S.A.* **77**, 1432–1436.

Grosschedl, R., and Birnstiel, M. L. (1980b). *Proc. Natl. Acad. Sci. U.S.A.* **77**, 7102–7106.

Grüss, P., Dhar, R., and Khoury, G. (1981). *Proc. Natl. Acad. Sci. U.S.A.* **78**, 943–947.

Guarente, L., and Ptashne, M. (1981). *Proc. Natl. Acad. Sci. U.S.A.* **78**, 2199–2203.

Guilfoyle, R., and Weinmann, R. (1981). *Proc. Natl. Acad. Sci. U.S.A.* **78**, 3378–3382.

Gundelfinger, E., Saumweber, H., Dallendörfer, A., and Stein, H. (1980). *Eur. J. Biochem.* **3**, 395–401.

Hagenbüchle, O., Larson, D., Hall, G. I., and Sprague, K. V. (1979). *Cell* **18**, 1217–1229.

Harada, F., and Kato, N. (1980). *Nucleic Acids Res.* **8**, 1273–1283.

Hattlen, L., and Attardi, G. (1971). *J. Mol. Biol.* **50**, 535–553.

Haynes, S. R., Toomey, T. P., Leinwand, L., and Jelinek, W. R. (1981). *Mol. Cell. Biol.* **1**, 573–583.

Heilig, R., Perrin, F., Gannon, F., Mandel, J. L., and Chambon, P. (1980). *Cell* **20**, 625–637.

Hentschel, C. C., and Birnstiel, M. L. (1981). *Cell* **25**, 301–313.

Hofstetter, H., Kressman, A., and Birnstiel, M. L. (1981). *Cell* **24**, 573–585.

Honda, B. M., and Roeder, R. G. (1980). *Cell* **22**, 119–126.

Houck, C. M., Rinehart, F. P., and Schmid, C. W. (1979). *J. Mol. Biol.* **132**, 283–306.

Hovemann, B., Sharp, S., Yamada, H., and Söll, D. (1980). *Cell* **19**, 889–895.

Ingles, C. J., Beatty, B. G., Guialis, A., Pearson, M. L., Crerar, M. M., Lobban, P. E., Siminovitch, L., and Buchwald, M. (1976). *In* "RNA Polymerase" (R. Losick and M. Chamberlin, eds.), pp. 835–853. Monograph Series, Cold Spring Harbor Lab., Cold Spring Harbor, New York.

Jacq, C., Miller, J. R., and Brownlee, G. G. (1977). *Cell* **12**, 109–120.

Jaehning, J. A., Woods, P. S., and Roeder, R. G. (1977). *J. Biol. Chem.* **252**, 8762–8771.

Jagadeeswaran, P., Forget, B. G., and Weissman, S. M. (1981). *Cell* **26**, 141–142.

Jahn, C., Hutchison, C. A., Philips, S. J., Weaver, S., Haigwood, N. L., Voliva, C. F., and Edgell, M. H. (1980). *Cell* **21**, 159–168.

Jelinek, W. R., and Leinwand, L. (1978). *Cell* **15**, 205–214.

Jelinek, W. R., Toomey, T. P., Leinwand, L., Duncan, C. H., Biro, P. A., Choudary, P. W., Weissman, S. M., Rubin, C. M., Houck, C. M., Deininger, P. L., and Schmid, C. W. (1980). *Proc. Natl. Acad. Sci. U.S.A.* **77**, 1398–1402.

Johnson, L. D., Henderson, A. S., and Atwood, K. C. (1974). *Cytogenet. Cell Genet.* **13**, 103–105.

Knapp, G., Ogden, R. C., Peebles, C. L., and Abelson, J. (1979). *Cell* **18**, 37–45.

Koch, W., Edwards, K., and Kössel, M. (1981). *Cell* **25**, 203–213.

Korn, L. J., and Brown, D. D. (1978). *Cell* **15**, 1145–1156.

Korn, L. J., and Gurdon, J. B. (1981). *Nature (London)* **289**, 461–465.

Koski, R. A., Clarkson, S. G., Kurjan, J., Hall, B. D., and Smith, M. (1980). *Cell* **22**, 415–425.

Krajev, A. S., Kramerov, D. A., Skryabin, K. G., Ryskov, A. P., Bayev, A. A., and Georgiev, G. P. (1980). *Nucleic Acids Res.* **8**, 1201–1215.

Kressmann, A., Clarkson, S. G., Pirrotta, V., and Birnstiel, M. L. (1978). *Proc. Natl. Acad. Sci. U.S.A.* **76**, 1176–1180.

Lacy, E., and Maniatis, T. (1980). *Cell* **21**, 545–553.

Lauer, J., Shen, C. K. J., and Maniatis, T. (1980). *Cell* **20**, 119–130.

Lerner, M. R., and Steitz, J. A. (1981). *Cell* **25**, 298–300.

Lerner, M. R., Andrews, N. C., Miller, G., and Steitz, J. A. (1981). *Proc. Natl. Acad. Sci. U.S.A.* **78**, 805–809.

Long, E. O., and Dawid, I. E. (1980). *Annu. Rev. Biochem.* **49**, 605–629.

Louis, C., Schedl, P., Semel, B., and Worcel, A. (1980). *Cell* **22**, 387–392.

McGee, J. D., and Felsenfeld, G. (1980). *Annu. Rev. Biochem.* **49**, 1115–1156.

Manley, J. L., Fire, A., Cano, A., Sharp, P. A., and Gefter, M. L. (1980). *Proc. Natl. Acad. Sci. U.S.A.* **72**, 3855–3860.

Mao, J., Schmidt, O., and Söll, D. (1980). *Cell* **20**, 589–596.

Mathews, S. M. (1980). *Nature (London)* **285**, 575–577.

Mathews, S. M., and Pettersson, U. (1978). *J. Mol. Biol.* **119**, 293–328.

Mathis, D. J., and Chambon, P. (1981). *Nature (London)* **290**, 310–315.

Mattoccia, E., Baldi, M. I., Carrara, G., Fruscoloni, P., Benedetti, P., and Tocchini-Valentini, G. P. (1979). *Cell* **18**, 643–648.

Melton, D. A., and Cortese, R. (1979). *Cell* **18**, 1165–1172.

Melton, D. A., De Robertis, E. M., and Cortese, R. (1980a). *Nature (London)* **284**, 143–148.

Melton, D. A., Cortese, R., De Robertis, E. M., Trendelenburg, M. F., and Gurdon, J. B. (1980b). *In* "Differentiation and Neoplasia" (R. G. McKinnel, M. A. Di Berardino, M. Blumenfeld, and R. D. Bergad, eds.), pp. 8–14. Springer-Verlag, Berlin and New York.

Miller, J. R., and Melton, D. A. (1981). *Cell* **24**, 829–835.

Monstein, H. J., and Philipson, L. (1981). *Nucleic Acids Res.* **9**, 4239–4250.

Müller, F., and Clarkson, S. G. (1980). *Cell* **19**, 345–353.

Murray, V., and Holliday, R. (1979). *FEBS Lett.* **106**, 5–7.

Ng, S. Y., Parker, C. S., and Roeder, R. G. (1979). *Proc. Natl. Acad. Sci. U.S.A.* **76**, 136–140.

Nishioka, Y., Leder, A., and Leder, P. (1980). *Proc. Natl. Acad. Sci. U.S.A.* **77**, 2806–2809.

Ogden, R. C., Beckman, J. S., Abelson, J., Kang, H. S., Söll, D., and Schmidt, O. (1979). *Cell* **17**, 399–406.

Ohe, K., and Weissman, S. M. (1971). *J. Biol. Chem.* **246**, 6991–7009.

Otsuka, A., de Paolis, A., and Tocchini-Valentini, G. P. (1981). *Mol. Cell. Biol.* **1**, 269–280.

Pan, J., Elder, J. T., Duncan, C. H., and Weissman, S. M. (1981). *Nucleic Acids Res.* **9**, 1151–1170.

Pardue, M. L., Brown, D. D., and Birnstiel, M. L. (1973). *Chromosoma* **42**, 191–203.

Paule, M. R. (1981). *Trends Biochem. Sci.* **6**, 128–131.

Peebles, C. L., Ogden, R. C., Knapp, G., and Abelson, J. (1979). *Cell* **18**, 27–35.

Pelham, H. R. B., and Brown, D. D. (1980). *Proc. Natl. Acad. Sci. U.S.A.* **77**, 4170–4174.

Pelham, H. R. B., Wormington, W. M., and Brown, D. D. (1981). *Proc. Natl. Acad. Sci. U.S.A.* **78**, 1760–1764.

Peterson, R. C., Doering, J. L., and Brown, D. D. (1980). *Cell* **20**, 131–141.

Prensky, W., Steffensen, D. M., and Hughs, W. L. (1973). *Proc. Nat. Acad. Sci. U.S.A.* **70**, 1060–1064.

Pribnow, D. (1979). *In* "Biological Regulation and Development" (R. F. Goldberger, ed.), pp. 250–277. Plenum, New York.

Prunell, A., and Kornberg, R. D. (1977). *Cold Spring Harbor Symp. Quant. Biol.* **42**, 103–108.

Pukkila, V. J. (1975). *Chromosoma* **53**, 71–89.

Roeder, R. G. (1976). *In* "RNA Polymerase" (R. Losik and M. Chamberlin, eds.), pp. 285–329. Monograph Series, Cold Spring Harbor Lab., Cold Spring Harbor, New York.

Rosa, M. D., Gottlieb, E., Lerner, M. R., and Steitz, J. A. (1981). *Mol. Cell. Biol.* **1**, 785–796.

Rosenberg, M., and Court, D. A. (1979). *Annu. Rev. Genet.* **13**, 319–353.

Rubin, C. M., Houck, C. M., Prescott, L. D., Friedmann, T., and Schmid, C. W. (1980). *Nature (London)* **284**, 372–374.

Sakano, H., Yamada, S., Ikemura, T., Shimura, Y., and Ozeki, H. (1974). *Nucleic Acids Res.* **1**, 355–371.

Sakonju, S., Bogenhaven, D. F., and Brown, D. D. (1980). *Cell* **19**, 13–25.

Sakonju, S., Brown, D. D., Engelke, D., Ng, S. Y., Shastry, B. S., and Roeder, R. G. (1981). *Cell* **23**, 665–669.

Santos, T., and Zasloff, M. (1981). *Cell* **23**, 699–709.

Schmidt, O., Mao, J., Ogden, R., Beckman, J., Sakano, H., Abelson, J., and Söll, D. (1980). *Nature (London)* **287**, 750–752.

Schultz, L. D., and Hall, B. D. (1976). *Proc. Natl. Acad. Sci. U.S.A.* **73**, 1029–1033.

Schweizer, E., McKechne, C., and Halvorson, H. O. (1969). *J. Mol. Biol.* **40**, 261–277.

Segall, J., Matsui, T., and Roeder, R. G. (1980). *J. Biol. Chem.* **255**, 11986–11991.

Silverman, S., Schmidt, O., Söll, D., and Hovemann, B. (1979). *J. Biol. Chem.* **254**, 10290–10294.

Singhal, R. P., and Fallis, P. A. M. (1979). *Prog. Nucleic Acid Mol. Biol.* **23**, 228–290.

Sklar, V. E., and Roeder, R. G. (1976). *J. Biol. Chem.* **251**, 1064–1073.

Sklar, V. E., Schwartz, L. B., and Roeder, R. G. (1975). *Proc. Natl. Acad. Sci. U.S.A.* **72**, 348–352.

Sklar, V. E., Jaehning, J. A., Gage, L. P., and Roeder, R. G. (1976a). *J. Biol. Chem.* **251**, 3794–3800.

Sklar, V. E., Yamamoto, M., and Roeder, R. G. (1976b). *In* "RNA Polymerase" (K. R. Losik and M. Chamberlin, eds.), pp. 803–817. Monograph Series, Cold Spring Harbor Lab., Cold Spring Harbor, New York.

Soderlund, H., Pettersson, U., Vennstrom, B., Philipson, L., and Mathews, M. B. (1976). *Cell* **7**, 585–593.

Sprague, K. U., Hagenbückle, O., and Zuniga, M. C. (1977). *Cell* **11**, 561–570.

Sprague, K. U., Larson, D., and Morton, D. (1980). *Cell* **22**, 171–178.

Strätling, W. H. (1979). *Biochemistry* **18**, 596–603.

Struhl, K. (1981). *Proc. Natl. Acad. Sci. U.S.A.* **74**, 5255–5259.

Telford, J. L., Kressmann, A., Koski, R. A., Grosschedl, R., Müller, F., Clarkson, S. G., and Birnstiel, M. L. (1979). *Proc. Natl. Acad. Sci. U.S.A.* **76**, 2590–2594.

Thimmappaya, B., Jones, N., and Shenk, T. (1979). *Cell* **18**, 947–954.

Thoma, F., Koller, T., and Keng, A. (1979). *J. Cell. Biol.* **83**, 403–427.

Traboni, C., Ciliberto, G., and Cortese, R. (1982). *EMBO J.* **1**, 415–420.

Traboni, C., Ciliberto, G., Cesareni, G., and Cortese, R. (1983). Submitted.

Tschudi, C., and Pirrotta, V. (1982). *In* "The Cell Nucleus" (H. Busch and L. Rothblum, eds.), Vol. II. Academic Press, New York.

Valenzuela, P., Venegas, A., Weinberg, F., Bishop, R., and Rutter, W. J. (1978). *Proc. Natl. Acad. Sci. U.S.A.* **75**, 190–194.

Vanin, E. F., Goldberg, G. I., Tucker, P. W., and Smithies, O. (1980). *Nature (London)* **286**, 222–226.

Venegas, A., Quiroga, M., Zaldivar, J., Rutter, W. J., and Valenzuela, P. (1979). *J. Biol. Chem.* **254**, 12306–12309.

Vennström, B., Pettersson, O., and Philipson, L. (1978a). *Nucleic Acids Res.* **5**, 195–204.

Vennström, B., Pettersson, O., and Philipson, L. (1978b). *Nucleic Acids Res.* **5**, 205–219.

Waldron, C., and Lacroute, F. (1975). *J. Bacteriol.* **122**, 855–865.

Wasylyk, B., Kedinger, C., Corden, J., Brison, O., and Chambon, P. (1980). *Nature (London)* **285**, 267–273.

Wegnez, M., Monier, R., and Denis, H. (1972). *Febs Lett.* **25**, 13–20.

Weil, P. A., Segall, J., Harris, B., Ng, S., and Roeder, R. G. (1979). *J. Biol. Chem.* **254**, 6163–6173.

Weiner, A. M. (1980). *Cell* **22**, 209–218.

Weinmann, R., and Roeder, R. G. (1974). *Proc. Natl. Acad. Sci. U.S.A.* **71**, 1790–1794.

Weinmann, R., Brendler, T. G., Raskas, H. J., and Roeder, R. G. (1976). *Cell* **7**, 557–566.

Wimber, D. E., and Steffensen, D. M. (1970). *Science* **170**, 639–641.

Wittig, B., and Wittig, S. (1979). *Cell* **18**, 1173–1183.

Wormington, W. M., Bogenhagen, D. F., Jordan, E., and Brown, D. D. (1981). *Cell* **24**, 809–817.

Wu, G. (1980). *J. Biol. Chem.* **255**, 251–258.

Yen, P. H., Sodja, A., Cohen, M., Jr., Conrad, S. E., Wu, M., Davidson, N., and Ilgen, C. (1977). *Cell* **11**, 736–777.

Zieve, G. V. (1981). *Cell* **25**, 296–297.

NOTE ADDED IN PROOF. Recently some results relevant to the issues discussed in this article have been reported. Bogenhagen *et al.* (1982) have now proposed a molecular mechanism based on the stability of the transcriptional complexes to explain the differential regulation of oocyte-specific and somatic 5 S RNA genes. Also recently, a number of newly isolated site-directed mutants in tRNA genes box A and B (Traboni *et al.,* 1982, 1983) and a detailed study of the transcriptional properties in eukaryotic systems of a tDNA^Tyr from *E. coli* (Dente *et al.,* 1982) have provided experimental evidence for the validity of the generalized boxes hypothesis. Finally we have demonstrated that the internal control region of 5 S RNA genes is separable into two distinct transcriptional signals, one of which is structurally and functionally equivalent to tRNA genes box A (Ciliberto *et al.,* 1983).

CHAPTER 4

THE FATE OF GENES, MESSENGERS, AND PROTEINS INTRODUCED INTO *XENOPUS* OOCYTES

Charles D. Lane

LABORATORY OF DEVELOPMENTAL BIOCHEMISTRY
NATIONAL INSTITUTE FOR MEDICAL RESEARCH
LONDON, ENGLAND

I. Introduction

The fully grown *Xenopus* oocyte, a giant cell over 1 mm in diameter, can be gripped on one side using watchmakers' forceps thereby enabling a glass needle, held by a semimicromanipulator, to be inserted from the other side. The glass micropipet is connected by oil-filled tubing to a micrometer screw. Thus fluid can be squirted into the living oocyte simply by turning the micrometer screw (Gurdon, 1974). Why over the past 10 years has this process been repeated in experiments described in more than 200 scientific papers? (For more detailed reviews see Asselbergs, 1979; Gurdon, 1974; Kressman and Birnstiel, 1980; Lane and Knowland, 1975; Marbaix and Huez, 1980; Wickens and Laskey, 1981; and for general reviews see de Robertis and Gurdon, 1979; de Robertis *et al.*, 1977a; Lane, 1976.) Why have experimentalists filled oocytes with DNA (see Section III), mRNA (see Section I), proteins (see Section II), and subcellular organelles (Gurdon, 1974; McKinnell, 1978)?

CURRENT TOPICS IN
DEVELOPMENTAL BIOLOGY, VOL. 18

The introduction of a substance into a living cell yields information of two kinds: first, the properties of a component operating within the natural milieu can be revealed, and such studies complement experiments performed *in vitro*. The *Xenopus* oocyte is a cell specialized for the synthesis and storage of components used later in embryogenesis (Davidson, 1976) but, in addition, the complex architecture of the frog cell reflects the subcellular systems involved in the export and import of proteins (Dumont and Brummett, 1978; Mohun *et al.*, 1981). The oocyte is therefore a rich source of materials for use *in vitro*, as are the egg and early embryo. Thus cell-free systems active in transcription (Birkenmeier *et al.*, 1978; Wormington *et al.*, 1981), replication (Benbow *et al.*, 1977; Goldberg *et al.*, 1981; Laskey *et al.*, 1979; Richter *et al.*, 1981), chromatin assembly (Laskey *et al.*, 1977a,b), mitochondrial protein synthesis (Swanson, 1971), membrane transfer of newly made proteins (Ohlsson *et al.*, 1981) but, surprisingly, not cytosolic protein synthesis itself, are easily prepared. Consequently the oocyte, egg, and early embryo can be used to study the properties of macromolecules or subcellular organelles both by microinjection and by addition to a cell-free extract. The full benefits of such complementarity are achieved only when, as in the above examples, both the *in vivo* and *in vitro* systems employ a given cell type.

In the second place, an injected foreign substance can serve as a probe and can reveal the nature and specificity of the biochemical pathways, in particular the control systems, in operation within the living cell. Nonetheless, artifacts can arise because of course the injection of substances, especially in large quantities, perturbs the natural state. For example, chicken ovalbumin messenger injected into oocytes translates, to a certain extent, in the wrong subcellular site, giving rise to protein molecules which cannot cross the endoplasmic reticulum (Colman *et al.*, 1981a; Lane *et al.*, 1979). Such effects can be quite revealing, especially if one wishes to study the rate-limiting steps in a particular pathway and it is therefore surprising that microinjection and kinetic studies have rarely been combined. Given interest in metabolic fluxes, it is not unexpected that one such study concerns the control of glucose metabolism (Ureta, 1980; Ureta and Radojkovic, 1978, 1979). Admittedly, from the outset (Moar *et al.*, 1971) there was interest in the kinetic consequences of varying the supply of mRNA to the oocyte. The elegant study of Laskey *et al.* (1977a) demonstrated that the supply of messenger does not limit to any significant extent the overall rate of protein synthesis (see also Asselbergs *et al.*, 1979a; Lane, 1976; Lingrel and Woodland, 1974).

II. The Fate of Injected Messenger RNA

A. TRANSLATION

What happens therefore when messenger RNA is injected into an oocyte? In physical terms surprisingly little is known and there is no compelling evidence to support the widely accepted view that the mRNA distributes itself evenly throughout the oocyte. Nonetheless within minutes of injection (Gurdon et al., 1971) some of the mRNA is translated: 7 hours later most stable messengers are fully established, although very large mRNAs such as those coding for vitellogenin or avian sarcoma virus take about twice as long to reach their maximum translational activity (Asselbergs et al., 1979a; Berridge and Lane, 1976; Huez et al., 1974). The rate-limiting step in messenger recruitment may well be diffusion. The generally accepted view is that heterologous messengers engage translational machinery within the oocyte that is neither species (Lane et al., 1971) nor phylum (Kindas-Mugge et al., 1974) specific: strictly speaking most of the mRNA injection experiments performed do not establish this point because crude mRNA preparations were used. It can always be argued that species-specific factors are required for translation and were formed from other heterologous mRNAs introduced into the frog cell. Furthermore, experiments with purified messengers from nonovarian tissues of foreign species do not even prove that the apparatus within the frog oocyte lacks cell type specificity, because the alien messenger might circumvent any translational restrictions associated with a particular differentiated state. Partially purified messengers from the specialized tissues of frogs have been translated in oocytes of the same amphibian species implying the existence of some machinery lacking cell type specificity (Berridge and Lane, 1976). It can still be argued that specific factors are required for the translation of specific messengers or specific classes of messenger, provided one assumes that the oocyte has a complete array of such factors. However, the large amounts of heterologous proteins made, the competition seen between different injected messengers (Asselbergs et al., 1979a), and the competition between injected and endogenous mRNAs (Laskey et al., 1977a) suggest that all messengers use at least some common machinery. Indeed it is generally assumed that all the engaged translational machinery is the same, although it will be interesting to see if the machinery involved in the translation of membrane-bound and free messengers is exactly equivalent. Whatever the underlying mechanism, it is clear that the frog oocyte can be programmed with a wide variety of eukaryotic messengers, including some from insects, mammals, birds, viruses (see Table I), fishes, and plants (see reviews listed in the introduction).

Are there any messengers that are read with low efficiency or are not translated at all? It is clearly very difficult to answer such a question because failure to find a heterologous protein may result from the milieu in which the foreign macromolecule is deposited, or it may merely reflect limitations in the detection method. The foreign protein may be unstable or it may not be correctly modified and may then have an anomalous gel mobility (Labarca and Paigen, 1977; Lane *et al.*, 1979, Wunner *et al.*, 1980). Evidence to date suggests that all bona fide eukaryotic mRNAs function in oocytes and that other kinds of messenger are inactive. Thus synthetic polynucleotides (Woodland and Ayers, 1974), bacteriophage mRNA (Gurdon *et al.*, 1971; Marbaix and

TABLE I

VIRAL PROTEINS MADE IN *Xenopus* OOCYTES UNDER THE DIRECTION
OF INJECTED RNA AND DNA

Viral RNA or DNA	Translation Products	Modifications	References
Encephalomyo carditis RNA	Viral polypeptides	Proteolytic cleavage of precursor protein	Laskey *et al.* (1972, 1977a)
Rauscher leukemia RNA	Viral polypeptides	Proteolytic cleavage of precursor protein, glycosylation of envelope protein	Van Zaane *et al.* (1977); Asselbergs *et al.* (1980); Salden *et al.* (1976a); Reynolds *et al.* (1978)
Avian myeloblastosis RNA	Viral core proteins	Proteolytic cleavage of core precursor protein	Salden *et al.* (1976b); Ghysdael *et al.* (1977a; b)
Avian sarcoma RNA	Viral polypeptides	Proteolytic cleavage of core precursor protein	Katz *et al.* (1979)
Bovine leukaemia RNA	Viral core proteins	Proteolytic cleavage	Ghysdael *et al.* (1977a, 1979)
Mouse mammary tumor RNA	Viral proteins	Proteolytic cleavage and phosphorylation of precursor protein	Nusse *et al.* (1978)
Moloney RNA	Viral proteins	—	Hesselink *et al.* (1981)
Rabies RNA	Viral proteins	—	Wunner *et al.* (1980)
Adenovirus RNA	Viral proteins	—	de Robertis *et al.* (1977b)
Reovirus RNAs	Viral polypeptides	—	McCrae and Woodland (1981)

TABLE I (*Continued*)

Viral RNA or DNA	Translation Products	Modifications	References
Simian virus 40 and polyoma RNA	Viral poly-peptides and tumor antigens	—	Lane *et al.* (1981a)
Alfa mosaic RNA	Viral proteins	—	Van Vloten-Doting *et al.* (1977); Rutgers *et al.* (1976); Rutgers (1977)
Barley mosaic RNA	Viral proteins	—	Rutgers *et al.* (1977)
Brome mosaic RNA	Viral proteins	—	Kondo *et al.* (1975)
Cucumber mosaic virus RNA	Viral proteins	—	Schwinghamer and Symons (1977)
Tobacco mosaic RNA	Viral proteins	Proteolytic cleavage	Knowland (1974)
Citrus exocortis RNA	None	—	Semancik *et al.* (1977)
Herpes DNA	Thymidine kinase	—	McKnight and Gavis (1980); Cordingley and Preston (1981)
Polyoma and simian virus 40 DNA	Viral proteins and tumor antigens	—	Rungger and Turler (1978); Rungger *et al.* (1979a); Lane *et al.* (1981a)

Huez, 1980), and mitochondrial mRNAs (Moorman *et al.,* 1977) all fail to produce detectable amounts of product. The results obtained by Moorman *et al.* (1977) are consistent with the finding that, within the mitochondria, the opal terminator codon UGA specifies tryptophan. It is difficult to reconcile these observations with those of Eggitt and Scragg (1975) who reported that yeast mRNAs injected into the cytosol produce normal mitochondrial proteins.

B. The Relationship between the Structure and Function of Injected Messengers

The behavior *in vivo* of macromolecules which have been modified *in vitro* is of considerable interest, although the effects observed are not necessarily of physiological significance. Prokaryotic messengers are uncapped and there is direct evidence (Paterson and Rosenberg, 1979) that such mRNAs are only translated efficiently in eukaryotic systems if they are artificially capped. Removing or breaking open the cap structure of globin mRNA causes a dramatic (>95%) reduction in its ability to direct globin synthesis in oocytes (Lockard and Lane, 1978). The pioneering study by Furuichi *et al.* (1977) suggests that the physical stability of reovirus RNA in oocytes is reduced, albeit from a fairly low level, by cap removal. More recent studies (McCrae and Woodland, 1981) indicate that the capped species are in fact quite stable and that cap removal greatly destabilizes all 10 reovirus messengers. Thus direct and indirect evidence suggests that a prokaryotic mRNA could not be translated in oocytes without being capped. Nonetheless naturally occurring uncapped eukaryotic mRNAs such as satellite tobacco necrosis virus RNA may both persist and function in the frog cell.

Are there also stringent requirements for an intact 3'-poly(A) tail? An elegant series of experiments (Huez *et al.*, 1974, 1975, 1977a,b, 1978, 1981; Marbaix *et al.*, 1975, 1979) has exploited to its furthest the oocyte as an *in vivo* system for studying the relationship between structure and function. Rabbit globin mRNA lacking a poly(A) tail lacks both physical and function stability: initially it is translated, but within 24 hours over half the tailless mRNA is degraded. In contrast, normal globin mRNA translates for weeks in cultured oocytes and is at least as stable as the average endogenous messenger (Gurdon *et al.*, 1973). Stability can be restored by adding back the poly(A) tail (Huez *et al.*, 1975). There appears to be a critical tail length of about 30 adenylic residues (Nudel *et al.*, 1976). In general, messengers possessing tails are stable, but naturally occurring mRNAs lacking tails are not necessarily unstable, as shown by McCrae and Woodland (1981) for all 10 reovirus mRNAs. At first it seemed that interferon mRNA, which normally has a tail, was rather unstable in oocytes whether or not it was polyadenylated (Sehgal *et al.*, 1978). However, Marbaix and Huez (1980) argued that exported protein had not been carefully accounted for, thereby leading to a false comparison between the stabilities of normal and deadenylated interferon messengers. Soreq *et al.* (1981) refute this argument and provide evidence that poly(A) removal has little or no effect on the decay, which is biphasic ($t_{1/2}$ is 6–10 hours phase 1 and 30 hours phase 2), of fibroblast interferon messengers.

Have these oocyte injection experiments solved the mystery of the poly(A) tail? Clearly, removal of the tail destabilizes globin messenger and this structure is therefore an essential part of the molecule, as is the cap. Furthermore, the effect of tail removal is the same in HeLa cells as it is in oocytes (Huez *et al.*, 1981). Yet one does not necessarily expect parts of molecules to be stable in living cytoplasm. It is therefore significant that intact human histone messenger can be stabilized by adding a poly(A) tail (Huez *et al.*, 1978). Poly(A) itself is stable in oocytes (Allende *et al.*, 1974) and one can argue that stability would be conferred by any polynucleotide resistant to exonucleases. Woodland and Wilt (1980a,b) have shown that injected sea urchin histone mRNAs are also unstable in both oocytes and early embryos, although in oocytes a small fraction of the injected mRNA is both stable and probably remains deadenylated. Hentschel *et al.* (1980) and Probst *et al.* (1979) report that histone mRNA made under the direction of injected sea urchin genes is quite stable. These intriguing observations reopen the whole question of an obligatory relationship between mRNA stability and polyadenylation, as do the findings that deadenylated mengovirus RNA (Revel and Groner, 1978) and interferon RNA (Soreq *et al.*, 1981) are stable in oocytes.

It should perhaps be emphasized that there has to date been no systematic and general study of mRNA stability in oocytes. The relationship between the amount of mRNA injected and mRNA half-life has not been investigated in detail, although Allende *et al.* (1974), using radioactive RNA presumed to be messenger, found that unengaged mRNA was rapidly degraded. Other authors, perhaps injecting smaller amounts of RNA, noted that the stability of deadenylated globin mRNA seemed inversely related to translational efficiency (Huez *et al.*, 1977a). McCrae and Woodland (1981) injected a mixture of similar amounts of 10 radioactive reovirus mRNA species and showed that mRNA stability was quite independent of translational efficiency. It is well known that injecting large amounts of messenger does not produce correspondingly large amounts of product, and, although it seems likely, there is no proof that some of this excess mRNA is degraded.

III. Posttranslational Events in *Xenopus* Oocytes

A. SECONDARY MODIFICATION OF FOREIGN PROTEINS

The fate of translation products as well as that of messengers can be studied using the oocyte system: the destiny of newly made foreign proteins was examined initially from the standpoint of secondary modification. Thus Berns *et al.* (1972) noticed that the N-terminal methionine of αA2 crystallin was N-acetylated whether the protein was formed in oocytes or calf lens cells. Such an experiment does not prove that frog enzymes within the oocyte are capable of modifying heterologous proteins. Although partially purified (14 S) crystallin mRNA was used, one can still argue that the acetylating enzyme was made by some minor messenger species present in the injected RNA. However, recent experiments (Cutler *et al.*, 1981) with highly purified

TABLE II

FUNCTIONAL PROTEINS MADE IN FROG OOCYTES UNDER THE DIRECTION OF
FOREIGN GENES AND MESSENGER RNAS

Source of messenger RNA injected into occytes	Translation product	Bioassay	Authors
Human fibroblast	Interferon	Inhibition of viral infection	Reynolds *et al.* (1975)
Mouse kidney	β-Glucuronidase	Enzyme activity	Labarca and Paigen (1977)
Pig colostrum	Immunoglobulin	Antigen binding	Kortbeek-Jacobs and Van der Donk (1978)
Xenopus liver	Vitellogenin	Uptake by oocytes	Lane, Champion, Colman, James, and Applebaum (unpublished)
Rat spleen	Immunoglobulin	Antigen binding	Deacon and Ebringer (1979)
Herpes virus (DNA)	Thymidine kinase	Enzyme assay	McKnight and Gavis (1980)
Rat liver	Cytochrome P-450	Enzyme assay (deethylase activity)	Ohlsson *et al.* (1981)
Torpedo electric organ	Acetylcholine receptor	α-Bungarotoxin binding	Sumikawa *et al.* (1981)

messenger have established that N-glycosylation and other modifications of chicken ovalbumin occur through the action of endogenous frog enzymes. The injected oocyte can, it appears, carry out a whole range (Asselbergs, 1979) of such enzymatic reactions (see Table II), ranging from phosphorylation, hydroxylation, glycosylation, and acetylation, to signal sequence removal and further cleavage of polypeptides including viral precursors (see Tables I, II, and III). The formation of disulfide bonds and the assembly of multimeric proteins also takes place. If, as seems likely, all these reactions are carried out by endogenous oocyte enzymes, why are these heterologous proteins modified in the manner expected of their parental cell types? Perhaps it is the nature of the substrate rather than the spectrum of enzymes that determines the processing pathway. Thus mouse kappa chains are glycosylated whether formed in oocytes or plasmacytoma cells, yet a mutant kappa chain remains unglycosylated (Jilka *et al.*, 1977) when made in either cell type. Similarly, newly made egg yolk precursor proteins from locust and frog are processed differently in *Xenopus* oocytes (see Fig. 1). The locust vitellogenin is processed extensively prior to export while the frog precursor is exported intact but is then imported, cleaved, and assembled into yolk platelets.

The formation of foreign proteins within oocytes does, however, provide some evidence albeit sparse of cell type specific enzymes. Certain newly made proteins such as mouse β-glucuronidase (Labarca and Paigen, 1977) and guinea pig caseins (Lane *et al.*, 1979) have anomalous gel mobilities. The oocyte lacks significant casein kinase activity and the proteins made from injected mammary gland mRNA cannot be labeled with ATP or phosphate. Thus caseins formed in oocytes appear underphosphorylated and indeed will only electrophorese with guinea pig milk caseins if the latter have been treated with phosphatase (Pas-

TABLE III

SECONDARY MODIFICATION AND SEGREGATION OF FOREIGN PROTEINS
MADE IN *Xenopus* OOCYTES

Modification in parental cell type	Protein	References (selected examples)[a,b]
N-Acetylation	Calf lens αA2 crystallin	Berns *et al.* (1972)
Hydroxylation	Mouse fibroblast collagen	Lane and Knowland (1975)
Glycosylation	Mouse plasmacytoma immunoglobulin	Jilka *et al.* (1977)
	Thyroid stimulating hormone	Kourides and Weintraub (1979); Kourides *et al.* (1979)
	Rat prostatic binding protein	Mous *et al.* (1979)
	Human chorionic gonadotrophin	Mous *et al.* (1980)
	Chicken ovalbumin	Colman *et al.* (1981b)
	Rat immunoglobulin	Deacon and Ebringer (1977, 1979)
Signal sequence removal	Mouse plasmacytoma immunoglobulin light chain	Mach *et al.* (1973)
	Mouse (MOPC 321) kappa chain	Jilka *et al.* (1979)
	Honey bee venom gland promelittin	Lane *et al.* (1981b)
Phosphorylation	Trout testis protamine	Gedamu *et al.* (1978)
Cleavage of polyprotein	*Xenopus* liver vitellogenin	Berridge and Lane (1976)
	Viral polyproteins	See Table I
S–S bond formation	Rabbit uteroglobulin	Beato and Rungger (1975)
	Immunoglobulins (Various)	Deacon and Ebringer (1977, 1979) Valle *et al.* (1981)

(*continued*)

TABLE III (*Continued*)

Modification in parental cell type	Protein	References (selected examples)[a,b]
Noncovalent assembly of protein subunits	Calf α- and β-crystallins	Asselbergs *et al.* (1978, 1979b)
	Mouse kidney β-glucuronidase	Labarca and Paigen (1977)
Noncovalent metalloporphyrin addition	Sumikawa *et al.* (1981²)
	Acetylcholine receptor	
	Rabbit hemoglobin (tetramer)	Lane (unpublished)
Protein export	Guinea pig milk proteins	Colman and Morser (1979)
Protein sequestration within vesicles	*Xenopus* liver albumin	Zehavi-Willner and Lane (1977)
	Mouse immunoglobulins	Winberry *et al.* (1980)
Insertion of integral membrane protein	Rat liver epoxide hydratase	Ohlsson *et al.* (1981)
Assembly into yolk platelets	*Xenopus* liver phosvitin and lipovitellin	Berridge and Lane (1976)
Assembly into ribosomal subunits	*E. coli* and *Artemia salina* acidic proteins	Kalthoff and Richter (1979)
Assembly into protein bodies	Maize storage proteins	Hurkman *et al.* (1981)
Entry into nuclei	*Xenopus* nuclear proteins	de Robertis *et al.* (1978)

[a] For a more complete set of references see Lane and Knowland (1975), Lane *et al.* (1981a), Colman *et al.* (1981a), and especially Asselbergs (1979). An attempt has been made to cite references which add to the extensive list compiled by the latter author.

[b] Acetylcholine receptors are, surprisingly, also present in uninjected oocytes (Kusano *et al.*, 1977).

cal, Boulton, Lane, and Craig, unpublished). Thyroglobulin is probably not iodinated (Vassart *et al.*, 1975) and β-crystallin fails to assemble correctly in oocytes (Asselbergs *et al.*, 1979a,b).

The frog cell also fails to remove the pro sequence from insulin (Rapoport, 1981), and promelittin, which is not even exported to any significant extent, also remains intact. Promelittin made in oocytes behaves anomalously and has therefore been analyzed in some detail (Kindas-Mugge *et al.*, 1974; Lane *et al.*, 1981b). The N-terminus of the molecule is "frayed" as is the promelittin of the venom gland cell: yet in the oocyte further removal of dipeptides is so slow that melittin formation cannot even be detected. At the C-terminus, the oocyte product fails to undergo transamidation to form the characteristic glutamine amide moiety. Thermodynamic calculations (Von Heijne, 1980) and the results of subcellular fractionation experiments suggest that the hydrophobic promelitting molecule becomes marooned within intracellular membranes of the oocyte. As a rule, however, foreign proteins are

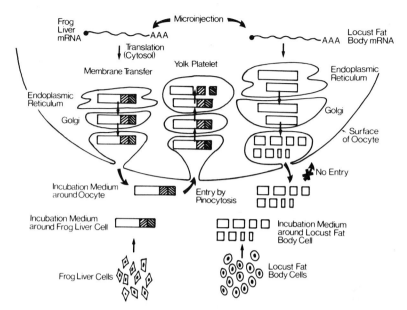

FIG. 1. The fate of *Xenopus* and locust vitellogenins made in *Xenopus* oocytes: an export–import-processing model. Microinjection of locust fat body or *Xenopus* liver messenger leads to the synthesis and sequestration within membranes of high-molecular-weight vitellogenin species. A single band of about M_r 210,000 is seen with frog mRNA while in oocytes programmed with locust messenger a doublet, shown by peptide mapping to be the products of two genes (Chen, 1980), is found in the range M_r 220,000–250,000. There is no direct evidence that the yolk precursors then progress through the Golgi and secretory vesicles, although such structures are present in oocytes: there is however direct evidence that some at least of the vitellogenin is exported, the locust protein probably being processed just prior to secretion. The pinocytotic uptake pathway shown is well established (see review by Wallace, 1978). The occurrence of intact frog vitellogenin in washed yolk platelets is consistent with the internally generated precursor adopting the pathway followed by exogenous frog vitellogenin. The four major locust polypeptides exported from oocytes programmed with fat body RNA migrate electrophoretically with the four major locust egg yolk proteins (vitellins). Processing of the minor locust polypeptides has not been investigated thoroughly, although minor species are seen in the expected molecular weight range. Thus as judged by SDS–gel electrophoresis, the egg yolk precursor processing pathways of the frog oocyte are characteristic of the cell used to prepare the injected RNA. The evidence that locust vitellogenins do not rapidly enter frog oocytes is provided by gel analysis of subcellular fractions, but entry followed by rapid degradation has not been ruled out. The above model is consistent with the effect on the conversion of internally generated *Xenopus* vitellogenin of a variety of externally applied agents. Thus mRNA directed yolk platelet formation is inhibited by antivitellogenin antibodies, excess unlabeled vitellogenin, other (uninjected) oocytes, and various drugs (tunicamycin, colchicine, and cytocholasin). There is evidence to suggest that at least the antibodies and the whole oocytes act externally. However it must be stressed that such observations do not prove the export–import-processing model nor do they exclude the existence or purely internal pathways of messenger directed platelet protein formation (Lane, Champion, Colman, James, and Applebaum, unpublished).

processed faithfully and are, therefore, biologically active (see Table III). Interferon mRNA is routinely assayed by microinjection (Reynolds *et al.,* 1975) and human fibroblast interferon exported from oocytes retains its cell type specificity (Morser and Colman, unpublished). Catalytically active thymidine kinase is formed in oocytes under the direction of DNA introduced directly into the nucleus, an elegant demonstration (Cordingley and Preston, 1981; McKnight and Gavis, 1980) that, if the appropriate naked DNA sequence is presented all subsequent steps in the gene expression pathway take place automatically (see reviews by de Robertis and Gurdon, 1979; Lane, 1976). Since protein processing enzymes are often topologically segregated, correct processing of foreign proteins implies correct interaction with the macromolecular sorting machinery of the frog cell.

B. The Fate of Foreign Proteins and Transfer RNAs in Oocytes

The mechanisms responsible for directing specific proteins to specific subcellular destinations are not well understood, and the *Xenopus* oocyte microinjection system provides an *in vivo* approach to the so ing problem. The direct injection of proteins permits analysis of the restrictions governing entry into the nucleus (Bonner, 1975a,b, 1980; Gurdon, 1970). Most nuclear proteins have a specific affinity for the nucleus of the oocyte (de Robertis *et al.,* 1978). Rather surprisingly, disrupting the nuclear membrane with a microinjection needle fails to abolish the selectivity of the uptake process (Feldherr and Ogburn, 1980).

The fate of nascent chains is often different from that of completed polypeptides and it is frequently more revealing to study the interaction with the protein sorting machinery of macromolecules formed *in situ.* In the first such experiment, liver mRNA was found to program the synthesis of vitellogenin which was subsequently converted to lipovitellin and phosvitin, the latter products being assembled into yolk platelets (Berridge and Lane, 1976). Injected vitellogenin was merely degraded and it seemed that the purified protein could only act as a precursor when presented to the surface of the oocyte (Wallace, 1978). Yet the oocyte was regarded as a closed system. The first light to be shed on this paradox came from further experiments combining mRNA injection with subcellular fractionation. Newly made albumin, milk proteins, and vitellogenin were found sequestered within membranous vesicles which could be isolated by sucrose gradient centrifugation (Zehavi-Willner and Lane, 1977). Then Lebleu *et al.* (1978) noticed that when oocytes were programmed with RNA from virus-infected mouse cells, interferon could be detected by bioassay in the surrounding medium. Proof that the oocyte is indeed a secretory cell was provided by the elegant work of Colman and Morser (1979), in which leakage artifacts were ruled out by coinjecting mRNAs coding for globin and milk proteins, only the latter being exported. The *Xenopus* oocyte can be used as a surrogate secretory system (Lane *et al.*, 1981a) and will export proteins made by messengers from plants, insects, birds, and mammals, the exception being honey been venom gland RNA which directs the synthesis but not the export, at least in detectable amounts, of melittin or promelittin (Lane *et al.*, 1981b).

The paradoxical results obtained with vitellogenin mRNA could now be explained by an export–import-processing model (see Fig. 1). The addition to the surrounding medium of antivitellogenin antibodies blocks mRNA-directed yolk platelet formation, as predicted by the model. Moreover, if defolliculated oocytes are used (the procedure seems to decrease recapture of secreted vitellogenin) yolk platelet proteins made under the direction of injected mRNA accumulate within the platelets of uninjected oocytes present in the same incubation vessel (Lane, Champion, Colman, James, and Appelbaum, unpublished).

What are the requirements for the secretion of foreign proteins from oocytes? Not surprisingly, topological segregation is a prerequisite for export: miscompartmentalized ovalbumin whether formed *in situ* (and lacking glycosyl residues) or introduced by injection, remains trapped within the cytosol while unglycosylated ovalbumin, made by tunicamycin treatment of oocytes, is secreted, as is the correctly modified eggwhite protein (Colman *et al.*, 1981a). The export of heterologous proteins is inhibited by colchicine. Cytocholasin acts synergistically suggesting that microtubules stabilized by microfilaments are required for the release of foreign proteins from oocytes (Colman *et al.*, 1981b). Certain aspects of the secretory process depend on the kind of protein being exported and indeed the oocyte system is well suited to the study of such interactions. Valle *et al.* (1981) have demonstrated that H and L immunoglobulin chains are exported only in a stoichiometric (1:1) ratio: there is an absolute requirement for light chains. Interaction at the protein subunit level can take place even when separated heavy and light chain mRNAs are injected into different poles of the oocyte. Thus either the mRNAs or their products diffuse thereby permitting subunit assembly.

Does the oocyte normally use the functional secretory system revealed by mRNA microinjection experiments? Mohun *et al.* (1981) answered this question by removing the layers of cells, including the tightly adhering follicle cells, which normally surround oocytes and then assaying the external medium for exported proteins. Two-dimensional gel electrophoresis revealed several polypeptides at least two of which could also be identified within a membrane vesicle fraction isolated from oocyte homogenates. These vesicles were known to be part of the secretory pathway. Further experiments showed that the surrounding layers of cells as well as the oocyte itself secrete proteins. Folliculated oocytes export proteases (Soreq and Miskin, 1981) whose activity can be abolished by adding a mixture of inhibitors.

Heterologous secretory proteins can be degraded inside as well as outside the oocyte, the extent of the loss varying with the nature of the protein and the time spent in the secretory pathway. Colman *et al.* (1981b) proposed a "conveyor belt" model, having noted that the rate of loss, allowing for both degradation and secretion, is constant for a given protein. Thus each species appears to move along the secretory pathway at a characteristic rate and is either exported or destroyed. Further evidence is required to substantiate such a model. It is nonetheless clear that different proteins, for example lysozyme and ovalbumin, are secreted at fundamentally different rates. Ovalbumin made under the direction of highly purified messenger maintains its characteristic rate of export, which suggests that the kinetics, at least in frog cells, are not influenced by any oviduct specific factors (Cutler *et al.*, 1981).

Microinjection experiments involving other subcellular compartments are rare, despite the promise of the oocyte system for studying the molecular traffic signals that govern the entry of proteins into mitochondria, lysosomes, storage granules, and membranes themselves. For example, heterologous mitochondria have been introduced into (Abramova, 1979) and survive in frog cytoplasm (Pinon *et al.*, 1975), and the oocyte is also packed with mitochondria of its own. Moreover, functional lysosomal enzymes can be made by injecting mouse cell mRNA (Labarca and Paigen, 1977). Yet there are no significant experiments on either of these two organelles. As regards storage proteins, two studies exist: first (Lane *et al.*, 1981a), it was shown that barley seed storage proteins are not exported, in contrast to other plant proteins made at the same time. Second, in a study (Hurkman *et al.*, 1979, 1981; Larkins *et al.*, 1980) which includes an improved method of subcellular fractionation, it was revealed that maize storage proteins are retained in the oocyte within structures that resemble plant protein bodies. Presumably such structures are induced by the storage proteins themselves being encoded directly by the injected mRNA. As regards membrane proteins, the synthesis, but not the fate, of the plasmalemmal glycoprotein 5'-nucleotidase was studied by Bergeron *et al.* (1975). Ohlsson *et al.* (1981) demonstrated the insertion of rat cytochrome P-450 and functional epoxide hydratase into intracellular membranes of the oocyte. The insertion process was then studied in further detail using an *in vitro* system containing *Xenopus* membranes. The frog membrane preparation provides a convenient alternative to, for example, systems which use endoplasmic reticulum from dog pancreas.

Microinjection is one obvious means of studying protein degradation *in vivo,* an important objective given the lack of suitable *in vitro* systems. Taking into account the specialized role played by storage, experiments were required to prove that the oocyte contains an active degradatory system. Studies in which protein export is disregarded (Wallace and Hollinger, 1979) do not prove the point. However, the lack of stability of primary translation products bearing detachable signal sequences provides such evidence, and has led to speculation (Lane *et al.,* 1979) that the oocyte contains proteases which correct errors of compartmentation. The concept of such error-correcting machinery can be generalized to include degradation within the cytosol of DNA (Wyllie *et al.,* 1977, 1978) or of RNA containing introns. Many injected proteins are destroyed with surprising rapidity, that is, in a matter of minutes, presumably by a nonlysosomal cytosolic enzyme system akin to that discovered in mammalian cells by Bigelow *et al.* (1981). Injected proteins can also serve as probes, for example, to prove the presence (presumably within the cytosol) of a particular protein kinase (Maller *et al.,* 1978; Masaracchia *et al.,* 1979); more generally, the introduction of specific antibodies into living oocytes is potentially very rewarding as an experimental approach. Nuclear injection of antihistone (Scheer *et al.,* 1979) and antiactin antibodies (Rungger *et al.,* 1979b) has been reported, and studies involving the introduction of antibodies raised against putative gene regulatory elements are eagerly awaited.

The fate of foreign transfer RNAs in oocytes is somewhat predictable: they appear quite stable (Allende *et al.,* 1974) and are functional (Gatica *et al.,* 1975, 1979; Gatica and Allende, 1977). Enzymes within the frog cell will catalyze the addition of 3'-terminal C-A nucleotides to tRNA species lacking these two residues (Solari *et al.,* 1977). The oocyte can therefore be used as a functional assay, for example, in the detection of eukaryotic suppressor tRNAs (Bienz *et al.,* 1980) or of impaired tRNAs produced, for example, by ethionine treatment of rats (Ginzburg *et al.,* 1979). Joshi *et al.* (1978) have demonstrated the aminoacylation and processing of turnip yellow mosaic virus RNA in oocytes, thereby confirming results obtained *in vitro* suggesting that the viral RNA is a surrogate tRNA. Specific tRNAs can also serve as probes and in the elegant experiments of Bienz *et al.* (1981) injection of suppressor tRNAs revealed that all three termination codons can be used by a given cell type, the *Xenopus* oocyte. Yeast mitochondrial tryptophanyl transfer RNA_{Trp} also functions as a suppressor when introduced into the cytoplasm of the frog cell (Grosjean *et al.*, 1981) provided that (Martin *et al.*, 1981), if the tRNA is not already activated, some *E. coli* acylating enzyme is coinjected. Such studies complement those on the microinjection of tRNAs, including suppressor tRNAs (Capecchi *et al.*, 1980), into somatic cells (see review by Celis *et al.*, 1980).

IV. The Introduction of Foreign Genes into Oocytes

DNA was first injected into eggs and oocytes of *Xenopus* in 1969 (Gurdon *et al.*, 1969; Gurdon and Speight, 1969), but the aim of this pioneering investigation was the study of gene replication. As reviewed by Harland and Laskey (1980), Laskey *et al.* (1979), and Laskey and Harland (1981) the above approach has born fruit. Transcription of microinjected templates was first investigated by Knowland (1971). Colman (1975) introduced synthetic, mammalian, and viral templates into eggs and oocytes: in these important experiments high voltage paper electrophoresis established beyond doubt that transcription of the heterologous DNA had occurred. However, the results were variable and a second breakthrough was required before the system could be used to study the control of transcription. Thus Gurdon *et al.* (1976a,b) found that nuclei could be deposited within the nucleus of the oocyte and once there swelled (Gurdon, 1976) and became transcriptionally very active. The nucleus of the oocyte is so large that direct injection of substances is really very easy, yet the prospect had daunted earlier investigators. Purified DNA molecules were soon injected (Mertz and Gurdon, 1977), the initial studies focusing on SV40 transcription. Genes transcribed by polymerase I were then shown to be active, whether derived from cloned ribosomal genes (Brown and Gurdon, 1977, 1978) or from purified ribosomal DNA (Gurdon and Brown, 1977, 1978). Individual transcription complexes formed by the injected DNA can be seen by electron microscopy (Trendelenburg *et al.*, 1978, 1980; Trendelenburg and Gurdon, 1978). In another important series of experiments Kressman *et al.* (1977, 1978, 1979) developed an even simpler method of injecting DNA (in this case tRNA genes) into nuclei. Oocytes were lightly centrifuged so as to bring the nucleus to the surface of the pigmented pole, where it could be seen as a translucent body lying just below the cell surface. Now the target was visible, it was easy to insert the micropipet to exactly the right distance. Using this method, the Swiss group have also analyzed in detail the relationship between sequence and function within the sea urchin histone gene repeating unit (Grosschedl and Birnstiel, 1980a,b; Hentschel et al., 1980; Probst et al., 1979). In this context, gene function includes the production of authentic histone proteins (Etkin and Maxson, 1980; de Robertis and Mertz, 1977). Such genes are of course transcribed by polymerase II and it only required further studies on heterologous tRNA genes, namely, those from yeast (de Robertis and Olson, 1979) and from nematodes (Cortese et al., 1978), to demonstrate that the oocyte system could be used to investigate transcription by all three classes of polymerase. The experiments on tRNA formation have also been very detailed and have shed light on sites of modification and processing, including splicing, as well as on transcription itself (Cortese et al., 1980; Hofstetter et al., 1981; Melton et al., 1980; Melton and Cortese, 1979; Telford et al., 1979). It is clear that the enzymes of the frog cell can recognize the splicing signals present on a variety of heterologous transcripts (Rungger and Turler, 1978). For example, ovalbumin is formed by injected ovalbumin genes, although splicing efficiency may well be lower than in the parental cell type (Wickens et al., 1980; see also Ladner et al., 1979). The splicing enzymes are located within the nucleus, but not apparently within the nuclear membrane (de Robertis et al., 1981).

Nuclear injection of centrifuged oocytes is described with clarity in the review by Kressman and Birnstiel (1980). Other oocyte microinjection systems have been described (Contreras et al., 1981; Hengst, 1977), that of Hitchcock and Friedman (1980) being semiautomatic, but it should be emphasized that nuclear injection is not a difficult technique (see apparatus described by Stephens et al., 1981). Consequently there is a rapidly growing literature on transcriptional studies in oocytes as can be seen from the review by Wickens and Laskey (1981). It is difficult even using centrifuged oocytes to ensure that DNA is always introduced into the nucleus and never into the cytoplasm. Fortunately, for most experiments this does not matter. If covalently closed, supercoiled DNA is injected into the cytoplasm the polymer is first relaxed, then nicked, then linearized, and then cleaved by an endonuclease. Similar polymers introduced into the nucleus are also relaxed but then form new supercoiled structures and finally, in the case of SV40 DNA, minichromosomes. Wyllie et al. (1977, 1978) concluded their important study on the fate of injected DNA by showing that linear species are degraded within the oocyte nucleus, presumably by an exonuclease, during which time however some transcripts are formed.

Why do oocytes transcribe injected genes? Why are the normal control mechanisms seemingly overridden? Nearly all DNA microinjection experiments reported have involved the infusion of vast numbers of genes, and so it is possible that the normal control mechanisms operate at physiological gene dosages. It is also conceivable that heterologous genes circumvent the control systems, and there are few examples of the injection of *Xenopus* genes, especially those coding for proteins. However, it is also possible that, if the right nucleotide sequences are present, naked DNA is always transcriptionally active. For example, Miller and Melton (1981) could detect the activity of a *Xenopus* 5 S RNA pseudogene which in *Xenopus* oocytes is normally dormant, or at least whose activity cannot be detected. Must the DNA be in the correct form, that is to say assembled into a chromosome, if the cytoplasm of the oocyte is to impose a specific pattern of gene expression on material introduced by microinjection? In an elegant series of experiments the Cambridge School (de Robertis *et al.*, 1977a,b,c; de Robertis and Gurdon, 1977, 1979; Gurdon, 1977) has shown that injected nuclei respond selectively to transcriptional control elements present in the cytosol of the oocyte. For example, kidney cell nuclei from newts express proteins characteristic of newt oocytes when injected into *Xenopus* oocytes, while kidney cell functions are repressed. The transcriptional control mechanisms within the *Xenopus* oocyte therefore lack species specificity, but cell type specificity manifests itself clearly.

How can the oocyte system be used to dissect out the components involved in such developmental regulation? One approach is to remove substances from nuclei until the latter begin to lack responsiveness to cytoplasmic signals, and then to find out which factors will restore the regulated state. Korn and Gurdon (1981) have done just this and have "activated" by salt extraction 5 S RNA genes within nuclei. It will be interesting to see if the repressible state can then be restored by adding back the extracted proteins. This type of experiment is, one hopes, the precursor to more detailed *in vivo* studies on developmental regulation. One should not, however, underestimate the usefulness of *in vitro* systems, including those derived from oocytes. It will be interesting to see what role the intriguing transcriptional control element, discovered (Engelke *et al.*, 1980; Pelham *et al.*, 1981; Pelham and Brown, 1980) during *in vitro* studies on 5 S RNA transcription, plays in modulating the activity of 5 S genes introduced into whole oocytes.

V. The Use of the Oocyte as a Surrogate Gene Expression System

Will the oocyte continue to be a useful experimental system? The work of the last decade has established the frog cell as a medium for surrogate gene expression. It is clear that machinery lacking either cell type or species specificity exists within the oocyte and that all the steps from transcription of the gene to the fate of the processed protein can therefore be studied. Nonetheless, there are many other surrogate systems. Informational macromolecules can be inserted into the cells of eukaryotes by direct addition (Wigler *et al.*, 1978) or by means of viral vectors (Berg, 1981), or via liposomes (Gregoriadis, 1980), or using red cell ghosts (Kriegler and Livingstone, 1977; Loyter *et al.*, 1975; Schlegel and Rechsteiner, 1978). Furthermore in addition to frog oocytes, other cell types, including cells of normal size, can be microinjected (Graessmann and Graessmann, 1971; Stacey and Allfrey, 1976), although inserting substances into the nuclei of such cells is difficult. Oocyte microinjection is not confined to *Xenopus* (Borovkov, 1975; Brachet *et al.*, 1973; May and Glenn, 1974) nor even to amphibia: indeed Brinster *et al.*, (1980, 1981a,b) using mouse oocytes have repeated many of the basic studies on transcription and translation of heterologous macromolecules, and Gordon *et al.* (1980) as well as Wagner *et al.* (1981) and Harbers *et al.* (1981) provide evidence of transformation by injected DNA. It is relatively easy to inject defined amounts into giant cells, for example the *Xenopus* oocyte, but other large cells, such as those of protozoa (Knowles *et al.*, 1978) or algae (Cairns *et al.*, 1978) are also available.

The oocyte offers a particularly convenient general system in which to test known amounts of substances within either the nuclear or cytoplasmic compartments. As such it should continue to enjoy a certain popularity. Doubtless the relationship between the structure and the fate or function of macromolecules will be explored further using oocytes. For example, sequence manipulation at the DNA level could be correlated with topological segregation of a given protein. In theory, microinjection combined with subcellular fractionation can be used to shed light on the function of an ill-characterized translation product or of an unknown gene or messenger. The oocyte is clearly an excellent system for studying posttranslational events, but progress with cell-free systems is so rapid that, except for those processes involving complex structures, the frog cell system may not in the end prove very useful, unless one wishes to study kinetics or control mechanisms.

The use of whole cell systems for the assay of messenger RNA can be justified only in terms of special requirements, such as the need to measure a biologically active end product, or the availability of only minute amounts of mRNA, or, because of problems *in vitro* with, for example, a very large messenger. Nonetheless, when it comes to the control of protein synthesis the system still has potential. The interaction of exogenous mRNAs with putative control elements, either exogenous (Giglioni *et al.,* 1973) or endogenous, can be investigated as can regulation of the endogenous mRNAs, many of which are at any given time unengaged and are possibly masked (Davidson, 1976). The engaged messenger fraction is found both attached to the endoplasmic reticulum and free in the cytosol, and the rules governing this allocation can also be studied by oocyte microinjection.

The mechanisms involved in transcription and processing are also amenable to analysis by oocyte injection, but once again *in vivo* work is likely to center on the control of these processes. It seems likely that the focus will be on developmental regulation, because many of the basic questions concerning promoters, splicing signals, and so forth can now be studied *in vitro.* Furthermore, interest in the mechanism behind variable gene expression leads to interest in the oocyte per se: hopefully, many studies will focus on the nature of the oocyte as the precursor to the totipotent egg cell. Microinjection experiments can of course be performed with eggs, and the potential of the *Xenopus* egg as a surrogate gene expression system should not be neglected. Stable macromolecules injected into eggs end up in differentiated cells, hence the interest in the system. Thus mammalian globin messengers persist (Gurdon *et al.,* 1974) and are translationally active within the tissues of both early (Froehlich *et al.,* 1977) and late frog embryos, and there is good evidence that even differentiated muscle cells can make rabbit globin (Woodland *et al.,* 1979). Injected frog muscle actin mRNA can be translated by early embryos while endogenous α-actin synthesis cannot be detected until the gastrula stage (Sturgess *et al.,* 1980). During early development, injected rabbit globin mRNA but not poly(A) is unequally distributed between different cell types (Froehlich *et al.,* 1977). Injected histone messenger has a short half-life (Woodland and Wilt, 1980b). Studies on interspecific hybrids have revealed that the maternal stockpile of histone mRNA is also turned over quite rapidly, and by the gastrula stage is largely replaced by newly synthesized transcripts (Woodland, 1980; Woodland *et al.,* 1979).

Globin genes introduced directly into the egg seem both to persist and to override the control mechanisms which so clearly repress the endogenous globin genes: heterologous transcripts can be detected, at least up to the gastrula stage. The injected foreign genes also seem to be replicated (Bendig, 1981). Integration has not as yet been studied, but the possibility that developmental regulation can be investigated by injecting genes into frogs eggs is causing considerable excitement. Thus the egg and oocyte of *Xenopus* are of intrinsic interest to the embryologist investigating amphibian development but these giant cells with their stockpiles of components can also be used for both *in vivo* and *in vitro* studies on genes from other organisms and other tissues.

ACKNOWLEDGMENTS

The ideas and assistance of J. Champion and R. Harris are gratefully acknowledged, as are the comments of Dr. R. Mohun, Dr. R. Craig, Dr. J. Morser, Dr. A. Boulton, Dr. J. Pascal, and Dr. A. Colman are thanked for giving access to results prior to publication.

REFERENCES

Abramova, N. B. (1979). *Ontogenez* **10**, 401–405.
Allende, C. C., Allende, J. E., and Firtel, R. E. (1974). *Cell* **2**, 189–196.
Asselbergs, F. A. M., Koopmans, M., Van Venrooij, W. J., and Bloemendal, H. (1978). *Eur. J. Biochem.* **91**, 65–78.
Asselbergs, F. A. M. (1979). *Mol. Biol. Rep.* **5**, 199–208.
Asselbergs, F. A. M., Van Venrooij, W. J., and Bloemendal, H. (1979a). *Eur. J. Biochem.* **94**, 249–254.
Asselbergs, F. A. M., Koopmans, M., Van Venrooij, W. J., and Bloemendal, H. (1979b). *Exp. Eye Res.* **28**, 475–482.
Asselbergs, F. A. M., Salden, M. H. L., and Bloemendal, H. (1980). *Eur. J. Biochem.* **109**, 395–403.
Beato, M., and Rungger, D. (1975). *FEBS Lett.* **59**, 305–309.
Benbow, R. M., Breaux, C. B., Joenje, H., Krauss, M. R., Lennox, R. W., Nelson, E. M., Wang, N. S., and White, S. H. (1977). *Cold Spring Harbor Symp. Quant. Biol.* 597–602.
Bendig, M. M. (1981). *Nature (London)* **292**, 65–67.
Berg, P. (1981). *Science* **213**, 296–303.
Bergeron, J. J. M., Berridge, M. V., and Evans, W. H. (1975). *Biochim. Biophys. Acta* **407**, 325–337.
Berns, A. J. M., Van Kraaikamp, M., Bloemendal, H., and Lane, C. D. (1972). *Proc. Natl. Acad. Sci. U.S.A.* **69**, 1606–1609.
Berridge, M. V., and Lane, C. D. (1976). *Cell* **8**, 283–297.
Bienz, M., Kubli, J., de Henau, S., and Grosjean, H. (1980). *Nucleic Acids Res.* **8**, 5169–5178.
Bienz, M., Kubli, E., Kohli, J., de Henau, S., Huez, G., Marbaix, G., and Grosjean, H. (1981). *Nucleic Acids Res.* **9**, 3835–3850.
Bigelow, S., Hough, R., and Rechsteiner, M. (1981). *Cell* **25**, 83–93.
Birkenmeier, E. H., Brown, D. D., and Jordan, E. (1978). *Cell* **15**, 1077–1086.Bonner, W. M. (1975a). *J. Cell Biol.* **64**, 421–430.
Bonner, W. M. (1975b). *J. Cell Biol.* **64**, 431–437.
Bonner, W. M. (1980). *In* "The Cell Nucleus" (H. Busch, ed.), Vol. 6, Chromatin Part C, pp. 97–144. Academic Press, New York.
Borovkov, A. I. (1975). *Dokl. Akad. Nauk. USSR* **223**, 751–753.
Brachet, J., Huez, G., and Hubert, E. (1973). *Proc. Natl. Acad. Sci. U.S.A.* **70**, 543–547.
Brinster, R. L., Chen, H. Y., Trumbauer, M. E., and Avarbock, M. R. (1980). *Nature (London)* **283**, 499–501.
Brinster, R. L., Chen, H. Y., and Trumbauer, M. E. (1981a). *Science* **211**, 397–398.
Brinster, R. L., Chen, H. Y., Trumbauer, M. E., and Paynton, B. V. (1981b). *Exp. Cell Res.* **134**, 291–296.

Brown, D. D., and Gurdon, J. B. (1977). *Proc. Natl. Acad. Sci. U.S.A.* **74,** 2064–2068.
Brown, D. D., and Gurdon, J. B. (1978). *Proc. Natl. Acad. Sci. U.S.A.* **75,** 2064–2068.
Cairns, E., Gschwender, H., Primke, M., Yamakawa, M., Traub, P., and Schweiger, H. (1978). *Proc. Natl. Acad. Sci. U.S.A.* **75,** 5557–5559.
Capecchi, M. R., von der Haar, R. A., Capecchi, N. E., and Sveda, M. M. (1980). *Cell* **12,** 371–381.
Celis, J. E., Kaltoft, K., Celis, A., Fenwick, R. G., and Laskey, C. T. (1980). *In* "Nonsense Mutations and tRNA Suppressors" (J. E. Celis and J. D. Smith, eds.), pp. 255–276. Academic Press, New York.
Chen, T. T. (1980). *Arch. Biochem. Biophys.* **201,** 266–276.
Colman, A. (1975). *Eur. J. Biochem.* **57,** 85–96.
Colman, A., and Morser, J. (1979). *Cell* **17,** 517–526.
Colman, A., Lane, C. D., Craig, R., Boulton, A., Mohun, T., and Morser, J. (1981a). *Eur. J. Biochem.* **113,** 339–348.
Colman, A., Morser, J., Lane, C. D., Besley, J., Wylie, C., and Valle, G. (1981b). *J. Cell. Biol.* **91,** 770–780.
Contreras, R., Cheroutre, H., and Fiers, W. (1981). *Anal. Biochem.* **113,** 185–187.
Cordingley, M. G., and Preston, C. M. (1981). *J. Gen. Virol.* **54,** 409–414.
Cortese, R., Melton, D., Tranquilla, T., and Smith, J. D. (1978). *Nucleic Acids Res.* **5,** 4593–4611.
Cortese, R., Harland, R., and Melton, D. (1980). *Proc. Natl. Acad. Sci. U.S.A.* **77,** 4147–4151.
Cutler, D., Lane, D. C., and Colman, A. (1981). *J. Mol. Biol.* **153,** 917–932.
Davidson, E. H. (1976). *In* "Gene Activity in Early Development" (E. H. Davidson, ed.). Academic Press, New York.
Deacon, N. J., and Ebringer, A. (1977). *FEBS Lett.* **79,** 191–194.
Deacon, N. J., and Ebringer, A. (1979). *Immunology* **38,** 137–144.
De Robertis, E. M., and Gurdon, J. B. (1977). *Proc. Natl. Acad. Sci. U.S.A.* **74,** 2470–2474.
De Robertis, E. M., and Gurdon, J. B. (1979). *Sci. Am.* **241,** 60–68.
De Robertis, E. M., and Mertz, J. E. (1977). *Cell* **12,** 175–182.
De Robertis, E. M., and Olson, M. (1979). *Nature (London)* **278,** 137–143.
De Robertis, E. M., Laskey, R. A., and Gurdon, J. B. (1977a). *TIBS* **2,** 250–252.
De Robertis, E. M., Partington, G. A., Longthorne, R. F., and Gurdon, J. B. (1977b). *J. Embryol. Exp. Morphol.* **40,** 199–214.
De Robertis, E. M., Gurdon, J. B., Partington, G. A., Mertz, J. E., and Laskey, R. A. (1977c). *Biochem. Soc. Symp.* **42,** 181–191.
De Robertis, E. M., Longthorne, R. F., and Gurdon, J. B. (1978). *Nature (London)* **272,** 254–256.
De Robertis, E. M., Black, P., and Nishikura, K. (1981). *Cell* **23,** 89–93.
Dumont, J. N., and Brummett, R. (1978). *J. Morphol.* **155,** 73–98.
Eggit, M. J., and Scragg, A. H. (1975). *Biochem. J.* **149,** 507–512.
Engelke, D. R., Ny, S.-Y., Shastry, B. S., and Roeder, R. G. (1980). *Cell* **19,** 717–728.
Etkin, L. D., and Maxson, R. E. (1980). *Dev. Biol.* **75,** 13–25.
Feldherr, C. M., and Ogburn, J. A. (1980). *J. Cell Biol.* **87,** 589–593.
Froehlich, J. P., Browder, L. W., and Schultz, G. A. (1977). *Dev. Biol.* **56,** 356–371.
Furuichi, Y., Lafiandra, A., and Shatkin, A. L. (1977). *Nature (London)* **266,** 235–239.
Gatica, M., and Allende, J. E. (1977). *Biochem. Biophys. Res. Commun.* **79,** 352–356.
Gatica, M., Tarrago, A., Allende, C. C., and Allende, J. E. (1975). *Nature (London)* **256,** 675–677.

Gatica, M., Solari, A., Arancibia, M., and Allende, J. E. (1979). *Arch. Biol. Med. Exp.* **12**, 427–432.

Gedamu, L., Dixon, G. H., and Gurdon, J. B. (1978). *Exp. Cell Res.* **117**, 325–334.

Ghysdael, J., Hubert, E., Travnicek, M., Bolognesi, D. P., Burny, A., Cleuter, Y., Huez, G., Kettmann, R., Marbaix, G., Portetelle, D., and Chantrenne, H. (1977a). *Proc. Natl. Acad. Sci. U.S.A.* **74**, 3230–3234.

Ghysdael, J., Hubert, E., Travnicek, M., Bolognesi, D. P., Cleuter, Y., Huez, G., Marbaix, G., Portetelle, D., and Chantrenne, H. (1977b). *Biochem. Soc. Trans.* **5**, 950–953.

Ghysdael, J., Hubert, E., and Cleuter, Y. (1977c). *Arch. Int. Phys. Biochem.* **85**, 978–979.

Ghysdael, J., Kettmann, R., and Burny, A. (1979). *J. Virol.* **29**, 1087–1098.

Giglioni, B., Gianni, A. M., Comi, P., Ottolenghi, S., and Rungger, D. (1973). *Nature (London) New. Biol.* **246**, 99–102.

Ginzburg, I., Cornelis, P., Giveon, D., and Littauer, U. Z. (1979). *Nucleic Acids Res.* **6**, 657–672.

Goldberg, E. Z., Naroditsky, B. S., Felgenhauer, P. E., Garaev, M. M., and Tikchonenko, T. I. (1981). *FEBS Lett.* **124**, 215–218.

Gordon, J. W., Scangos, G. A., Plotkin, D. J., Barbosa, J. A., and Ruddle, F. H. (1980). *Proc. Natl. Acad. Sci. U.S.A.* **77**, 7380–7384.

Graessmann, A., and Graessmann, M. (1971). *Hoppe-Seylers Physiol. Chem.* **352**, 527.

Gregoriadis, G. (1980). "Liposones in Biological Systems." Wiley, New York.

Grosjean, H., Dehenau, S., Sibler, A. P., Martin, R., Dirheimer, G., Keith, G., and Kohli, J. (1981). *Arch. Int. Physiol. Biochem.* **89**, B58–59.

Grosschedl, R., and Birnstiel, M. L. (1980a). *Proc. Natl. Acad. Sci. U.S.A.* **77**, 1432–1436.

Grosschedl, R., and Birnstiel, M. L. (1980b). *Proc. Natl. Acad. Sci. U.S.A.* **77**, 7102–7106.

Gurdon, J. B. (1970). *Proc. R. Soc. London Ser. B* **176**, 303–314.

Gurdon, J. B. (1974). *In* "The Control of Gene Expression in Animal Development." Oxford and Harvard Univ. Press, London and New York.

Gurdon, J. B. (1976). *J. Embryol. Exp. Morphol.* **36**, 523–540.

Gurdon, J. B. (1977). *Proc. R. Soc. London Ser. B* **198**, 211–247.

Gurdon, J. B., and Brown, D. D. (1977). *In* "The Molecular Biology of the Mammalian Genetic Apparatus" (P. Tso, ed.), Vol. 2, pp. 111–123. North-Holland Publ., Amsterdam.

Gurdon, J. B., and Brown, D. D. (1978). *Dev. Biol.* **67**, 346–356.

Gurdon, J. B., and Speight, V. A. (1969). *Exp. Cell Res.* **55**, 253–256.

Gurdon, J. B., Birnstiel, M. L., and Speight, V. A. (1969). *Biochim. Biophys. Acta* **174**, 614–628.

Gurdon, J. B., Lane, C. D., Woodland, H. R., and Marbaix, G. (1971). *Nature (London)* **233**, 177–182.

Gurdon, J. B., Lingrel, J. B., and Marbaix, G. (1973). *J. Mol. Biol.* **80**, 539–551.

Gurdon, J. B., Woodland, H. R., and Lingrel, J. B. (1974). *Dev. Biol.* **39**, 125–133.

Gurdon, J. B., De Robertis, E. M., and Partington, G. (1976a). *Nature (London)* **260**, 116–120.

Gurdon, J. B., Partington, G. A., and De Robertis, E. M. (1976b). *J. Embryol. Exp. Morphol.* **36**, 541–553.

Harbers, K., Jahner, D., and Jaenisch, R. (1981). *Nature (London)* **293**, 540–542.

Harland, R. M., and Laskey, R. A. (1980). *Cell* **21**, 761–771.

Heijne, G., von (1980). *Eur. J. Biochem.* **103**, 431–438.

Hengst, R. T. (1977). *Mikroskopie* **32**, 345–350.

Hentschel, C., Probst, E., and Birnstiel, M. L. (1980). *Nature (London)* **288**, 100–102.

Hesselink, W. G., van der Kamp, A. C. M., and Bloemers, H. P. J. (1981). *Virology* **110**, 375–384.

Hitchcock, M. J. M., and Friedman, R. M. (1980). *Anal. Biochem.* **109**, 338–344.

Hofstetter, H., Kressmann, A., and Birnstiel, M. L. (1981). *Cell* **24**, 573–585.

Huez, G., Marbaix, G., Hubert, E., Leclercq, M., Nudel, U., Soreq, H., Solomon, R., Lebleu, B., Revel, M., and Littauer, U. Z. (1974). *Proc. Natl. Acad. Sci. U.S.A.* **71**, 3142–3146.

Huez, G., Marbaix, G., Hubert, E., Cleuter, Y., Leclercq, M., Chantrenne, H., Soreq, H., Nudel, U., and Littauer, U. Z. (1975). *Eur. J. Biochem.* **59**, 589–592.

Huez, B., Marbaix, G., Burny, A., Hubert, E., Leclercq, M., Cleuter, Y., Chantrenne, H., Soreq, H., and Littauer, U. Z. (1977a). *Nature (London)* **266**, 473–474.

Huez, G., Marbaix, G., Weinberg, E., Gallwitz, D., Hubert, E., and Cleuter, Y. (1977b). *Biochem. Soc. Trans.* **5**, 936–937.

Huez, G., Marbaix, G., Gallwitz, D., Weinberg, E., Devos, R., Hubert, E., and Cleuter, Y. (1978). *Nature (London)* **271**, 572–573.

Huez, G., Bruck, C., and Cleuter, Y. (1981). *Proc. Natl. Acad. Sci. U.S.A.* **78**, 908–911.

Hurkman, W. J., Pederson, K., Smith, L. D., and Larkins, B. A. (1979). *Plant Physiol.* **63**, 94.

Hurkman, W. J., Smith, L. D., Richter, J., and Larkins, B. A. (1981). *J. Cell Biol.* **89**, 292–299.

Jilka, R., Cavalieri, R. L., Yaffe, L., and Pestka, S. (1977). *Biochem. Biophys. Res. Commun.* **79**, 625–630.

Jilka, R., Familletti, P., and Pestka, S. (1979). *Arch. Biochem. Biophys.* **192**, 290–295.

Joshi, S., Haenni, A. L., Hubert, E., Huez, G., and Marbaix, G. (1978). *Nature (London)* **275**, 339–341.

Kalthoff, H., and Richter, D. (1979). *Biochemistry* **18**, 4144–4147.

Katz, R. A., Maniatis, E. M., and Guntaka, R. V. (1979). *Biochem. Biophys. Res. Commun.* **86**, 447–453.

Kindas-Mügge, I., Lane, C. D., and Kreil, G. (1974). *J. Mol. Biol.* **87**, 451–462.

Knowland, J. S. (1971). Doctoral thesis, Bodleian Library, University of Oxford.

Knowland, J. (1974). *Genetics* **78**, 383–394.

Knowles, J. K. C., Lipps, H. J., and Nook, A. (1978). *Biochem. Biophys. Res. Commun.* **80**, 897–904.

Kondo, M., Marbaix, G., Moens, L., Huez, G., Cleuter, Y., and Hubert, E. (1975). *FEBS Meet. 10th, Paris* Abstract No. 352.

Korn, L. J., and Gurdon, J. B. (1981). *Nature (London)* **289**, 461–465.

Kortbeek-Jacobs, N., and van der Donk, H. (1978). *J. Immunol. Methods,* **24**, 195–199.

Kourides, I. A., and Weintraub, B. D. (1979). *Proc. Natl. Acad. Sci. U.S.A.* **76**, 298–302.

Kourides, I., Vamvakopoulos, N. C., and Maniatis, C. M. (1979). *J. Biol. Chem.* **254**, 11106–11110.

Kressmann, A., and Birnstiel, M. L. (1980). *In* "Transfer of Cell Constituents into Eukaryotic Cells" (J. E. Celis, A. Graessmann, and A. Loyter, eds.), pp. 383–407. Plenum, New York.

Kressmann, A., Clarkson, S. G., Telford, J. L., and Birnstiel, M. L. (1977). *Cold Spring Harbor Symp. Quant. Biol.* **42**, 1077–1082.

Kressmann, A., Clarkson, S. G., Pirrotta, V., and Birnstiel, M. L. (1978). *Proc. Natl. Acad. Sci. U.S.A.* **75**, 1176–1180.

Kressmann, A., Hofstetter, H., di Capua, E., Grosschedl, R., and Birnstiel, M. L. (1979). *Nucleic Acids Res.* **7**, 1749–1763.

Kriegler, M. P., and Livingstone, D. M. (1977). *Somatic Cell Genet.* **3**, 603–611.

Kusano, K., Miledi, R., and Stinnakre, J. (1977). *Nature (London)* **270**, 739–741.

Labarca, C., and Paigen, K. (1977). *Proc. Natl. Acad. Sci. U.S.A.* **74**, 4462–4465.

Ladner, M. B., Chan, L., and O'Malley, B. W. (1979). *Biochem. Biophys. Res. Commun.* **86**, 1227–1233.

Lane, C. D. (1976). *Sci. Am.* **235**, 60–71.

Lane, C. D., and Knowland, J. S. (1975). *In* "The Biochemistry of Animal Development" (R. A. Weber, ed.), Vol. 3, pp. 145–181. Academic Press, New York.

Lane, C. D., Marbaix, G., and Gurdon, J. B. (1971). *J. Mol. Biol.* **61**, 73–91.

Lane, C. D., Shannon, S., and Craig, R. (1979). *Eur. J. Biochem.* **101**, 485–495.

Lane, C. D., Colman, A., Mohun, T., Morser, J., Champion, J., Kourides, I., Craig, R., Higgins, S., James, T. C., Applebaum, S. W., Ohlsson, R. I., Paucha, E., Houghton, M., Matthews, J., and Miflin, B. J. (1981a). *Eur. J. Biochem.* **111**, 225–235.

Lane, C. D., Champion, J., Haiml, L., and Kreil, G. (1981b). *Eur. J. Biochem.* **113**, 273–281.

Larkins, B. A., Pedersen, K., Handa, A. K., Hurkman, W. J., and Smith, L. D. (1980). *Proc. Natl. Acad. Sci. U.S.A.* **76**, 6448–6452.

Laskey, R. A., and Harland, R. M. (1981). *Cell* **24**, 283–284.

Laskey, R. A., Gurdon, J. B., and Crawford, L. V. (1972). *Proc. Natl. Acad. Sci. U.S.A.* **69**, 3665–3669.

Laskey, R. A., Mills, A. D., Gurdon, J. B., and Partington, G. A. (1977a). *Cell* **11**, 345–352.

Laskey, R. A., Honda, B. M., Mills, A. D., Norris, N. R., Wyllie, A. H., Mertz, J. E., De Robertis, E. M., and Gurdon, J. B. (1977b). *Cold Spring Harbor Symp. Quant. Biol.* **42**, 171–178.

Laskey, R. A., Gurdon, J. B., and Trendelenburg, M. (1979). *Symp. Br. Soc. Dev. Biol., 4th* pp. 65–80.

Lebleu, B., Hubert, E., Content, J., De Wit, L., Braude, I. A., and de Clerq, E. (1978). *Biochem. Biophys. Res. Commun.* **82**, 665–673.

Lingrel, J. B., and Woodland, H. R. (1974). *Eur. J. Biochem.* **47**, 47–56.

Lockard, R. E., and Lane, C. D. (1978). *Nucleic Acids Res.* **5**, 3237–3247.

Loyter, A., Zakai, N., and Kulka, R. G. (1975). *J. Cell Biol.* **66**, 292–304.

McCrae, M. A., and Woodland, H. R. (1981). *Eur. J. Biochem.* **116**, 467–470.

McKinnell, R. G. (1978). "Cloning: Nuclear Transplantation in Amphibia. A Critique of Results Obtained with the Technique to Which Is Added a Discourse on the Methods of the Craft," Vol. 12, p. 319. Univ. of Minnesota Press, Minneapolis.

McKnight, S. L., and Gavis, E. R. (1980). *Nucleic Acids Res.* **8**, 5931–5948.

Mach, B., Faust, C. F., Vassali, P., and Rungger, D. (1973). *Mol. Biol. Rep.* **1**, 3–6.

Maller, J. L., Kemp, B. E., and Krebs, E. G. (1978). *Proc. Natl. Acad. Sci. U.S.A.* **75**, 248–251.

Marbaix, G., and Huez, G. (1980). *In* "The Transfer of Cell Constituents into Eukaryotic Cells" (J. E. Celis, A. Graessmann, and A. Loyter, eds.), Vol. 31, pp. 347–382. NATO Advanced Study Institutes Series A. Plenum, New York.

Marbaix, G., Huez, G., Burny, A., Cleuter, Y., Hubert, E., Leclercq, M., Chantrenne, H., Soreq, H., Nudel, U., and Littauer, V. Z. (1975). *Proc. Natl. Acad. Sci. U.S.A.* **72**, 3065–3067.

Marbaix, G., Huez, G., Soreq, H., Gallwitz, D., Weinberg, E., Devos, R., Hubert, E., and Cleuter, Y. (1979). *FEBS Meet. Gene Functions, 12th* **51**, 427–436.

Martin, R. P., Sibler, A. P., Dirheimer, G., de Henau, S., and Grosjean, H. (1981). *Nature (London)* **293**, 235–237.

Masaracchia, R. A., Maller, J. L., and Walsh, D. A. (1979). *Arch. Biochem. Biophys.* **194**, 1–12.

May, B. K., and Glenn, A. R. (1974). *Aust. J. Biol. Sci.* **27**, 585–589.

Melton, D. A., and Cortese, R. (1979). *Cell* **18**, 1165–1172.

Melton, D. A., de Robertis, E. M., and Cortese, R. (1980). *Nature (London)* **284**, 143–148.

Mertz, J. E., and Gurdon, J. B. (1977). *Proc. Natl. Acad. Sci. U.S.A.* **74**, 1502–1506.

Miller, J. R., and Melton, D. A. (1981). *Cell* **24**, 829–835.

Moar, V. A., Gurdon, J. B., Lane, C. D., and Marbaix, G. (1971). *J. Mol. Biol.* **61**, 93–104.

Mohun, T. J., Lane, C. D., Colman, A., and Wylie, C. C. (1981). *J. Embryol. Exp. Morphol.* **61**, 367–383.

Moorman, A. F. M., Verkley, F. N., Asselbergs, F. A. M., and Grivell, L. A. (1977). *In* "Genetics and Biogenesis of Mitochondria" (E. Kaudwitz, R. J. Schwegen, W. Bandlow, and K. Wolf, eds.), pp. 385–399. De Gruyter, Berlin.

Mous, J., Peeters, B., Rombauts, W., and Heyns, W. (1979). *FEBS Lett.* **103**, 81–84.

Mous, J., Peeters, B., and Rombauts, W. (1980). *FEBS Lett.* **122**, 105–108.

Nudel, U., Soreq, H., Littauer, U. Z., Marbaix, G., Huez, G., Leclercq, M., Hubert, E., and Chantrenne, H. (1976). *Eur. J. Biochem.* **64**, 115–121.

Nusse, R., Asselbergs, F. A. M., Salden, M. H. L., Michalides, R. J. A. M., and Bloemendal, H. (1978). *Virology* **91**, 106–115.

Ohlsson, R. I., Lane, C. D., and Guengerich, F. P. (1981). *Eur. J. Biochem.* **115**, 367–373.

Paterson, B. M., and Rosenberg, M. (1979). *Nature (London)* **279**, 692–696.

Pelham, H. R. B., and Brown, D. D. (1980). *Proc. Natl. Acad. Sci. U.S.A.* **77**, 4170–4174.

Pelham, H. R. B., Wormington, W. M., and Brown, D. D. (1981). *Proc. Natl. Acad. Sci. U.S.A.* **78**, 1760–1764.

Pinon, H., Barat, M., Dufresne, C., and Mounolou, J. C. (1975). *In* "Molecular Biology of Nucleocytoplasmic Relationships" (M. Puiseux-Dao, ed.), pp. 129–133. Elsevier, Amsterdam.

Probst, E., Kressman, A., and Birnstiel, M. L. (1979). *J. Mol. Biol.* **135**, 709–732.

Rapoport, T. A. (1981). *Eur. J. Biochem.* **115**, 665–669.

Revel, M., and Groner, Y. (1978). *Annu. Rev. Biochem.* **47**, 1079–1126.

Reynolds, F. H., Premkumar, E., and Pitha, P. M. (1975). *Proc. Natl. Acad. Sci. U.S.A.* **72**, 4881–4885.

Reynolds, R. K., Van De Ven, W. J. M., and Stephenson, J. R. (1978). *J. Virol.* **28**, 665–670.

Richter, A., Otto, B., and Knippers, R. (1981). *Nucleic Acids Res.* **9**, 3793–3807.

Rungger, D., and Turler, H. (1978). *Proc. Natl. Acad. Sci. U.S.A.* **75**, 6073–6077.

Rungger, D., Huber, J.-P., and Turler, H. (1979a). *Cell Biol. Int. Rep.* **3**, 183–188.

Rungger, D., Rungger-Brandle, E., Chaponnier, C., and Gabbiani, G. (1979b). *Nature (London)* **282**, 320–321.

Rutgers, A. S. (1977). Ph.D. Thesis, State University of Leiden.

Rutgers, T., Neeleman, L., Van Vloten-Doting, L., Cleuter, Y., Hubert, E., Huez, G., and Marbaix, G. (1976). *Arch. Int. Physiol. Biochem.* **84**, 654–655.

Rutgers, T., Van Vloten-Doting, L., Marbaix, G., Huez, G., Hubert, E., and Cleuter, Y. (1977). *FEBS Meet., 11th, Copenhagen* Abstracts A2-5/205/3.

Salden, M. H. L., Selten-Versteegen, A.-M., and Bloemendal, H. (1976a). *Biochem. Biophys. Res. Commun.* **72**, 610–618.

Salden, M., Asselbergs, F. A. M., and Bloemendal, H. (1976b). *Nature (London)* **259**, 696–699.

Scheer, U., Somerville, J., and Bustin, M. (1979). *J. Cell Sci.* **40**, 1–20.

Schlegel, R. A., and Rechsteiner, M. C. (1978). *Methods Cell Biol.* **20**, 341–354.

Schwinghamer, M. W., and Symons, R. H. (1977). *Virology* **79**, 88–108.

Sehgal, P., Soreq, H., and Tamm, I. (1978). *Proc. Natl. Acad. Sci. U.S.A.* **75**, 5030–5033.

Semanck, J. S., Conejero, V., and Gerhart, J. (1977). *Virology* **80**, 218–221.

Solari, A., Gatica, M., and Allende, J. E. (1977). *Nucleic Acids. Res.* **4**, 1873–1880.

Soreq, H., and Miskin, R. (1981). *FEBS Lett.* **128**, 305–310.

Soreq, H., Sagar, A. D., and Sehgal, P. B. (1981). *Proc. Natl. Acad. Sci. U.S.A.* **78**, 1741–1745.

Stacey, D. W., and Allfrey, V. G. (1976). *Cell* **9**, 725–732.

Stephens, D. L., Miller, T. J., Silver, L., Zipser, D., and Mertz, J. E. (1981). *Anal. Biochem.* **114**, 299–309.

Sturgess, E. A., Ballantine, J. E. M., Woodland, H. R., Mohun, R. M., Lane, C. D., and Dimitriadis, G. J. (1980). *J. Embryol. Exp. Morphol.* **58**, 303–320.

Sumikawa, K., Houghton, M., Emtage, J. S., Richards, B. M., and Barnard, E. A. (1981). *Nature (London)* **292**, 862–864.

Swanson, R. F. (1971). *Nature (London)* **231**, 31–34.

Telford, J. L., Kressman, A., Koski, R. A., Grosschedl, R., Miller, F., Clarkson, S. G., and Birnstiel, M. L. (1979). *Proc. Natl. Acad. Sci. U.S.A.* **76**, 2590–2594.

Trendelenburg, M. F., and Gurdon, J. B. (1978). *Nature (London)* **276**, 292–294.

Trendelenburg, M. F., Zentgraf, H., Franke, W. W., and Gurdon, J. B. (1978). *Proc. Natl. Acad. Sci. U.S.A.* **75**, 3791–3795.

Trendelenburg, M. F., Mathis, D., and Oudet, P. (1980). *Proc. Natl. Acad. Sci. U.S.A.* **77**, 5984–5988.

Ureta, T., and Radojkovic, J. (1978). *Fed. Proc. Fed. Am. Soc. Exp. Biol.* **37**, 1716.

Ureta, T., and Radojkovic, J. (1979). *Acta Cient. Venez.* **30**, 396–400.

Ureta, T., and Radojkovic, J. (1980). *Fed. Proc. Fed. Am. Soc. Exp. Biol.* **39**, 2143.

Van Vloten-Doting, L., Bol, J., Neeleman, L., Rutgers, T., Van Dalen, D., Castel, A., Bosch, L., Marbaix, G., Huez, G., Hubert, E., and Cleuter, Y. (1977). *In* "Nucleic Acid and Protein Synthesis in Plants" (L. Borograd and J. H. Weil, eds.), pp. 387–411. Plenum, New York.

Van Zaane, D., Gielkins, A. L. J., Hesselink, W. G., and Bloemers, H. P. J. (1977). *Proc. Natl. Acad. Sci. U.S.A.* **74**, 1855–1859.

Valle, G., Besley, J., and Colman, A. (1981). *Nature (London)* **291**, 338–339.

Vassart, G., Refetoff, S., Brocas, H., Dinsart, C., and Dumont, J. E. (1975). *Proc. Natl. Acad. Sci. U.S.A.* **72**, 3839–3843.

Wagner, E. F., Stewart, T. A., and Mintz, B. (1981). *Proc. Natl. Acad. Sci. U.S.A.* **78**, 5016–5020.

Wallace, R. A. (1978) *In* "Vertebrate Ovary" (R. E. Jones, ed.), pp. 469–502. Plenum, New York.

Wallace, R. A., and Hollinger, T. G. (1979). *Exp. Cell Res.* **119**, 277–287.

Wickens, M. P., and Laskey, R. A. (1981). *In* "Genetic Engineering" (R. Williamson, ed.), pp. 104–107. Academic Press, New York.

Wickens, M. P., Woo, S., O'Malley, R. W., and Gurdon, J. B. (1980). *Nature* (London) **285**, 628–634.

Wigler, M., Pellicer, A., Silverstein, S., and Axel, R. (1978). *Cell* **14**, 725–731.

Winberry, L., Marks, A., and Baumal, R. (1980). *J. Immunol.* **124**, 1174–1182.

Woodland, H. R. (1980). *FEBS Lett.* **121**, 1–7.

Woodland, H. R., and Ayers, S. E. (1974). *Biochem. J.* **144**, 11–19.

Woodland, H. R., and Wilt, F. H. (1980a). *Dev. Biol.* **75**, 214–221.

Woodland, H. R., and Wilt, F. H. (1980b). *Dev. Biol.* **75**, 199–213.

Woodland, H. R., Gurdon, J. B., and Lingrel, J. B. (1974). *Dev. Biol.* **39**, 134–140.

Woodland, H. R., Flynn, J. M., and Wyllie, A. J. (1979). *Cell* **18,** 165–171.

Wormington, M. W., Bogenhagen, D. F., Jordan, E., and Brown, D. D. (1981). *Cell* **24,** 809–817.

Wunner, W. H., Curtis, P. J., and Wiktov, T. J. (1980). *J. Virol.* **36,** 133–142.

Wyllie, A. H., Gurdon, J. B., and Price, J. (1977). *Nature (London)* **268,** 150–152.

Wyllie, A. H., Laskey, R. A., Finch, J., and Gurdon, J. B. (1978). *Dev. Biol.* **64,** 178–188.

Zehavi-Willner, T., and Lane, C. D. (1977). *Cell* **11,** 683–693.

CHAPTER 5

CELL–CELL CONTACT, CYCLIC AMP, AND GENE EXPRESSION DURING DEVELOPMENT OF *DICTYOSTELIUM DISCOIDEUM*

Giorgio Mangiarotti,* Salvatore Bozzaro,† Scott Landfear,‡ and Harvey F. Lodish‡

* CATTEDRA DI BIOLOGIA GENERALE
UNIVERSITY OF TURIN
TURIN, ITALY

† MAX-PLANCK INSTITUT FÜR BIOCHEMIE
MARTINSRIED, FEDERAL REPUBLIC OF GERMANY

‡ DEPARTMENT OF BIOLOGY
MASSACHUSETTS INSTITUTE OF TECHNOLOGY
CAMBRIDGE, MASSACHUSETTS

117

I. Introduction

Dictyostelium discoideum and related cellular slime mold species have been the subject of intense study in recent years because they are unicellular in the vegetative stage of their life cycle, are easily handled in large quantity, are readily amenable to mutant selection, and, most important of all, undergo a rather complex and interesting developmental process in synchrony. The predominant feature of the developmental cycle is the aggregation of unicellular, free-living amoebae into a multicellular organism (Cappuccinelli and Ashworth, 1977; Bonner, 1967; Loomis, 1975). Differentiation of amoebae within the newly formed aggregates generates the three distinct cell types found in the mature fruiting body: spore cells, stalk cells, and basal discs. *Dictyostelium discoideum* exhibits many features of development seen in more complex eukaryotic organisms: specific cell–cell contacts are found; a homogeneous cell population differentiates into discrete cell types; and there is specific cell migration and pattern formation. These morphogenetic changes are accompanied by major changes in the pattern of gene expression. As we shall discuss here, the transcription of these genes is controlled by many of the same factors that affect gene expression in other differentiating systems, in particular, by cell–cell contact and by an extracellular hormone, cyclic AMP. Additionally, and unexpectedly, cell–cell contact in *Dictyostelium* is essential for stabilizing a large class of regulated mRNAs.

II. The Developmental Cycle

A. Induction of Development

Growth and morphogenesis in *Dictyostelium* are temporally separated. During the growth phase the cells behave as unicellular amoebae, feeding on bacteria or growing on an axenic medium, and duplicating by fission. The differentiation pathway is induced by starvation; deprivation of one or more amino acids appears to be the key factor (Marin, 1976). Development is fueled by endogenous energy reserves, and there is extensive turnover of RNA, carbohydrate, and protein as differentiation proceeds (Cocucci and Sussman, 1970; Hames and Ashworth, 1974; Mangiarotti *et al.*, 1981a). Most DNA synthesis ceases during the first few hours; thus, there does not appear to be any coupling between DNA replication and differentiation. However, there may be some synthesis of DNA in a subset of the cells at the stage of late aggregation (Bonner and Frascella, 1952; Katz and Bourguignon, 1974; Zada-Hames and Ashworth, 1978).

The formation of the multicellular aggregates, each containing about 10^5 cells, begins at about 6 hours, and by 12 hours the mounds of cells have differentiated a well-defined "tip" at the top (Fig. 1). At this stage the mounds begin synthesis of an extracellular protein–carbohydrate complex which coats the organism (Freeze and Loomis, 1977).

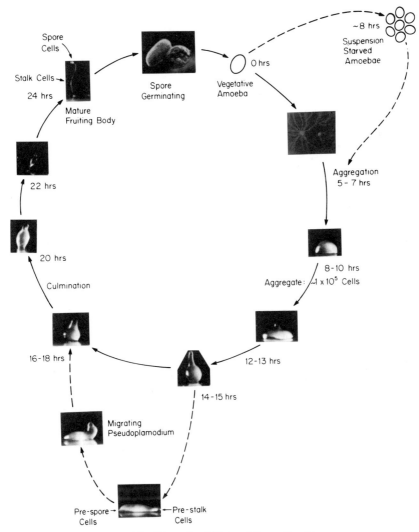

FIG. 1. The life cycle of *Dictyostelium discoideum*.

B. CHEMOTAXIS

The formation of multicellular aggregates is a combination of two separable processes: chemotaxis, the streaming of cells toward local centers, and cellular adhesion, the formation of specific tight cell junctions (reviewed in Loomis, 1979). Growing cells are incapable of either response. Both of these processes require the elaboration, during the preaggregation phase, of specific cell-surface macromolecules. The production of these entities by a cell is highly dependent on signals received from other aggregating cells (Marin, 1977).

Aggregation involves cell–cell signaling by the pulsatile release of an extracellular chemotactic agent. An individual cell responds to a gradient of cAMP by several actions. It moves several microns up the gradient, toward the source of cAMP (Konijn *et al.*, 1967, 1968; Bonner *et al.*, 1969; Alcantara and Monk, 1974), it synthesizes and releases its own pulse of cAMP (Gerisch and Wick, 1975; Shaffer, 1975; Roos *et al.*, 1975), and then becomes refractory for a period of several minutes. Under most natural conditions, the cAMP signal is amplified by the cell, in that it synthesizes and releases more cAMP than was present in the original stimulus. This relaying results in cell to cell propagation of the cAMP signal (Shaffer, 1975; Roos *et al.*, 1975; Devreotes and Steck, 1979). Proper functioning of this response requires a number of macromolecules, all of which are absent or present in low amounts in growing cells and which are produced during the immediate preaggregation time: adenylcyclase, the enzyme which synthesizes 3′,5′ cAMP from ATP (Klein, 1976, 1977; Roos *et al.*, 1977), a surface cAMP receptor, which binds the extracellular hormone (Malchow and Gerisch, 1974; Green and Newell, 1975; Henderson, 1975; Mato and Konijn, 1975; Wallace and Frazier, 1978), and an extracellular and a surface cAMP phosphodiesterase, which degrades cAMP to 5′ AMP (Riedel and Gerisch, 1971; Malchow *et al.*, 1972; Gerisch, 1976). The phosphodiesterase is essential as it prevents cells from responding to their own "pulse" of cAMP, and prevents the hormone from building up to such a level that any gradients are swamped out. Additional regulation is provided by an inhibitor of the phosphodiesterase (Gerisch *et al.*, 1972; Klein and Darmon, 1977; Yeh *et al.*, 1978; Kessin *et al.*, 1979).

An important feature of chemotaxis in *Dictyostelium discoideum* is that cells are attracted to the cAMP released by adjacent cells; there is no control source of chemoattractant to which all cells are attracted (reviewed in Newell, 1977). A homogeneous lawn of cells resting on a solid substratum rapidly breaks up into aggregation centers, each of which contain about 10^5 cells. This is initiated by random cells releasing pulses of cAMP. Pulsatile waves of cAMP signaling radiate outward from these "initiator" cells within a period of 3 to 5 minutes (Alcantara and Monk, 1974; Gross *et al.*, 1976; Tomchik and Devreotes, 1981). Concomitantly, there is a pulsatile movement of the cells inward toward the centers. Eventually, these concentric circular waves of cells break into streams (Shaffer, 1962; Robertson, 1972); while inward movement is still pulsatile, cells are now attracted into inward moving streams of cells, and thence to the center.

A key unanswered question concerns the mechanism by which the pulses of cAMP are amplified—by which the signal of cAMP bound to the surface of a cell causes the intracellular synthesis and then release of additional cAMP. Cyclic GMP has been proposed to be one such intracellular signal (Gerisch *et al.*, 1977; Mato *et al.*, 1977b; Malchow *et al.*, 1978). Additionally, movements of Ca^{2+} and H^+ ions across the plasma membrane accompany this signaling process (Wick *et al.*, 1978); they, too, may be intracellular mediators.

C. CELL–CELL COHESION

As the cells are chemotactically attracted into streams and assemble in aggregates, they form stable contacts with each other. This cohesiveness is developmentally regulated (Gerisch, 1961; Beug *et al.*, 1973) and species-specific (Bozzaro and Gerisch, 1979; Nicol and Garrod, 1978; Springer and Barondes, 1978; Gerisch, 1980). Vegetative cells do not adhere to each other or else form loose aggregates which lack species specificity (Bozzaro and Gerisch, 1978; Nicol and Garrod, 1978).

Gerisch and his co-workers defined two cell–cell "contact sites" classes by showing that antibodies raised against two cell surface antigens prevented cell–cell adhesion (Beug *et al.*, 1973). Expression of one of these antigens, "contact sites B" (cs-B) is not developmentally regulated. The identifying characteristic of cs-B is EDTA-sensitive cell–cell adhesion, suggesting a role for divalent cations in this stage of the adhesion process. "Contact sites A" (cs-A), on the other hand, is a developmentally regulated glycoprotein of MW 80,000 (Müller and Gerisch, 1978). Cell–cell adhesion mediated by "contact sites A" or gp80 is seen as end-to-end cell contacts which form as the amoebae stream toward centers. These gp80-induced cell aggregates are EDTA-resistant. Monoclonal antibodies have confirmed that the gp80 protein is under developmental control and its appearance is correlated with the ability of the cells to form stable cell–cell contacts (Ochiai *et al.*, 1982).

cs-A persists during the postaggregative stages, though the level of cs-A on the cell surface declines (Ochiai *et al.*, 1982). Beginning at the aggregation stage two other glycoproteins accumulate and may take over the cell-contact function of cs-A. One has a MW of 95,000 and begins to be synthesized at the tip stage (Steinemann and Parish, 1980). The other one, gp150, begins to appear on the cell membrane during the aggregation stage and was reported to act as a "contact site" at this stage (Geltosky *et al.*, 1979). However, Fab directed against this molecule apparently exerts significant inhibition of adhesion only in the postaggregative stages (Lam *et al.*, 1981), contrary to a previous report (Geltosky *et al.*, 1979). Immunoelectron microscopy has demonstrated that in 18-hour cellular aggregates the concentration of gp150 is highest at the regions of cell–cell contact (Geltosky *et al.*, 1980). By fluorescence analysis, these 18-hour cell aggregates appear to contain two cell populations differing in the amount of gp150 displayed on their surface, raising the possibility that this molecule may be differentially expressed in prespore and prestalk cells.

Two other molecules supposed to be involved in cell adhesion during aggregation are discoidin I and II, cytoplasmic lectins, a small portion of which is found on the cell surface (Simpson *et al.*, 1975; Chang *et al.*, 1975). Although at least discoidin I appears to be required for normal development (Schinnick and Lerner, 1980), the function of these lectins in cell adhesion remains a controversial question (Rosen *et al.*, 1973; Bozzaro and Gerisch, 1978; Ochiai *et al.*, 1982).

Despite the identification of these various candidate cell–cell adhesion molecules, the precise molecular interactions which lead to the formation of tight cellular aggregates remain unclear. Each of these molecules may, for example, interact with a specific receptor molecule on adjacent cells but no specific receptor or ligand has been identified for gp80, gp95, or gp150. Finally, the evidence, to be discussed below, that cell–cell contact is a crucial step in the activation of postaggregation genes suggests that studies of *Dictyostelium* may provide valuable clues as to how events occurring at the cellular membrane alter gene expression.

D. DIFFERENTIATION OF SPORE AND STALK CELLS

Following aggregation and tip formation, the mound transforms into a migrating "pseudoplasmodium" or, colloquially, a "slug" with the "tip" as the "leading edge." Depending on the environmental conditions, these slugs can be made to migrate for several days; they are both phototactic and thermotactic (Cappuccinnelli and Ashworth, 1977; Bonner, 1967; Loomis, 1975). Fate mapping studies have indicated that some cellular specialization has occurred at this stage: the front third of the cells will eventually become stalk cells; the rear two-thirds are destined to become spore cells (Raper, 1940) and most contain prespore vacuoles which contain spore surface antigen (Hohl and Hammamoto, 1969; Ikeda and Takeuchi, 1971). This commitment to a specific cell type is reversible; certain treatments can cause "prespore" cells to become "prestalk" cells, and vice versa. In particular, if the "slug" is cut in half, and culmination (see below) is immediately induced, the front section will yield a disporportionately large stalk, and the rear, spore cells. However if culmination is not induced for several hours, the slugs will reproportion themselves, and, notably, a new "tip" will be formed from the rear section. Induction of culmination then results in the production of two half-sized, but perfectly proportioned, fruiting bodies (Raper, 1940; Bonner and Frascella, 1952; Bonner *et al.*, 1955; Gregg, 1965, 1968). These redifferentiations can occur in the absence of mitosis (Bonner and Frascella, 1952; Bonner, 1952; Gregg, 1965, 1968).

Culmination is the terminal stage of morphogenesis. It is initiated by overhead light, in conjunction with a suitable ionic environment (Raper, 1940; Sliflan and Bonner, 1952; Newell *et al.*, 1969; Schindler and Sussman, 1977a,b). The slug rights itself, so that the "tip" and the prestalk cells are on top. These cells elongate and vacuolate, pushing down through the mass of differentiating spore cells (George *et al.*, 1972). This results in the mass of spore cells being elevated on the elongating stalk. By 24 hours of differentiation the spore cells, now dehydrated and containing a multilayered spore coat, surmount the dead, vacuolated stalk.

III. Gene Expression during Development

A. OVERALL METABOLISM OF RIBOSOMAL RNA AND MESSENGER RNA DURING THE DEVELOPMENTAL CYCLE

Although our main focus will be on the specifics of messenger RNA (mRNA) regulation, it is important to discuss first the overall rates of ribosomal RNA (rRNA) and mRNA production. A growing amoebae contains about 2×10^6 ribosomes and 2×10^5 mRNA molecules. During development the ribosome content per cell decreases exponentially, with a half-life of 10 to 12 hours; culminating cells contain only about one-third the initial number of ribosomes. In spite of the net loss of ribosomes, cells continue to synthesize rRNA during differentiation. By determining the rate of dilution of ribosomal particles (growing cells) with particles newly made during development, we found that the rate of synthesis of rRNA during development is less than 15% of that of growing cells (Mangiarotti *et al.*, 1981a).

Why differentiating cells keep forming new ribosomes, while they are degrading the old and new ribosomal particles (Mangiarotti and Hames, 1979), is unclear. Contrary to an early indication that developmental ribosomes might be preferentially utilized for protein synthesis during development (Cocucci and Sussman, 1970) ribosomal particles synthesized during growth and differentiation were found to be functionally indistinguishable by several criteria. This is in line with the observation that the primary structure of rRNA synthesized during growth and development is the same (Batts-Young *et al.*, 1980). It is noteworthy that in late aggregation a new set of proteins different from those present during growth can be found on ribosomes (Ramagopal and Ennis, 1981). Whether these protein can exchange with those already assembled on preexisting ribosomes or must be assembled on newly formed rRNA remains to be determined.

From the absolute rate of synthesis of rRNA, the rate of synthesis of total mRNA could be determined, based on the finding that the fraction of RNA synthesized at any time during growth or development which is polyadenylated is practically constant (Mangiarotti *et al.*, 1981a). In both growing and differentiating cells, at least half of newly made polyadenylated RNA is mRNA. We conclude that the rate of synthesis of mRNA is reduced during differentiation as much as is that of rRNA, to a level less than 15% of growing cells.

In growing cells, nuclear pre-mRNA is converted to cytoplasmic mRNA extremely quickly; less than 4 minutes are required for a newly made mRNA to be processed and exit from the nucleus. This time is lengthened considerably during differentiation; pulse–chase experiments on total polyadenylated RNA suggest that the processing time for nuclear pre-mRNA may be as long as 60 minutes (Firtel and Lodish, 1973). Since individual mRNAs have not been subjected to such analyses, it is not known whether the rate-limiting step in processing is splicing, capping, or transport from the nucleus.

As we discuss in detail later, the average half-life of all mRNAs in growing and differentiating cells is about 4 hours, although a few mRNAs are much less stable (Margolskee and Lodish, 1980a). Culminating cells at 24–26 hours of development contain about half the amount of mRNA as do growing cells. Thus, the population of mRNA molecules is turned over and replenished several times during differentiation.

B. Changes in Protein Synthesis during Differentiation

Important studies beginning in the late 1960s established that the activities of a number of enzymes increased or decreased at defined times during the developmental cycle (reviewed in Loomis, 1975; Sussman and Sussman, 1969). Most of these changes appeared to be part of a "developmental program," in that mutations or other treatments which caused differentiation to be blocked at a specific morphological stage generally resulted in the inhibition of all changes in enzyme levels characteristic of all later stages (Loomis et al., 1976, 1977). While these changes in enzyme activities provided markers for specific developmental stages, such studies could provide little information concerning the number or timing of regulated genes or insights to the mechanisms of regulation. Experiments with inhibitors (actinomycin D and cycloheximide) indicated that the accumulation of several of the marker enzymes (UDPG pyrophosphorylase trehalose-6-P synthetase, UDPGal 4 epimerase, and UDPGal polysaccharide transferase) required new RNA and protein synthesis (Roth et al., 1968; Sussman and Sussman, 1969; Telser and Sussman, 1971). However, for only two enzymes (UDP glucose pyrophosphorylase and glycogen phosphorylase) was it actually shown that an increase in enzyme activity was specifically correlated with an increased rate of synthesis of the polypeptide chain (Franke and Sussman, 1973; Thomas and Wright, 1976).

Information concerning the timing of gene expression during differentiation came from the studies in which cells were pulse-labeled with [^{35}S]methionine at hourly intervals and the protein products resolved on two-dimensional polyacrylamide gels (Alton and Lodish, 1977a). Growing cells synthesized about 400 resolvable discrete polypeptide chains. Note that this is a minimum estimate, since proteins translated from mRNAs present at a low level (less than 10–20 copies per cell) would not have been detected. Most of these 400 proteins continued to be synthesized throughout differentiation, a result which implied that most of the predominant mRNAs present in these cells persist throughout differentiaton. This analysis resolved about 80 proteins whose synthesis was induced during differentiation, or whose rate of synthesis increased or decreased markedly. As might be expected, changes in the pattern of protein synthesis were observed at all times during the cycle (Fig. 2). The surprising result was that synthesis of fully half of the developmentally regulated proteins was induced at one stage—that of late cell–cell aggregation. The induction of synthesis of these 40 proteins was correlated with the appearance in the cytoplasm of the homologous translatable mRNAs; thus, synthesis of these proteins appeared to be regulated by the synthesis (or stability) of mRNA (Alton and Lodish, 1977a). More recent studies indicated that synthesis of the majority of these predominant aggregation-stage proteins

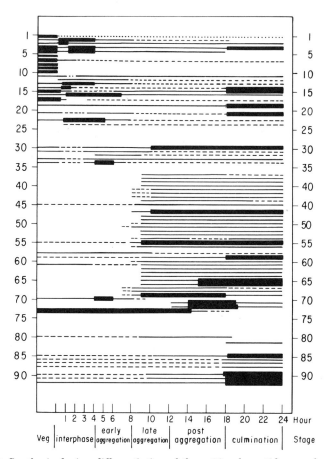

FIG. 2. Synthesis during differentiation of those 80 polypeptides, resolved by two-dimensional gel electrophoresis, which are developmentally regulated. Not shown here are the approximately 300 polypeptides which are synthesized both during growth and throughout differentiation. A dotted line indicates barely detectable synthesis, a solid line indicates synthesis of the protein, and a thick black line indicates that the protein is one of the predominant species made during the indicated interval. The numbers identify specific protein spots on the two dimensional gels. (From Alton and Lodish, 1977a.)

occurs both in stalk and spore cells and presumably occurs in all of the cells of the aggregate (Coloma and Lodish, 1981).

C. Protein Synthesis in Spore and Stalk Cells

During the culmination stage, the maturing spore and stalk cells show specific profiles of protein synthesis which can be used as markers of cytodifferentiation. A few predominant polypeptides, synthesized only after 19 hours of development, are differentially segregated between spore and stalk cells (Coloma and Lodish, 1981; Orlowski and Loomis, 1979). Thus, during culmination there is a second, less dramatic induction of newly synthesized developmentally regulated proteins. In addition, at this stage, synthesis of several "constitutive" polypeptides as well as proteins induced at earlier stages of development appear to be regulated differently in each cell type. Interestingly, this is the case for actin, whose synthesis is specifically inhibited in the maturating spores during culmination (Coloma and Lodish, 1981).

While the predominant spore- or stalk-specific polypeptides are only made during culmination, gene expression in the two cell types may begin to diverge earlier in development (Raper, 1940; Bonner, 1952). By 9 hours of development, cells can be separated into distinct prespore and prestalk fractions by density centrifugation (Maeda and Maeda, 1974; Feinberg *et al.,* 1979) which are selectively cohesive (Feinberg *et al.,* 1979). Additionally, cells of the prestalk fraction contain higher concentrations of intracellular cAMP and calcium, and are also more chemotactic to cAMP (Tsang and Bradbury, 1981; Feinberg *et al.,* 1979; Bonner, 1949; Rubin, 1976; Brenner, 1977; Matsukuma and Durston, 1979). By 16 hours of development, prestalk cells possess a higher cAMP phosphodiesterase activity as compared with prespore cells (Tsang and Bradbury, 1981; Brown and Rutherford, 1980). This preculmination cell type divergence is also reflected by differences in protein synthesis detected between anterior (prestalk) and posterior regions of the migrating pseudoplasmodium (Alton and Brenner, 1979; Morrissey *et al.,* 1981).

D. THE NUMBER OF DEVELOPMENTALLY REGULATED GENES

More definitive estimates of the number of developmentally regulated genes have come from several cDNA–mRNA and single-copy DNA–mRNA hybridization studies (Firtel, 1972; Blumberg and Lodish, 1980a,b, 1981).

As is summarized in Table I, growing *Dictyostelium* cells contain around 4000–5000 discrete species of mRNA (Blumberg and Lodish, 1980a). Approximately 600 of these sequences are present in greater than 160 copies per cell; the rest are present, on the average, at 14 copies per cell. These mRNAs represent the transcription products of 19% of the single-copy *Dictyostelium* genome.

The number of mRNA species does not change significantly by 6 hours of differentiation (preaggregation stage) (Blumberg and Lodish, 1980b). Cross-hybridization studies showed, moreover, that the population of mRNAs present in growing and preaggregating cells were extremely similar. While other types of studies show that expression of some genes is induced in the preaggregation stage, the number of such genes must be relatively low (Alton and Lodish, 1977a; Williams and Lloyd, 1979; Margolskee and Lodish, 1980b).

By contrast, the polysomes of postaggregation cells contain 7000 discrete mRNA species, the transcription products of 30% of the single-copy genome (Blumberg and Lodish, 1980b). The majority of the 4000–5000 mRNA species present before aggregation remains in the cells throughout development, although the average abundance of these mRNAs decreases with time. About one-third of the mass of mRNAs in the postaggregation cells is comprised of the 2500 mRNA species which appear only after aggregation. Thus, an additional 11% of the single-copy genome is expressed as polysomal polyadenylated RNA, presumably mRNA, after aggregation. Of these aggregation-stage mRNAs, 100 to 150 sequences are present at 80 copies per cell; the remainder are present at 5 copies per cell.

The population of mRNAs present in culminating cells is indistinguishable, by cross-hybridization, from that in postaggregation cells. Both contain the same 7500 different species of mRNA. Although synthesis of spore- and stalk-specific proteins occurs during the culmination stage, they are not encoded by a significant fraction of the mRNA sequences present in these cells (Alton and Lodish, 1977a; Coloma and Lodish, 1981; Blumberg and Lodish, 1980b).

An independent estimate of the number of mRNA species which accumulate only in aggregated cells has come from screening several thousand cloned fragments of genomic DNA for developmentally controlled genes by a competition-hybridization technique (Mangiarotti *et al.*, 1981b).

An example of the screening analysis is shown in Fig. 3 and some properties of several selected clones are illustrated in Fig. 4. To identify and quantitate the amount of mRNA homologous to these cloned DNAs at different stages of development, we subjected equal amounts of cytoplasmic polyadenylated RNA to gel electrophoresis under denaturing conditions. The RNAs were then blotted onto and immobilized to nitrocellulose paper. After hybridization with ^{32}P-labeled cloned DNA, the paper was washed and exposed to X-ray film. Three classes of cloned DNA fragments (average size 9 kb) can be recognized. Some (like clone GM27) contain a single gene whose RNA can be found only in late aggregates. Some (like clone GM55) contain two genes, one corresponding to an mRNA present both in growing and developing cells, the other to an mRNA present only in aggregated cells. Finally other clones (like GM45) contain sequences corresponding to several mRNAs whose abundance clearly increases during development.

A. [³²P] Vegetative RNA

C. [³²P] 13 h RNA

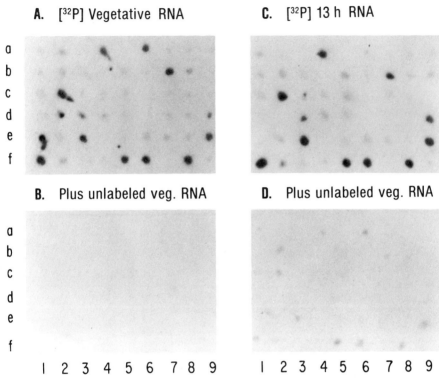

B. Plus unlabeled veg. RNA

D. Plus unlabeled veg. RNA

FIG. 3. Screening a random sample of λ-*Dictyostelium* clones by hybridization competition. A random sample of plaques, each derived from a single recombinant phage, was picked into wells of a microtiter tray and replicated directly onto four agar plates as described in Mangiarotti *et al.* (1981b). DNA from the plaques was blotted onto a nitrocellulose filter and hybridized. In (A) 0.2 μg (1,000,000 cpm) *in vitro* labeled cytoplasmic poly(A⁺) RNA extracted from vegetative cells was added to the hybridization mixture; (B) as in (A), except 1.0 mg total cytoplasmic RNA extracted from vegetative cells was added; (C) the same amount of poly(A⁺) RNA from 13 hour cells, with comparable specific radioactivity, was added; (D) as in (C) except 1.0 mg RNA from vegetative cells was added. Some of the clones shown in this figure are also shown in the following figure. Cone GM 45 is A6 and GM 55 is F4. (A) and (C) show that at least three-fourths of the clones formed a hybrid with ³²P-labeled polyadenylated RNA derived from both growing and aggregated cells. The addition of a several-fold excess of unlabeled polyadenylated RNA extracted from growing cells abolished all hybridization of labeled polyadenylated RNA also derived from growing cells (B) but it did not prevent the hybridization of labeled polyadenylated RNA from differentiating cells to a substantial fraction of the clones (D). (From Mangiarotti *et al.*, 1981b.)

Out of the 3000 random DNA clones so far examined by the competition hybridization test, at least 90% hybridized to mRNA derived from developing cells, and about 30% appeared to contain at least one developmentally regulated gene. Sixty clones, randomly chosen from

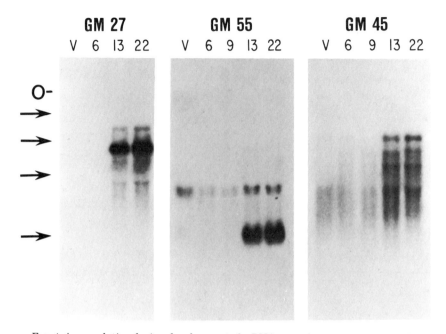

FIG. 4. Accumulation during development of mRNAs complementary to some selected clones. Poly(A⁺) RNA species extracted from growing cells (4 μg) and from cells at the indicated stages of development (2 μg) were separated by electrophoresis and blotted onto nitrocellulose paper as described in Mangiarotti *et al.* (1981b). DNA extracted from the indicated clones was labeled by nick-translation and hybridized to the nitrocellulose filter. The arrows correspond to marker DNA (from top to bottom) of 9500, 4300, 2100, and 1300 bases. "O" indicates the origin. (From Mangiarotti *et al.*, 1981b.)

the library, were analyzed more thoroughly by identifying and quantitating the homologous mRNAs by RNA gel analyses similar to Fig. 4. Again, about one-third of the mRNAs encoded by these clones were present only in aggregated cells (Mangiarotti *et al.*, 1982b). The results are in qualitative agreement with the previous estimate (Blumberg and Lodish, 1980a,b) that about one-fifth of the single-copy *Dictyostelium* genome is expressed as mRNA throughout growth and differentiation, while transcripts from about one-tenth is present in mRNA only during development.

E. The Timing of Transcription of Developmentally Regulated Genes

Though modulation of the levels of mRNAs occurs throughout the developmental cycle (Alton and Lodish, 1977a,b; Williams and Lloyd, 1979; Williams *et al.*, 1979; Rowekamp *et al.*, 1980), the results reported above show that mRNA species fall into two major classes, those present both in growth and development ("constitutive" mRNAs) and those present only in aggregated cells ("late" mRNAs).

Two lines of evidence indicate that the appearance of aggregation-stage mRNAs is under transcriptional control. First, as judged by hybridization of single copy DNA to RNA, the vast majority of aggregation-specific mRNA species are absent from the nuclear RNA of growing or preaggregating cells (Blumberg and Lodish, 1981). Following aggregation, an additional 26% of the single-copy genome is expressed as total nuclear plus cytoplasmic polyadenylated RNA transcripts. Of these sequences, 40%, equivalent to transcripts of 11% of the single-copy genome, emerge in the cytoplasm as mRNA (Table I) (Blumberg and Lodish, 1981). It appears that if genes encoding late mRNAs are transcribed in preaggregation cells, the transcripts are destroyed immediately.

Second, *in vitro* transcription by nuclei isolated from cells at different stage of development have been employed to follow the synthesis of

TABLE I

COMPLEXITY OF NUCLEAR AND CYTOPLASMIC POLYADENYLATED RNA[a,b]

Developmental stage	Percentage single copy DNA expressed in total nuclear plus cytoplasmic polyadenylated RNA	Percentage single copy genome expressed in cytoplasmic polyadenylated RNA (mRNA)	Number of genes expressed as mRNA
Vegetative	53.4	19.3	4820
6 hours (preaggregation)	54.0	19.3	4800
13 hours (postaggregation)	82.2	29.8	7420
22 hours culmination	76.8	31.0	7750
Mixture: vegetative plus 13 hour cells	79.4	31.0	7750

[a] Percentage single copy DNA expressed is determined from the fraction of the single copy DNA rendered double stranded after hybridization with either total nuclear plus cytoplasmic polyadenylated RNA (column 1) or cytoplasmic polyadenylated RNA alone (column 2) (data from Blumberg and Lodish 1980a,b, 1981). The assumption is made that only one strand of the DNA is transcribed. Therefore the percentage of genomic DNA which is expressed is twice the percentage rendered double stranded in the RNA-driven hybridization reactions.

[b] The number of genes expressed as average sized cytoplasmic polyadenylated RNA species (column 3) is calculated assuming that *Dictyostelium* mRNA has a weight average molecular weight of 400,000 (Firtel and Lodish, 1973) and the size of the single copy portion of the genome is 2×10^{10} daltons.

individual mRNA precursors (Landfear *et al.*, 1982). In these experiments hybridization of ^{32}P-labeled transcripts to cloned cDNAs or genomic DNAs spotted onto nitrocellulose paper has been used to analyze synthesis of specific RNA sequences. Since isolated nuclei do not reinitiate *in vitro* synthesis of new chains very efficiently but do complete synthesis of RNAs already initiated *in vivo,* the labeled product of the *in vitro* transcriptions represents those RNAs which were being synthesized by the cells at the time nuclei were isolated. The main result of this analysis is that "constitutive" mRNAs are synthesized from nuclei derived both from growing cells and from cells at any stage of development, while "late" mRNAs are synthesized only from nuclei derived from cells at 8 to 12 hours of development or later.

One example of this analysis is shown in Fig. 5. Here two sets of cloned DNAs were used: clones CZ5, CZ9, CZ22, SC29, and SC79 encode unique constitutive mRNAs. Their corresponding mRNAs are synthesized from nuclei derived from cells at all stages of development. Clones PL1, PL3, D15, D18, and D19 encode a unique developmentally regulated gene. None of the mRNA homologous to these clones was synthesized by nuclei isolated from either growing or 4 hour (preaggregation) cells. The RNAs corresponding to clones PL1, D15, and D18 were synthesized by nuclei from 8 hour cells as well as by nuclei from later stages of development; the RNAs corresponding to clones PL3 and D19 were synthesized only by nuclei isolated at 12 hours or later.

RNA gel analyses indicate that the mRNAs corresponding to clones PL1, D15, and D18 begin to accumulate between 4 and 8 hours of differentiation, while those homologous to clones PL3 and D19 accumulate between 8 and 12 hours (Fig. 6). Thus, there is a good correspondence between initiation of transcription and accumulation of the corresponding mRNA. These results also indicate that transcription of "late" genes is not coordinate. At least two and possibly more classes of "late" mRNA exist, whose synthesis starts at different times during development. It should be noted that by 8 hours cells can establish EDTA-resistant contacts, but they have not yet formed tight mounds.

Preliminary *in vivo* pulse-labeling experiments have indicated that some RNA capable of hybridizing to some regulated genes is synthesized even at earlier times (Mangiarotti, unpublished data). While the labeled RNA sequences have not yet been fully characterized, the possibility must be kept in mind that for some developmentally regulated mRNA a considerable interval may lapse between the time when synthesis is started and when they can be detected as a component of the mRNA population present in the cell.

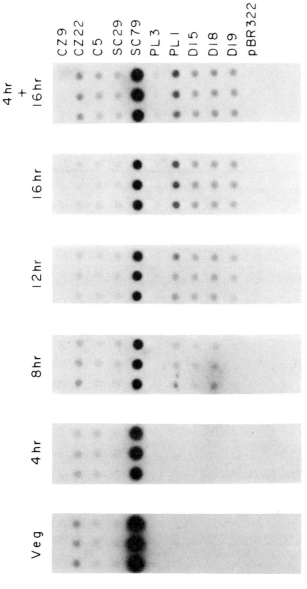

FIG. 5. *In vitro* transcription of regulated and constitutive RNAs using nuclei from different stages of development. Nuclei were isolated from vegetative cells (veg) and from cells at 4, 8, 12, and 16 hours of development. *In vitro* transcription reactions were performed, as detailed in Landfear *et al.* (1982), in the presence of [α-^{32}P]UTP, and hybridized to cloned DNAs spotted onto nitrocellulose. Constitutive clones CZ9, CA22, C5, SC29, SC79 and regulated clones PL3, PL1, D15, D18, and D19 were used to quantitate transcription of individual mRNA precursors. After hybridization and washing, the nitrocellulose filter was exposed to Kodak XAR-5 film using an intensifying screen. (From Landfear *et al.*, 1982.)

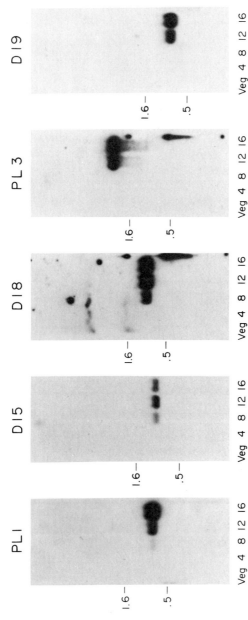

Fig. 6. Accumulation of individual mRNAs during development. Cytoplasmic polyadenylated RNA was isolated from the same cells (veg, 4, 8, 12, and 16 hours) used to prepare the nuclei in Fig. 5. Equal amount (2 μg) of each RNA was applied to each lane of the gel (Landfear *et al.*, 1982); after electrophoresis, the RNA was blotted onto nitrocellulose and hybridized with nick-translated cloned DNA (PL1, D15, D18, PL3, D19). Size markers were 1.6 and 0.5 kb. (From Landfear *et al.*, 1982.)

While transcription is presumed to play an important role in regulation of gene activity in any organism, the actual demonstration of control at this level has been limited to a relatively small number of systems (e.g., Ringold *et al.*, 1977; Yamamoto *et al.*, 1977; Schutz *et al.*, 1977; Derman *et al.*, 1981). In *Dictyostelium discoideum* a control at the level of transcription had been shown only for a few genes (e.g., for discoidin gene, Williams *et al.*, 1979, 1981). The existence of a major transcriptional control during the postaggregation stage of development of *Dictyostelium discoideum* is now finally established. Whether this is the only level at which the expression of "late" genes is regulated, or posttranscriptional controls are superimposed on it remains an open question.

F. STABILITY OF mRNAs DURING DIFFERENTIATION

The level of an mRNA species in a cell is a function not only of its rate of synthesis, but also of its decay. It is thus important to determine half-lives of mRNA, particularly since, as is discussed below, the stability of the entire class of "regulated" mRNAs is a function of tight cell–cell contact. Two methods have been used to determine the stability of *Dictyostelium* mRNA during differentiation: approach to steady-state labeling of mRNA, and addition of inhibitors of mRNA biosyn-

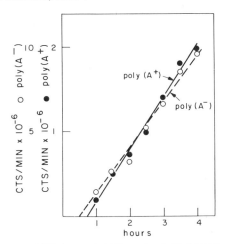

FIG. 7. Incorporation of ^{32}P into poly(A$^+$) and poly(A$^-$) RNA during development. Cells (5 × 10^7) were labeled with [^{32}P]orthophosphate beginning at 13 hours of development. At the indicated times poly(A$^+$) and poly(A$^-$) RNA were isolated from the cytoplasm of labeled cells. An aliquot of each RNA preparation was precipitated with cold trichloroacetic acid and the amount of ^{32}P label incorporated measured in a scintillation spectrophotometer. ●--●, poly(A$^+$) RNA; ○-----○, poly(A$^-$) RNA. (From Mangiarotti *et al.*, 1982a.)

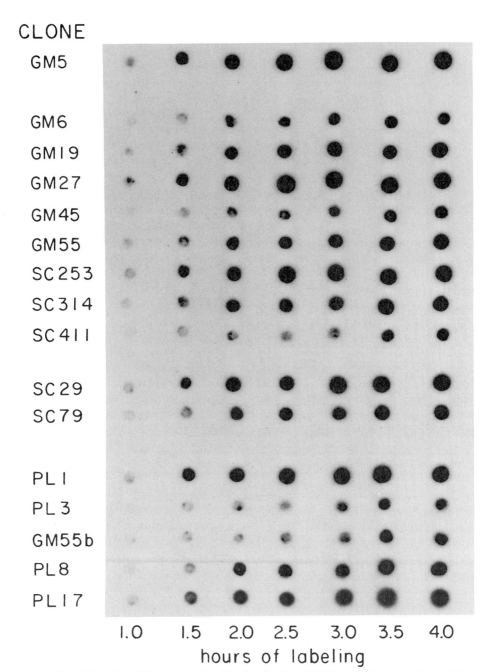

Fig. 8. Uptake of ^{32}P into cytoplasmic polyadenylated RNA species between 13 and 17 hours in continuous labeling during normal development. The poly(A[+]) RNA preparations described in Fig. 7 were hybridized to cloned DNAs described in the text. The poly(A[+]) RNA obtained from 2×10^7 labeled cells was added to each hybridization mix-

thesis (Mangiarotti *et al.*, 1982a; Margolskee and Lodish, 1980a). Both methods showed that during growth (8 hour cell doubling) and differentiation, the average half-life of all mRNA in the cell is about 4 hours. Of greater importance, after aggregation both individual "constitutive" and "regulated" mRNA species have the same half-life—about 4 hours (Mangiarotti *et al.*, 1982a; Chung *et al.*, 1981).

This point is documented by the study described in Mangiarotti *et al.* (1982a) and further depicted in Figs. 7–9, in which *Dictyostelium* cells are labeled with $[^{32}P]PO_4$ from 13 to 17 hours of development, a period chosen because it is characterized by the accumulation of late mRNAs (Mangiarotti *et al.*, 1981b; Chung *et al.*, 1981). Initially, the incorporation of ^{32}P into both poly(A^+) and poly(A^-) cytoplasmic RNA exhibits a 30 to 45 minute lag, which presumably reflects the time required for the RNA precursors to reach a constant specific radioactivity and for the RNA to exit from the nucleus into the cytoplasm. Following the lag period, the incorporation of ^{32}P label into poly(A^+) and poly(A^-) RNA is linear for several hours, and declines significantly only in the last hour of labeling. Assuming, as is the case (Mangiarotti *et al.*, 1982a), that the rate of synthesis of both rRNA and mRNA is constant during this period, this result indicates that the bulk of newly made cytoplasmic polyadenylated RNA as well as rRNA is relatively stable, as suggested by previous experiments (Margolskee and Lodish, 1980a; Chung *et al.*, 1981): the rate at which the amount of radioactivity in a species or population of RNA reaches a steady state (i.e., where synthesis of a labeled species is balanced by its destruction) is a function only of the rate of decay of that species or population.

In order to determine the kinetics of incorporation of ^{32}P into conserved and late mRNA species the above ^{32}P-labeled RNA preparations were hybridized to a series of immobilized, cloned DNAs encoding both constitutive mRNAs (clones GM5, SC29, SC79) and aggregation-dependent mRNAs (all of the others). In the experiment depicted in Fig. 8, DNA purified from each clone was spotted in seven equal aliquots in a horizontal line on a sheet of nitrocellulose paper. The paper was cut in vertical strips, each containing a spot corresponding to each of the clones and each strip was hybridized to 0.2 µg of a

---

ture. To ensure that the amount of any specific hybridizable sequence would be the same in all hybridizations, an excess of unlabeled total cytoplasmic RNA derived from aggregated cells was added to each hybridization mixture. Under these conditions, the amount of label in the RNA hybridized to a clone DNA is proportional to the specific activity of that sequence in the hybridization mixture (Mangiarotti *et al.*, 1982). This precaution allows accurate quantitation of hybridizations, even if the annealing reaction has not gone to saturation. (From Mangiarotti *et al.*, 1982a.)

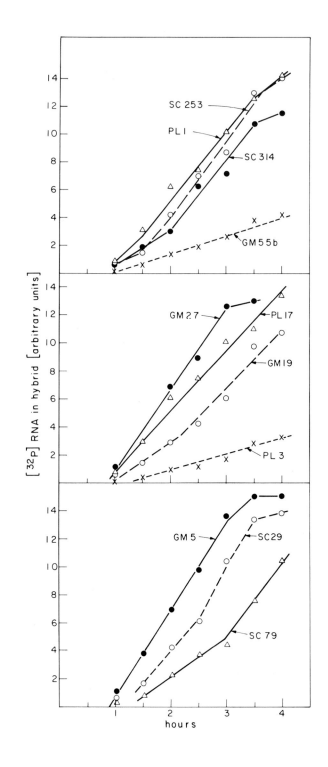

different labeled poly(A⁺) RNA preparation under conditions where the extent of hybridization is proportional to the amount of radioactivity in the homologous mRNA. As can be seen (Fig. 9) the incorporation of ^{32}P into poly(A⁺) RNA hybridizing to all of the cloned DNAs continues at a linear rate for several hours. No difference is observed between the group of clones that had been shown previously to hybridize only to conserved mRNAs (clones GM5, SC29, and SC79) and all the other clones, which hybridize exclusively or mainly to late mRNAs. We conclude that all mRNAs, both conserved and late, complementary to the tested DNA clones, have a half-life of at least 3 hours.

IV. Cell–Cell Contacts, cAMP, and Gene Expression

A. FORMATION OF TIGHT CELL–CELL CONTACTS IS REQUIRED FOR INDUCTION OF "LATE" mRNAS

About 2500 new mRNAs appear at the time of formation of tight cell–cell contacts. Most studies indicate that these cell interactions are an essential prerequisite for expression of these genes, although there are some apparently contradictory results.

Cells of most strains of *Dictyostelium discoideum* which have been starved for 15 hours in a vigorously shaken suspension culture in the same solution as used for differentiation become aggregation competent (Gerisch, 1968). They possess the cAMP receptor and phosphodiesterase required for cAMP cell signaling, as well as all known cell surface proteins required for cohesion, such as cs-A. In fact, the entire population of such aggregation-competent cells in a suspension culture will release pulses of cyclic AMP every 5 to 6 minutes, a process due to coordinate cell–cell signaling of cAMP (Gerisch and Hess, 1974). When plated on a solid surface they rapidly form mounds with prominent tips within 7 to 9 hours, several hours faster than plated growing cells induced to differentiation. Our laboratory strain, AX3, becomes only partially aggregation competent when starved in suspension culture. Pulsatile addition of cAMP to micromolar levels for several hours will render them fully competent (R. Chisholm, personal communication). In the presence of EDTA, added to inhibit formation of stable cell contacts, such aggregation-competent cells fail to induce significant levels

FIG. 9. Quantitation of the autoradiograph shown in Fig. 8. Different exposures of the radiogram were scanned in a Joyce-Lobel microdensitometer using a full-scale pen deflection of 1.16 optical density units, a value within the linear range of the film. The height of each peak thus obtained is reported in arbitrary units. (From Mangiarotti *et al.*, 1982a.)

of most if not all aggregation stage mRNA (Chung *et al.*, 1981, and unpublished data).

Studies on gene expression in mutant cells which are blocked at different stages of morphogenesis do demonstrate an excellent correlation between the formation of EDTA-resistant cell–cell contacts and induction of synthesis of 2500 "late" mRNAs:

1. All mutants which fail to aggregate (irrespective of the nature of the mutated gene), do not induce any late mRNA tested (Table II, Blumberg *et al.*, 1982).

2. Two mutants undergo normal chemotaxis, and form mounds of cells. However, they do not form EDTA-resistant cell–cell contacts and, importantly, induce synthesis of no regulated mRNAs while exhibiting a normal level of the "constitutive" species (Table II, Blumberg *et al.*, 1982). These mutants establish that cell–cell signaling with cAMP and chemotaxis is not sufficient for induction of regulated mRNAs.

3. All mutants which form morphologically normal cell aggregates, in which a wild-type level of EDTA-resistant cell contacts is formed, make normal amounts of most late mRNAs even though they fail to differentiate further (Table II). One of these mutants forms a "tip"; the other does not.

It is possible that the act of forming tight (EDTA-resistant) cell contacts triggers a cellular response leading to induction of gene transcription. Alternatively, cell contact could be required simply to increase the concentration of some diffusible secreted molecule which, together with cAMP, causes some cells to induce stalk- or spore-specific molecules.

B. Gene Expression Is Dependent on Continued Cell–Cell Interactions

Abundant evidence indicates that continued synthesis of aggregation-specific polypeptides and enzymes is dependent on continued cell–cell interactions. Disaggregation of pseudoplasmodia results in immediate cessation of accumulation of developmentally regulated enzymes such as UDP-glucose pyrophosphorylase and UDP-galactose polysaccharide transferase (Newell and Sussman, 1970; Newell *et al.*, 1971, 1972). Likewise, synthesis of the predominant polypeptides whose synthesis initiates after aggregation ceases when the aggregates are dispersed and kept from reattaching to each other by constant shaking (Alton and Lodish, 1977b; Okamoto, 1982; Landfear and Lodish, 1980).

More recent studies have used two types of hybridization experiments to investigate the synthesis and stability of "aggregation-dependent" and "constitutive" mRNAs in disaggregated cells: hybridization of mRNA to a cDNA probe specific for the population of 2500 regulated sequences; and hybridization of mRNA to cloned cDNAs encoding individual "regulated" or "constitutive" mRNAs (Mangiarotti *et al.*, 1982a; Chung *et al.*, 1981). Both assays indicate that metabolism of all 2000 to 3000 regulated mRNAs is coordinately affected by disaggregation. First, synthesis of virtually all "aggregation-dependent" mRNA ceases when slugs are disaggregated and are kept apart by constant shaking. Synthesis of the "constitutive" species, those synthesized both during growth and differentiation, are unaffected. Second, and more surprisingly, the stability of "aggregation-dependent" mRNAs in the cytoplasm is markedly and specifically reduced by disaggregation. In disaggregated cells the half-life of individual "late" mRNA falls from the value of several hours, characteristic of growth and normal development, to 25 to 40 minutes; the stability of "constitutive" mRNAs by contrast is unaffected by cell–cell contact (Mangiarotti *et al.*, 1982a; Chung *et al.*, 1981).

An example of the selective destruction of individual regulated mRNAs is depicted in Figs. 10 and 11. Cytoplasmic polyadenylated RNA was prepared from cells plated for development for 15 hours, or disaggregated after 15 hours and maintained as a vigorously shaken single cell suspension for up to 5 hours following disaggregation. The level of several constitutive and late-specific mRNAs was measured by "Northern" gel analysis (Figs. 10 and 11). The constitutive RNAs, bands 79, 314b, 314c, 29, and 55a, remain at the same level following disaggregation, whereas the late specific RNAs, 253b, 314a, 315b, and 55b, are rapidly lost following disaggregation. This study indicates that 2.5 hours after cells are disaggregated, the level of late mRNA sequences is only 6% that in plated cells, by 5 hours, it is only 2.5%. This indicates that upon disaggregation the late mRNAs are lost from the cytoplasm with a $t_{1/2}$ of 25 to 45 minutes. (This is a minimum estimate, and it assumes no synthesis of these mRNAs after disaggregation. Any continued synthesis would result in a shorter half-life.) Since the half-lives of regulated mRNAs in multicellular aggregates is at least 4 hours, disaggregation induces a six- to ninefold increase in the decay constants for regulated, but not constitutive, mRNAs (Mangiarotti *et al.*, 1982a; Chung *et al.*, 1981).

How the aggregation-stage mRNAs are specifically labilized upon disaggregation is not known. Among several possibilities, disaggregation could increase the synthesis or activity of a specific mRNA-

TABLE II

PROPERTIES OF DEVELOPMENTALLY BLOCKED MUTANTS[a]

Strain	Parent	Source	Very early development[b]	45 minutes[c]	PDE[d]	cAMP-B[e]	EDTA contacts[f]	Terminal morphology[g]	Level of aggregation-dependent mRNAs (%)[h]	Aggregation-dependent proteins[i]
Agg2	AX3	D. McMahon	+	−	−	−	−	agg⁻	0.4	−
WL3	AX3	W. F. Loomis	+	+	−	−	−	agg⁻	0.2	−
JM41	AX3	J. Margolskee	+	+	−	−	ND[j]	agg⁻	0.4	−
HC72	HC6	M. B. Coukell	+	+	+	−	−	agg⁻	0.2	−
HC54	HC6	M. B. Coukell	+	+	+	+	−	agg⁻	0.2	−
HJR-1	NC4	R. A. Lerner	ND	ND	ND	ND	−	Ripples, loose aggregates	0.3	ND
JM84	AX3	J. Margolskee	+	+	+	+	−	Ripples, loose aggregates	6	−
GM2	AX3	W. F. Loomis	+	+	+	+	+	Mounds	39.8	+
JM35	AX3	J. Margolskee	+	+	+	+	+	Mounds with tips	100	+
AX3	NC4	W. F. Loomis	+	+	+	+	+	Culminates	100	+

[a] From Blumberg *et al.* (1982).

[b] Very early development. + indicates induction of synthesis of the enzyme *N*-acetylglucosaminidase. It also indicates a two- to four-fold induction of actin synthesis between 0 and 30 minutes of development as well as a sharp drop in actin synthesis at 90 minutes of development (Margolskee and Lodish, 1980a,b).

[c] 45 minutes. + indicates induction of the synthesis of two early proteins (the "45 minute" proteins) synthesized between 45 and 90 minutes of development (Margolskee and Lodish, 1980b).

[d] PDE. Induction of the activity of the cell-bound phosphodiesterase. + indicates that the mutant cells developed by starvation for 15 hours in a rapidly shaken suspension culture expressed a level of the enzyme at least fourfold above the background activity observed in growing cells. AX3 wild-type cells starved in suspension culture for 15 hours expressed a level 13-fold above the growth phase background (cf. Blumberg *et al.*, 1982, for details).

[e] cAMP-B. Cell surface cAMP binding activity. + indicates that the mutant cells developed by starvation in a rapidly shaken suspension culture for 8 or 15 hours induce a level of binding which is at least four times above the level detected in growing cells. Wild type AX3 cells induced a sixfold increase under these conditions.

[g] Agg⁻ means a failure to aggregate.

[h] Taken from data in Blumberg *et al.* (1982).

[i] Taken from data shown in Blumberg *et al.* (1982).

[j] ND, Not done.

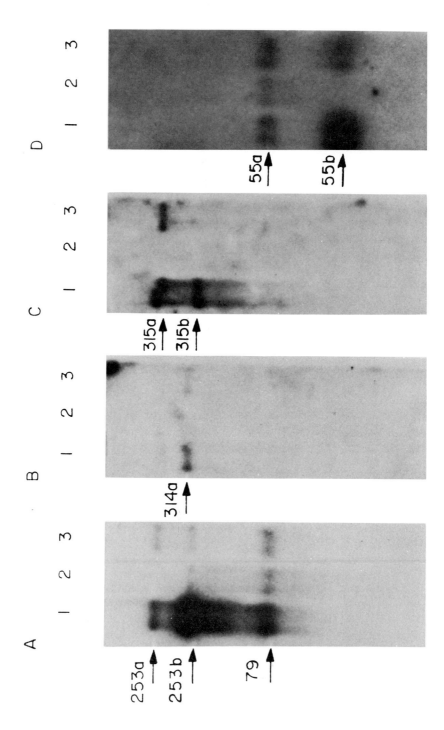

degrading enzyme. Such activation of specific mRNA nucleases has been observed in mammalian cells treated with interferon (Nilsen *et al.*, 1980). We envisage differential stability of mRNAs as providing flexibility to a developing system such as *Dictyostelium*. Until very late in the developmental program, when formation of actual spores and stalk cells begins, differentiation is reversible, as disaggregated cells will resume normal growth when placed in axenic culture.

C. CYCLIC AMP AND GENE EXPRESSION

During the preaggregation stages, cAMP serves the dual role of chemotactic agent and inducer of development. When growing cells are transferred to starvation buffer and shaken in suspension to prevent formation of aggregates, they become "aggregation competent" and will, after several hours, begin to emit spontaneous, periodic pulses of cAMP (Gerisch, 1968; Gerisch and Hess, 1974). If these cells are subjected to externally applied pulses of cAMP starting before the onset of spontaneous cAMP emission, the amoebae will induce prematurely high levels of several developmentally regulated preaggregation stage proteins. In particular, several proteins required for chemotaxis (the cAMP receptor, adenyl cyclase, the membrane bound and extracellular phosphodiesterases) and cellular aggregation ("contact sites A") appear in cAMP pulsed cells several hours before they would appear in cells not treated with cAMP (Gerisch *et al.*, 1975; Darmon *et al.*, 1975; Klein, 1975; Klein and Juliani, 1977). In general, these developmental events are advanced most effectively by pulses of cAMP rather than by continuous application of the nucleotide. Marin and Rothman (1980), by contrast, find that stimulatory effects of cAMP pulsing are found only when the developmental rate is suboptimal. They find cAMP has no effect when cells are differentiating in optimal concentrations of ions.

We have shown that, in disaggregated cells, cAMP specifically stimulates the synthesis of most but not all of the aggregation-

---

FIG. 10. Specific degradation of late messages upon disaggregation, and preservation of late messages by cAMP. Two micrograms of cytoplasmic polyadenylated RNA was loaded on each lane of the gel, electrophoresed, blotted, and immobilized on nitrocellulose paper as described in Chung *et al.* (1981). Filters were hybridized to ^{32}P-labeled DNA of clones 253, 314, 315, 55, and 79, respectively. The RNA encoded by these clones are indicated by the arrows. Lane 1 contains RNA from 15 hour plated cells; lane 2 contains RNA from cells that were plated for 15 hours and then disaggregated for 5 hours; and lane 3 contains RNA from cells plated for 15 hours and then disaggregated for 5 hours in the presence of 100 μM cAMP. Bands 79 and 55a are constitutive mRNAs and bands 253a, 253b, 314a, 315b, and 55b are late, aggregation specific mRNAs. (From Chung *et al.*, 1981.)

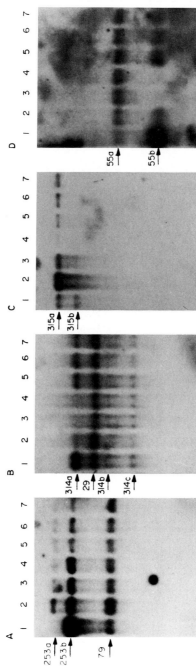

Fig. 11. Rate of degradation of late message upon disaggregation and restoration of late messages in disaggregated cells by cAMP. The gel separation hybridization was the same as in Fig. 2. Lane 1 contains RNA from 15 hour plated cells; lane 2 contains RNA from cells that were plated for 15 hours and then disaggregated for 1.25 hours; lane 3, for 2.5 hours; and lane 4, for 5 hours. Lanes 5, 6, and 7 contain RNA from cells that were treated the same way as those in lane 2, 3, and 4, respectively, except that at the end of the disaggregation period cAMP was added and the cells were shaken for another 3 hours. (A) Clones 79 and 253; (B) clones 314 and 29; (C) clone 315; (D) clone 55. (From Chung et al., 1981.)

dependent mRNAs. As noted above, we find that regardless of the time of addition, cAMP does not induce synthesis of the aggregation-stage regulated mRNAs in cells shaken in suspension from the beginning of differentiation, i.e., aggregation competent cells which are not and have not been in physical contact with other cells (Chung *et al.*, 1981; Landfear *et al.*, 1982). We believe that cell–cell contact induces the *ability* of cells to respond to extracellular cAMP, resulting in the transcription of 2500 "regulated" mRNAs. Specifically, 2.5 hours after disaggregation the level of all "regulated" mRNAs is only 6% that of control cells and is about 2% at 5 hours (Figs. 10 and 11). Within 3 hours after cAMP is added to either of these two populations of cells, the level of late mRNAs is restored to a value at least 50% that of plated cells (Fig. 11). Cyclic AMP stimulates the rate of synthesis of "regulated" mRNAs by these cells *at least* 4.5-fold (Chung *et al.*, 1981).

Experiments on RNA synthesis by isolated nuclei have reinforced the notion that cAMP can affect gene transcription (Landfear *et al.*, 1982). Nuclei from disaggregated cells synthesize, *in vitro*, low levels of "aggregation-dependent" mRNAs, but normal amounts of the "constitutive" species. When disaggregated cells were treated with cAMP and nuclei then isolated, synthesis of most "aggregation-dependent" mRNAs was increased and was similar to that of nuclei from normal aggregated cells.

Besides stimulating the transcription of "late" genes, cAMP appears to stabilize the late mRNAs in disaggregated cells (Mangiarotti *et al.*, 1982b). In this study, cells were labeled with [^{32}P]PO$_4$ from 13 to 17 hours, and then disaggregated. In the absence of cAMP, the labeled "late" mRNAs were specifically degraded. Their half-life was 20–30 minutes, in agreement with a previous report (Mangiarotti *et al.*, 1982a). If millimolar cAMP was added, however, the labeled "late" mRNAs were stable, with a half-life of greater than 3 hours.

The notion that cell–cell contact is an essential prerequisite for activation of developmentally regulated genes is disputed by Kay, Gross, and their colleagues. They showed that isolated amoebae of certain "sporogenous" mutants of the *Dictyostelium* mutant strain V12M2 can differentiate into mature stalk and prespore cells. This differentiation requires that the cells be bound to a special plastic surface, and is dependent on high levels of cAMP and on an exact ionic composition. The frequency of mature stalk cells decreases as the density of the monolayer of cells is decreased, indicating that something in addition to cAMP is required for stalk cell induction (Kay *et al.*, 1978). A dialyzable factor has been identified which, together with cAMP, can induce isolated amoebae to differentiate into mature stalk cells (Town and

Stanford, 1979). The pathway for mature spore formation also requires cAMP as well as some other form of cell interaction, possibly a substance which diffuses only over a short range since close cell proximity but not actual cell contact appears to be required (Kay *et al.*, 1978, 1979; Gross *et al.*, 1981; Kay and Trevan, 1981). It should be noted that isolated wild-type cells cannot differentiate into spore or stalk cells under similar circumstances, and the nature of the mutation(s) which result in the sporogenous phenotype is obscure. The mutation itself and/or the presence of the adhesive plastic surface may allow the normal requirement of cell–cell contact for morphogenesis and regulated gene expression to be bypassed.

In related studies, Gross *et al.* (1981) have shown that the activity of one developmentally regulated enzyme, glycogen phosphorylase, can be induced by the addition of very high levels of cAMP (1 m*M*) to a starved suspension of single wild-type cells. Under similar conditions, however, another late enzyme, UDP-galactose polysaccharide transferase, as well as other late polypeptides cannot be induced (Okamoto, 1982; Alton and Lodish, 1977b; Landfear and Lodish, 1980). Thus it is important to emphasize that while a great many late gene products are not expressed in aggregation competent suspension starved cells and are not induced in these cells by the addition of cAMP, there are some late gene products which may be exceptions.

D. Cyclic AMP and Differentiation of Spore and Stalk Cells

Several lines of evidence suggest that cAMP might influence the differentiation of spore and stalk cells in the multicellular aggregate. The action of cAMP in stimulating postaggregative mRNA expression may be, in fact, a reflection of a larger role of cAMP as an inducer of differentiation (Bonner, 1970; Hamilton and Chia, 1975; Kay, 1979; Town *et al.*, 1976; Town and Stanford, 1979). Cell contact could be required simply to increase the concentration of some diffusible secreted molecule which, together with cAMP, causes some cells to induce stalk- or spore-specific molecules.

How such components actually interact with a cell and induce a committment to differentiate along the prespore or prestalk pathway is a key question. An attractive hypothesis is that the position of a cell in the aggregate determines its neighboring interaction and thus its committment to the spore or stalk pathway (Farnsworth and Wolpert, 1971; Loomis, 1972; McMahon, 1973; Rubin and Robertson, 1975). More recent evidence, however, suggests that the committment to spore or stalk differentiation precedes the formation of the positional (tip–prestalk–prespore) axis (Bonner *et al.*, 1971; Forman and Garrod,

1977; Tasaka and Takeuchi, 1982). Amoebae starved in suspension culture form spherical aggregates; development proceeds on the same time scale as in cells undergoing normal morphogenesis (Forman and Garrod, 1977; Tasaka and Takeuchi, 1982). After 12 to 14 hours, prespore cells appear randomly throughout the aggregate. It is only later, upon prolonged incubation that the prespore cells collect toward the center of the aggregate and prestalk cells form a ring around the periphery.

Thus, it is more likely that properties of the precommitted cells are responsible for the developmental pattern. One such property may be differences in cellular cohesion between the prespore and prestalk cells (Feinberg *et al.,* 1979). The polarity or directional axis of the prepattern may be determined by differences in the ability of the prespore and prestalk cells to chemotax to cAMP (Sussman and Schindler, 1978; Matsukuma and Durston, 1979; Sternfeld and David, 1982). When nonpolar spherical aggregates are suspended at the interface between a buffer containing cAMP and one lacking it, prestalk cells will sort toward the higher cAMP concentration, thus imposing a polarity upon the previously nonpolar aggregates (Sternfeld and David, 1982). Also, stained prestalk cells within a mound migrate toward a microelectrode emitting cAMP in excess of 5×10^{-5} M (Matsukuma and Durtson, 1979). Regardless of the initial position of the electrode, the prestalk cells attracted by the cAMP become the tip of the slug. The prespore cells within the same mounds, by contrast, gave no signs of being chemotactically active toward these levels of cAMP.

Thus, as in the early stages of aggregation, postaggregative development is also characterized by a dual role for cAMP. Chemotaxis to cAMP aids in orienting the prespore–prestalk pattern. Together with other components cAMP also acts as an inducer of differentiation and regulator of late gene expression.

V. Conclusion

The value of *Dictyostelium discoideum* as a system for investigating several key problems of developmental biology at the molecular level is just now being realized. As one example, formation of specific cell–cell contacts is dependent on a number of developmentally regulated surface proteins. Importantly, formation of these tight cell–cell contacts is essential for both the transcription and the stability of about 2500 regulated mRNA species. It should be possible to determine precisely not only how these surface molecules function in cell–cell recognition, but also how interactions at the cell surface are transmitted to the nucleus and cytoplasm in order to affect gene expression. Many aspects of the role of cAMP as a chemotactic agent are now understood, at least in outline. There is growing evidence that cAMP also induces or accelerates at least part of the developmental program and may also induce the cytodifferentiation and segregation of prestalk and prespore cells. In particular, cAMP increases the synthesis and the stability of the 2500 mRNA species which are induced at aggregation; addition of this compound to disaggregated cells (which have ceased transcription specifically, of this class of mRNAs) restores synthesis of these mRNAs. It will be of considerable interest to learn whether, as in prokaryotic cells, cAMP enters the cell and whether cAMP binding proteins interact directly with regulatory sequences in DNA. Intracellular transmitter molecules are believed to mediate the response to extracellular cAMP during chemotaxis, resulting in the pulsatile synthesis and secretion of cAMP. It is also possible that these or other compounds mediate the effects of extracellular cAMP on gene expression. The identification of the nature and mode of action of these intracellular mediators will be of considerable importance.

ACKNOWLEDGMENTS

Work from the author's laboratories was supported by grants 79-00839 from the National Science Foundation and GM29897 from the National Institutes of Health to H.F.L. and by a grant from the C.N.R. to G.M. We thank Miriam Boucher for her skill in reading the illegible.

REFERENCES

Alcantara, F., and Monk M. (1974). *J. Gen. Microbiol.* **85**, 321.

Alton, T. H., and Brenner, M. (1979). *Dev. Biol.* **71**, 1.

Alton, T. H., and Lodish, H. F. (1977a). *Dev. Biol.* **60**, 180.

Alton, T. H., and Lodish, H. F. (1977b). *Dev. Biol.* **60**, 207.

Batts-Young, G., Lodish, H. F., and Jacobson, A. (1980). *Dev. Biol.* **78**, 352.

Beug, H., Katz, F. E., and Gerisch, G. (1973). *J. Cell Biol.* **56**, 647.

Blumberg, D. D., and Lodish, H. F. (1980a). *Dev. Biol.* **78**, 268.

Blumberg, D. D., and Lodish, H. F. (1980b). *Dev. Biol.* **78**, 285.

Blumberg, D. D., and Lodish, H. F. (1981). *Dev. Biol.* **81**, 74.

Blumberg, D. D., Margolskee, J. P., Chung, S., Barklis, E., Cohen, N. S., and Lodish, H. F. (1982). *Proc. Natl. Acad. Sci. U.S.A.* **79**, 727.

Bonner, J. T. (1949). *J. Exp. Zool.* **110**, 259.

Bonner, J. T. (1952). *Am. Nat.* **86**, 79.

Bonner, J. T. (1967). "The Cellular Slime Molds" (2nd Ed.). Princeton Univ. Press, Princeton, New Jersey.

Bonner, J. T. (1970). *Proc. Natl. Acad. Sci. U.S.A.* **65**, 110–113.

Bonner, J. T., and Frascella, E. B. (1952). *J. Exp. Zool.* **121**, 561.

Bonner, J. T., Chiquoine, A. D., and Kolderie, M. Q. (1955). *J. Exp. Zool.* **130**, 133.

Bonner, J. T., Barkley, D. S., Hall, E. M., Konijn, T. M., Mason, J. W., O'Keefe, G., III, and Wolfe, P. B. (1969). *Dev. Biol.* **20**, 72.

Bonner, J. T., Sieja, T. W., and Hall, E. M. (1971). *J. Embryol. Exp. Morphol.* **25**, 457.

Bozzaro, S., and Gerisch, G. (1978). *J. Mol. Biol.* **120,** 265.

Bozzaro, S., and Gerisch, G. (1979). *Cell Differ.* **8,** 112.

Brenner, M. (1977). *J. Biol. Chem.* **252,** 4073.

Brown, S. S., and Rutherford, C. L. (1980). *Differentiation* **16,** 173.

Cappuccinelli, P., and Ashworth, J. M., eds. (1977). "Development and Differentiation in the Cellular Slime Moulds." Elsevier, Amsterdam.

Chang, C. M., Reitherman, R. W., Rosen, D. D., and Barondes, S. M. (1975). *Exp. Cell Res.* **95,** 136.

Chung, S., Landfear, S. M., Blumberg, D. D., Cohen, N. S., and Lodish, H. F. (1981). *Cell* **24,** 785.

Cocucci, S., and Sussman, M. (1970). *J. Cell Biol.* **45,** 399.

Coloma, A., and Lodish, H. F. (1981). *Dev. Biol.* **81,** 238.

Darmon, M., Brachet, P., and Pereira da Silva, L. H. (1975). *Proc. Natl. Acad. Sci. U.S.A.* **72,** 3163.

Derman, E., Karauter, K., Walling, L., Weinberger, C., Ray, M., and Darnell, J. E. (1981). *Cell* **23,** 731.

Devreotes, P. N., and Steck, T. L. (1979). *J. Cell Biol.* **80,** 300.

Farnsworth, P., and Wolpert, L. (1971). *Nature (London)* **231,** 329.

Feinberg, A. P., Springer, W. R., and Barondes, S. H. (1979). *Proc. Natl. Acad. Sci. U.S.A.* **76,** 3977.

Firtel, R. A. (1972). *J. Mol. Biol.* **66,** 363.

Firtel, R. A., and Lodish, H. F. (1973). *J. Mol. Biol.* **79,** 295.

Forman, D., and Garrod, D. R. (1977). *J. Embryol. Exp. Morphol.* **40,** 229.

Franke, J., and Sussman, M. (1973). *J. Mol. Biol.* **81,** 173.

Freeze, H., and Loomis, W. F. (1977). *J. Biol. Chem.* **252,** 820.

Geltosky, J. E., Weseman, J., Bakke, A., and Lerner, R. (1979). *Cell* **18,** 391.

Geltosky, J. E., Birdwell, C. R., Weseman, J., and Lerner, R. A. (1980). *Cell* **21,** 339.

George, R. P., Hohl, H. R., and Raper, K. B. (1972). *J. Gen. Microbiol.* **70,** 477.

Gerisch, G. (1961). *Exp. Cell Res.* **25,** 535.

Gerisch, G. (1968). *Curr. Toop. Dev. Biol.* **3,** 157.

Gerisch, G. (1976). *Cell Differ.* **5,** 21.

Gerisch, G. (1980). *Curr. Top. Dev. Biol.* **14,** 157.

Gerisch, G., and Hess, B. (1974). *Proc. Natl. Acad. Sci. U.S.A.* **71,** 2118.

Gerisch, G., and Wick, U. (1975). *Biochem. Biophys. Res. Commun.* **65,** 364.

Gerisch, G., Malchow, D., Riedel, V., and Miller, E. M. (1972). *Nature (London)* **235,** 90.

Gerisch, G., Fromm, H., Hensgen, A., and Wick, U. (1975). *Nature (London)* **255,** 547.

Gerisch, G., Maeda, Y., Malchow, D., Roos, W., Wick, U., and Wurster, B. (1977). "Development and Differentiation in the Cellular Slime Molds" (P. Cappuccinelli and J. Ashworth, eds.), p. 105 Elsevier, Amsterdam.

Gerisch, G., Krelle, H., Bozzaro, S., Eitle, E., and Guggenheim, R. (1980). *In* "Cell Adhesion and Motility" (A. S. G. Curtis and J. Pitts, eds.) p. 293. Cambridge Univ. Press, Cambridge.

Green, A., and Newell, P. (1975). *Cell* **6,** 129.

Gregg, J. H. (1965). *Dev. Biol.* **12,** 377.

Gregg, J. H. (1968). *Exp. Cell Res.* **51,** 633.

Gross, J. D., Peacey, M. J., and Trevan, D. J. (1976). *J. Cell Sci.* **22,** 645.

Gross, J. G., Town, C. D., Brookman, J. J., Jermyn, K. A., Peacey, M. J., and Kay, R. R. (1981). *Philos. Trans. R. Soc. London. Ser. B* **295,** 497.

Hames, B. D., and Ashworth, J. M. (1974). *Biochem. J.* **142,** 301.

Hamilton, I. D., and Chia, W. K. (1975). *J. Gen. Microbiol.* **91,** 295.

Henderson, E. (1975). *J. Biol. Chem.* **250**, 4730.
Hohl, H. R., and Hammamoto, S. T. (1969). *J. Ultrastruct. Res.* **26**, 442.
Ikeda, T., and Takeuchi, I. (1971). *Dev. Growth Differ.* **13**, 221.
Katz, E., and Bourguignon, L. (1974). *Dev. Biol.* **36**, 82.
Kay, R. R., and Trevan, D. J. (1981). *J. Embryol Exp. Morphol.* **62**, 369.
Kay, R. R. (1979). *J. Embryol. Exp. Morphol.* **52**, 171.
Kay, R. R., Garrod, D., and Tilly, R. (1978). *Nature (London)* **271**, 58.
Kay, R. R., Town, C. D., and Gross, J. D. (1979). *Differentiation* **13**, 7.
Kessin, R. H., Orlow, S. J., Shapiro, R. I., and Franke, J. (1979). *Proc. Natl. Acad. Sci. U.S.A.* **76**, 5450.
Klein, C. (1975). *J. Biol. Chem.* **250**, 7134.
Klein, C. (1976). *FEBS Lett.* **68**, 125.
Klein, C. (1977). *FEBS Lett.* **71**, 17.
Klein, C., and Darmon, M. (1977). *Nature (London)* **268**, 76.
Klein, C., and Juliani, M. H. (1977). *Cell* **10**, 329.
Konijn, T. M., Van De Meene, J. G. C., Bonner, J. T., and Barkley, D. S. (1967). *Proc. Natl. Acad. Sci. U.S.A.* **58**, 1152.
Konijn, T. M., Barkley, D. S., Chang, Y. Y., and Bonner, J. T. (1968). *Am. Nat.* **102**, 225.
Lam, T. V., Pickering, G., Geltowsky, J., and Siu, C. M. (1981). *Differentiation* **20**, 22.
Landfear, S. M., and Lodish, H. F. (1980). *Proc. Natl. Acad. Sci. U.S.A.* **77**, 1044.
Landfear, S., Chung, S., Lefebvre, P., and Lodish, H. F. (1982). *Cell* (in press).
Loomis, W. F., Jr. (1972). *Nature (London) New Biol.* **240**, 6.
Loomis, W. F. (1975). "Dictyostelium discoideum: A Developmental System." Academic Press, New York.
Loomis, W. F. (1979). *Dev. Biol.* **70**, 1.
Loomis, W. F., White, S., and Dimond, R. L. (1976). *Dev. Biol.* **53**, 171.
Loomis, W. F., Dimond, R., Free, S., and White, S. (1977). *In* Eukaryotic Microbes as Model Development Systems" (D. O'Day and P. Hougen, eds.), p. 177. Dekker, New York.
McKnight, G. S., and Palmiter, R. D. (1979). *J. Biol. Chem.* **254**, 9050.
McMahon, D. (1973). *Proc. Natl. Acad. Sci. U.S.A.* **70**, 2396.
Maeda, Y., and Maeda, M. (1974). *Exp. Cell Res.* **84**, 88.
Malchow, D., and Gerisch, G. (1974). *Procl Natl. Acad. Sci. U.S.A.* **71**, 2423.
Malchow, D., Nägele, B., Schwarz, H., and Gerisch, G. (1972). *Eur. J. Biochem.* **28**, 136.
Malchow, D., Nanjundiah, V., Wurster, B., Eckstein, F., and Gerisch, G. (1978). *Biochim. Biophys. Acta* **538**, 473.
Mangiarotti, G., and Hames, D. H. (1979). *Exp. Cell Res.* **119**, 428.
Mangiarotti, G., Chung, S., Zuker, C., and Lodish, H. F. (1981a). *Nucleic Acids Res.* **9**, 947.
Mangiarotti, G., Altruda, F., and Lodish, H. F. (1981b). *Mol. Cell. Biol.* **1**, 35.
Mangiarotti, G., Lefebvre, P., and Lodish, H. F. (1982a). *Dev. Biol.* **89**, 82.
Mangiarotti, G., Ceccarelli, A., and Lodish, H. F. (1982b). *Nature (London)*, Submitted.
Margolskee, J. P., and Lodish, H. F. (1980a). *Dev. Biol.* **74**, 37.
Margolskee, J. P., and Lodish, H. F. (1980b). *Dev. Biol.* **74**, 50.
Marin, F. T. (1976). *Dev. Biol.* **48**, 110.
Marin, F. (1977). *Dev. Biol.* **60**, 389.
Marin, F., and Rothman, F. (1980). *J. Cell Biol.* **87**, 823.
Mato, J., and Konijn, T. (1975). *Biochim. Biophys. Acta* **385**, 173.
Mato, J., Kreus, F., Van Haastert, P., and Konijn, T. (1977a). *Biochem. Biophys. Res. Commun.* **77**, 399.

Mato, J., Kreus, F., Van Haastert, P., and Konijn, T. (1977b). *Proc. Natl. Acad. Sci. U.S.A.* **74**, 2348.

Matsukuma, S., and Durston, A. J. (1979). *J. Embryol. Exp. Morphol.* **50**, 243.

Morrissey, J. H., Farnsworth, P., and Loomis, W. F. (1981). *Dev. Biol.* **83**, 1.

Müller, K., and Gerisch, G. (1978). *Nature (London)* **274**, 445.

Newell, P. C. (1977). *In* "Microbial Interactions (Receptors and Recognition)" (J. L. Reissig, ed.), Ser. B., Vol. 3. Chapman Hall, London.

Newell, P. C., and Sussman, M. (1970). *J. Mol. Biol.* **49**, 627–637.

Newell, P. C., Telser, A., and Sussman, M. J. (1969). *Bacteriology* **100**, 763.

Newell, P. C., Longlands, M., and Sussman, M. (1971). *J. Mol. Biol.* **58**, 541.

Newell, P. C., Franke, J., and Sussman, M. (1972). *J. Mol. Biol.* **63**, 373.

Nicol, A., and Garrod, D. R. (1978). *J. Cell Biol.* **32**, 377.

Nilsen, T. W., Weissman, S. G., and Baglioni, C. (1980). *Biochemistry* **19**, 5574.

Ochiai, H., Schware, N., Merkl, R., Wagle, G., and Gerisch, G. (1982). *Cell Differ.* **11**, 1.

Okamoto, K. (1982). *J. Gen. Micro biol.* (in press).

Orlowski, M., and Loomis, W. F. (1979). *Dev. Biol.* **71**, 297.

Ramagopal, S., and Ennis, H. L. (1981). *Proc. Natl. Acad. Sci. U.S.A.* **78**, 3083.

Raper, K. B. (1940). *J. Elisha Mitchell Sci. Soc.* **56**, 241.

Riedel, V., and Gerisch, G. (1971). *Biochem. Biophys. Res. Commun.* **42**, 119.

Ringold, G. M., Yamamoto, K. R., Bishop, J. M., and Varmus, H. E. (1977). *Proc. Natl. Acad. Sci. U.S.A.* **74**, 2879.

Robertson, A. (1972). *Lect. Math. Life Sci.* **4**, 47.

Roos, W., Nanjundiah, W., Malchow, D., and Gerisch, G. (1975). *FEBS Lett.* **53**, 139.

Roos, W., Scheidegger, C., and Gerisch, G. (1977). *Nature (London)* **266**, 259.

Rosen, S. D., Kafka, J. A., Simpson, D. L., and Barondes, S. H. (1973). *Proc. Natl. Acad. Sci. U.S.A.* **70**, 2554.

Roth, R., Ashworth, J. M., and Sussman, M. (1968). *Proc. Natl. Acad. Sci. U.S.A.* **59**, 1235.

Rowekamp, W., Poole, S., and Firtel, R. A. (1980). *Cell* **20**, 495.

Rubin, J. (1976). *J. Embryol. Exp. Morphoe.* **36**, 261.

Rubin, J., and Robertson, A. (1975). *J. Embryol. Exp. Morphol.* **33**, 227.

Schindler, J., and Sussman, M. (1977a). *Biochem. Biophys. Res. Commun.* **79**, 611.

Schindler, J., and Sussman, M. (1977b). *J. Mol. Biol.* **116**, 161.

Schinnick, T. M., and Lerner, R. A. (1980). *Proc. Natl. Acad. Sci. U.S.A.* **77**, 4788.

Schutz, G., Nguyen-Huu, M. C., Giescke, K., Hynes, N. E., Groner, B., Wurtz, T., and Sippel, A. E. (1977). *Cold Spring Harbor Symp. Quant. Biol.* **42**, 617.

Shaffer, B. M. (1962). *Adv. Morphog.* **2**, 109.

Shaffer, B. M. (1975). *Nature (London)* **255**, 549.

Simpson, D. L., Rosen, S. D., and Barondes, S. H. (1975). *Biochim. Biophys. Acta* **412**, 709.

Sliflan, M. K., and Bonner, J. T. (1952). *Biol. Bull.* **102**, 273.

Springer, W. R., and Barondes, S. M. (1978). *J. Cell Biol.* **78**, 837.

Steinemann, C., and Parish, R. W. (1980). *Nature (London)* **286**, 621.

Sternfeld, J., and David, C. N. (1982). *Differentiation* (in press).

Sussman, M., and Schindler, J. (1978). *Differentiation* **10**, 1.

Sussman, M., and Sussman, R. R. (1969). *Symp. Soc. Gen. Microbiol.* **19**, 403.

Tasaka, M., and Takeuchi, I. (1982). *Differentiation* (in press).

Telser, A., and Sussman, M. (1971). *J. Biol. Chem.* **246**, 2252.

Thomas, D. A., and Wright, B. E. (1976). *J. Biol. Chem.* **251**, 1258.

Tomchik, K. J. and Devreotes, P. N. (1981). *Science* **212**, 443.

Town, C., and Stanford, E. (1979). *Proc. Natl. Acad. Sci. U.S.A.* **76**, 308.

Town, C. D., Gross, J. D., and Kay, R. R. (1976). *Nature (London)* **262,** 717.

Tsang, A., and Bradbury, J. M. (1981). *Exp. Cell Res.* **132,** 433.

Wallace, L. J., and Frazier, W. A. (1979). *Proc. Natl. Acad. Scil U.S.A.* **76,** 4250.

Wick, V., Malchow, D., and Gerisch, G. (1978). *Cell Biol. Int. Rep.* **2,** 71.

Williams, J. G., and Lloyd, M. M. (1979). *J. Mol. Biol.* **129,** 19–38.

Williams, J. G., Lloyd, M. M., and Devine, J. M. (1979). *Cell* **17,** 903.

Williams, J. G., Tsnag, A. S., and Mahbubani, H. (1981).*Proc. Natl. Acad. Sci. U.S.A.* **77,** 7171.

Yamamoto, K. R., Stallcup, M. R., Ring, J., and Ringold, G. M. (1977). *Cold Spring Harbor Symp. Quant. Biol.* **42,** 625.

Yeh, R. P., Chan, F. K., and Coukell, M. B. (1978). *Dev. Biol.* **66,** 361.

Zada-Hames, I. M., and Ashworth, J. M. (1978). *Dev. Biol.* **63,** 307.

CHAPTER 6

DEVELOPMENTAL AND EXPERIMENTAL CHANGES IN RETINAL GLIA CELLS: CELL INTERACTIONS AND CONTROL OF PHENOTYPE EXPRESSION AND STABILITY

A. A. Moscona and P. Linser

LABORATORY FOR DEVELOPMENTAL BIOLOGY
CUMMINGS LIFE SCIENCE CENTER
UNIVERSITY OF CHICAGO
CHICAGO, ILLINOIS

I. Introduction

This article is concerned with the differentiation of neural retina cells. It focuses mainly on the glia cells, and on the role of contact interactions with neurons in the control of their phenotypic characteristics. Our main purpose is to bring together findings and interpretations within a framework of a unifying working hypothesis, rather than review in detail the voluminous body of data related to this subject.

The vertebrate neural retina (NR)* arises in the early embryo as an extension of the brain, starting out as a simple neuroepithelium that contains the progenitors of the two major categories of retina cells,

* Abbreviations: NR, neural retina; MC, Müller glia cells; CA-C, carbonic anhydrase-C; GS, glutamine synthetase; PE, pigment epithelium; AAA, α-aminoadipic acid; BrdU, 5-bromo-2′-deoxyuridine.

CURRENT TOPICS IN
DEVELOPMENTAL BIOLOGY, VOL. 18

neurons and glia. Its development transforms it into a system specialized for reception of light signals and their transmission into visual centers in the brain. The divergence of the progenitor cells and their differentiation into definitive neurons and glia is accompanied by cellular compartmentalization of specific enzymes and other products. As in other developing systems, some of these processes may be preprogrammed already in the precursor cells; others evolve in response to successive external "signals" provided by microenvironment, "positional information," and contact-relationship of the cells.

Our studies have been concerned mainly with the characteristics of glia cells in the NR of the chick embryo. There is growing awareness of the importance of glia cells in the development and function of the NR, prompting increased interest in their properties. It is generally believed that among the key functions of glia cells is the regulation of the neuronal extracellular milieu, in part, because of their ability to take up and metabolize various transmitters and other products released from nerve terminals (Kuffler and Nicholls, 1976), and, in part, because they contribute to nerve cells and their immediate microenvironment metabolic and physical conditions essential for normal activity. The enzymic and other mechanisms that enable glia cells to fulfill these functions arise during embryonic development. This article reviews published and ongoing work on the developmental programs of two "markers" of definitive glia cells in the NR, the enzymes carbonic anhydrase-C and glutamine synthetase; it then describes experiments on modification of definitive glia cells into lens-like cells; and it proposes that the cell surface and cell interactions play a key role in the expression and stability of Müller glia phenotype.

II. Müller Glia Cells

Unlike the brain, the avian NR contains only a single kind of glia known as Müller fibers, or Müller cells; these versatile cells combine functions that in other parts of the nervous system are fulfilled by diverse types of gliocytes (Linser and Moscona, 1981a). They are the only cells that, from early stages of development, span the whole width of the NR, thus serving as the primary scaffolding in the morphogenesis of this tissue. They extend from the outer limiting membrane to the inner limiting membrane (Cajal, 1973; Mayerson and Moscona, 1979), and send fine vertical (radial) processes into the inner plexiform and ganglion cell layers; these processes become increasingly numerous and pervasive as development of the NR advances (Fig. 1).

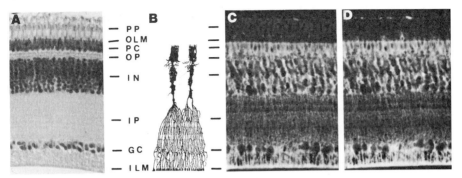

FIG. 1. Structure of mature chicken NR, Müller cell morphology, and simultaneous localization of CA-C and GS by double-label indirect immunofluorescence. (A) Hematoxylin–eosin-stained section of mature NR. PP, photoreceptor processes; OLM, outer limiting membrane; PC, photoreceptor cell layer; OP, outer plexiform layer; IN, inner nuclear layer; IP, inner plexiform layer; GC, ganglion cell layer; ILM, inner limiting membrane. (B) Morphology of mature avian Müller glia cells (after Cajal, 1973) showing numerous arborizations. (C and D) Same section of NR double-immunostained with antisera to CA-C (D) and GS (C). Immunofluorescence confined to Müller cells. The staining patterns of both enzymes closely overlap and correspond to the structural characteristics of Müller cells (×240). For detection of CA-C the section was treated with rabbit antiserum to CA-C, followed by rhodamine-conjugated goat anti-rabbit IgG Fab' fragments. For detection of GS, mouse antiserum to GS was used, followed by fluorescein isothiocyanate-conjugated rabbit anti-mouse IgG. (Modified from Linser and Moscona, 1981a.)

Hence, each Müller cell is juxtaposed along its length to virtually all the types of neurons in the NR, as it passes and arborizes through the different retinal layers. This situation would make it possible for Müller cells to interact with various neurons by way of surface contact, junctions, and metabolite exchanges. Such interactions, which are undoubtedly reciprocal, might be expected to play an important role in development, expression, and stabilization of the cells' phenotype, as well as in the physiological functions of the mature NR.

Definitive Müller cells in the mature avian NR are characterized by the presence of the enzymes carbonic anhydrase-C (CA-C) and glutamine synthetase (GS). This has been demonstrated immunohistochemically by showing that monospecific antisera to each of these two proteins react exclusively with Müller cells (Fig. 1; Linser and Moscona, 1979, 1981a). Taking advantage of the fact that antiserum to GS of avian NR cross-reacts with GS in the NR of other vertebrates, we determined that this enzyme is confined to Müller cells also in the NR of quail (Moscona and Degenstein, 1981a), fish, frog, and mouse (Linser and Moscona, unpublished). Also in rat NR, GS is found only in these glia cells (Riepe and Norenberg, 1978). Therefore, compartmentalization of GS in Müller cells is characteristic of vertebrate NR. This is consistent with the suggestion that these cells are the locus of the "small glutamate compartment" in which GS is a key component (Moscona et al., 1980).

A similar survey could not yet be done with CA-C, because the antiserum generated to chicken CA-C (Linser and Moscona, 1981a) shows only slight cross-reactions in other species. However, using monospecific antiserum directed against mammalian (mouse) CA-C we found that, also in the NR of mature mice Müller cells immunostain intensely for CA-C (Linser and Moscona, 1982b). Carbonic anhydrase was detected in mammalian Müller cells also by methods based on enzymatic activity (Musser and Rosen, 1973; Bhattacharjee, 1976). Therefore, a high level of this enzyme and of GS appears to be a characteristic feature of definitive Müller cells in the mature vertebrate NR. In the adult brain (mammalian) these two enzymes are compartmentalized in different cells: GS in astroglia (Norenberg, 1979) and CA-C in oligodendroglia (Ghandour et al., 1979) and in choroid cells (Giacobini, 1962). Evidently, definitive Müller glia cells fulfill multiple roles that in the brain are partitioned into several kinds of cells.

Although in mature NR both CA-C and GS are coexpressed in the same cells, the developmental programs of these two enzymes in the embryonic NR differ markedly with respect to temporal, spatial, and regulatory parameters. We will now describe these programs and review what is known about their developmental regulation.

III. Carbonic Ahydrase-C (CA-C)

CA-C (EC 4.2.1.1) catalyzes the hydration of metabolic CO_2 and the dehydration of bicarbonate, thereby facilitating removal of CO_2; it functions in regulation of Na^+ and Cl^- movement and in fluid balance, and therefore is important in cell and tissue homeostasis (Maren, 1967). The level of CA-C in the adult chicken NR is very high and represents approximately 3% of the total protein of this tissue (Linser and Moscona, 1981a). Since CA-C is confined to Müller cells which represent approximately one-fifth of the cells in the NR, their content of this enzyme is exceptionally high. In adult mouse NR, the level of CA-C is only one-tenth of that in the chicken NR. This difference may be due to the fact that the avian NR is avascular, unlike that of most mammals; therefore, homeostasis and other CA-C-dependent processes in the avian eye place added demands on the Müller cells, and the high level of CA-C may reflect this situation.

A. Changes in CA-C Levels during NR Development

Carbonic anhydrase enzyme activity has long been known to be present in NR of very young chick embryos (Clark, 1951), but detailed quantitative changes and the cellular localization of this enzyme at various developmental stages have been examined only recently. Using monospecific antiserum to purified avian CA-C, we determined by quantitative immunoelectrophoresis the developmental profile of CA-C in the chick NR, i.e., the age-dependent changes in the concentration of this antigen in the total NR; next, we investigated immunohistochemically the cellular localization of CA-C at progressive stages of development (Linser and Moscona, 1981a).

Figure 2 shows changes in CA-C levels in the embryonic NR. For reference, this figure also shows the growth curve of the NR (changes in total protein) and the developmental profile of GS specific activity (to be discussed further on). It is important to note that the chick embryo NR completes its overall growth by the twelfth day of development; total protein, cell number and DNA content increase at a fast rate till the eighth to ninth day, then at a slowing rate, and plateau by day 12, as shown in Fig. 4 (Moscona and Moscona, 1979). From then on, cells in the NR are engaged predominantly in functional differentiation and specialization which progresses fastest in the region of the fundus and slowest near the ciliary margin.

The overall level of CA-C in the NR shows a biphasic relationship to embryonic age (Fig. 2). Between days 3 and 5 of development, CA-C level rises very sharply, from being undetectable by these methods, to

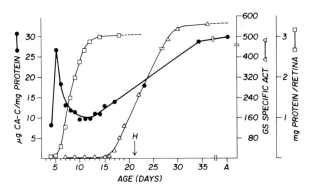

FIG. 2. Developmental profile of CA-C in the neural retina of chicken embryos compared with that of GS and with growth of the retina. ●, CA-C in retina; □, protein per retina; △, GS specific activity. H, Hatching; A, adult stage. Units of GS-specific activity here were derived from an assay with improved sensitivity over that used in older work reviewed in this article. (From Linser and Moscona, 1981a.)

25–27 μg/mg of total protein by the fifth day. After that, the relative concentration of CA-C drops markedly and continues to decline until day 11, while total protein in the NR continues to increase. Following cessation of retina growth, CA-C concentration again begins to increase, rising gradually and reaching a plateau after hatching at approxqmately 30 μg/mg total protein. These overall changes are reflected in changes in the cellular localization of the enzyme.

B. CELLULAR LOCALIZATION OF CA-C IN THE NR

The localization of CA-C in the embryonic NR changes markedly during development (Fig. 3). In early 3-day embryos, when CA-C first becomes immunohistochemically detectable, the prospective NR is still at the stage of an undifferentiated neuroepithelium and is continuous with the future pigment epithelium (PE) as a double lamina (Fig. 3A). CA-C first appears at the fold of this lamina adjacent to the lens vesicle, in the upper temporal quadrant of the eye. Then it extends around the margin of the lens in both the NR and the PE, and spreads gradient-like from the margin toward the fundus (Fig. 3B). By day 5, CA-C is present in practically all the cells throughout the NR and the PE (Fig. 3C). It is noteworthy that, concurrently with its appearance in the prospective NR and PE, CA-C also appears in the early lens cells; in later stages, the level of CA-C remains high in the lens epithelium, but declines in the lens fibers. Thus, early in the development of the eye, the posterior and vitreal eye chambers become surrounded by Ca-C-containing cells.

With the appearance of recognizable neurons in the NR, the cellular distribution of CA-C begins to change; progressively the enzyme is "lost" by the differentiating neurons, and becomes restricted to Müller glia cells. By day 6, the first definitive neurons, the ganglion cells, are present in the fundus (Meller and Glees, 1965; Kahn, 1974), and they are distinguished by absence of CA-C (Fig. 3D). As histogenesis progresses, other neurons lose their capacity to immunostain for CA-C, with the exception of certain amacrine neurons at the border of the inner plexiform layer (Cajal, 1973) that retain the enzyme longer (Figs. 3E and F). Eventually, CA-C in these, as in all other neurons, decreases to background level.

In contrast to the neurons, immunostaining of Müller cells for CA-C intensifies with development and spreads into their arborizing processes (Fig. 3E–G). In the fundus (developmentally the most advanced region of the NR), CA-C is confined predominantly to Müller cells already by day 10–11; at the ciliary margin (the least advanced region), it is still present in most of the cells as late as day 13. By day

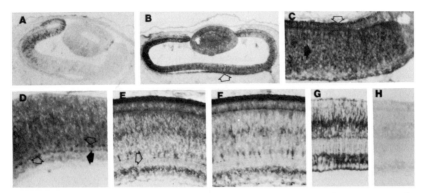

FIG. 3. Localization by immunoperoxidase reaction of CA-C in embryonic retina during development: progressive changes in regional and cellular compartmentalization of the antigen. (A) Section through the eye region of a day 3 chicken embryo showing onset of detectable immunostaining for CA-C in the dorsal aspect of the neural retina (NR) and the pigment epithelium (PE) near the developing lens (×150). (B) Section of eye of day 4 embryo showing staining of the NR, most intensely in the dorsal aspect, and generalized staining of the PE (open arrow) and lens (×56). (C) Retina of day 5 embryo showing generalized staining for CA-C in most cells of the NR (solid arrow) and PE (open arrow) (×250). (D) Section of day 8 NR showing reduction or absence of staining in ganglion cells (solid arrow) and staining in double row of prospective amacrine neurons (open arrow) that border the inner plexiform layer (IP) (×250). (E) Day 13 embryonic NR sectioned in a region close to the ciliary margin showing immunostaining for CA-C in the amacrine neurons and how their lateral arborizations form a continuous line running horizontally through the IP (open arrow). Note also the intensified immunostaining of Müller cell perikarya in the central region of the inner nuclear layer (IN) (×250). (F) Same NR as in (E), but sectioned closer to the fundus, showing the still intense staining of the amacrine neurons and their arborizations. Elsewhere staining is reduced, except in the perikarya of Müller cells (center of the IN) and their endings (i.e., near the PE and around the ganglion cells) (×250). (G) Day 16 NR showing that staining for CA-C is confined to Müller cells (×250). (H) Control section for (G), stained with previously absorbed CA-C antiserum (×250). (From Linser and Moscona, 1981a.)

15–16, CA-C is confined to Müller cells almost throughout the NR. After hatching, it is not detectable outside of Müller cells.

To substantiate these observations further, we have recently generated several monoclonal antibodies to chicken CA-C by the technique of Köhler and Milstein (1976). These were used to determine whether the above changes in cellular localization of the enzyme represented isozyme differences that could not be distinguished by the polyclonal antiserum. However, all the monoclonal antibodies which reacted with mature Müller cells revealed the same developmental changes in enzyme localization as those described above (Linser and Moscona, 1982b).

The transition in CA-C distribution in the NR from generalized to Müller cell-specific suggests that genes coding for CA-C are initially "turned on" in all the retinoblasts, beginning at the margin of the eye; later, their expression is "turned off" in the developing neurons, but continues in Müller cells so that, in the maturing and adult NR, CA-C becomes a characteristic "marker" of Müller cells. So far, we have been unable to modify the temporal program or the cellular distribution of CA-C by treatment with corticosteroid hormones, or with other experimental interventions that modify the expression of GS. Although these results are not finite, they strongly indicate that the development of CA-C in embryonic and fetal NR is subject to different regulatory mechanisms than that of GS (see below).

The very early expression of CA-C in the developing eye precedes its appearance in other tissues of the chick embryo and raises questions about causes and functions. CA-C appears almost simultaneously in the NR, PE, and lens as these three tissues meet at the anterior eye margin. This suggests that interactions among these three tissues, or between them and the regional microenvironment trigger the expression of CA-C. As to the function of CA-C at this early stage of eye development, it is significant that its appearance is temporally correlated with closure of the eyeball (the choroid fissure) and formation of the eye chambers. A possible lead to function is suggested by the need for intraoccular fluid pressure in the expansion of the embryonic eyeball (Coulombre, 1956), and by the role of CA-C in the regulation of fluid balance and intraoccular pressure (Maren, 1976). Therefore, the early expression of CA-C in the eye may be specifically related to the rapid accumulation of intraoccular fluid. Confirmation of this will show that CA-C plays an important role in eye morphogenesis in the early embryo.

IV. Glutamine Synthetase (GS)

GS (EC 6.3.1.2) catalyzes the amidation of glutamate to glutamine, an essential precursor in a variety of biosynthetic pathways (Meister, 1974). GS is of special importance in the vertebrate nervous system; it is a key enzyme in the "small glutamate compartment" and is involved in the recycling of putative amino acid neurotransmitter molecules, such as glutamate and GABA, released by physiologically active neurons (Hamberger et al., 1979; Tapia, 1980). Therefore, the development, cellular localization, and control of GS during neurodifferentiation are of considerable interest.

GS is found throughout the nervous system, but its level is particularly high in adult NR (Moscona, 1972; Moscona et al., 1980). On the other hand, GS activity is very low in embryonic NR. Its developmental profile in the NR of the chick embryo is shown in Fig. 2. GS begins to rise sharply only on the sixteenth day of incubation, i.e., 4 days after cessation of growth and cell multiplication in the NR. Its increase coincides with the final stages of functional maturation of the retina. GS activity increases over 100-fold in 6 to 7 days, and then plateaus at this high level (Moscona, 1972; Moscona and Moscona, 1979). GS has a very similar developmental pattern also in the quail NR (Moscona and Degenstein, 1981a). In the rat and mouse NR, GS begins to increase postnatally, since in these species the retina matures functionally only several days after birth (Chader, 1971; LaVail and Reif-Lehrer, 1971).

A. INDUCTION OF GS

The sharp rise of GS in the chick embryo is elicited by adrenal corticosteroids (Piddington, 1967) subsequent to their increase in the embryo after the fourteenth day of development. The question arose whether the NR becomes responsive (competent) for this induction at the same time. Quite unexpectedly we found (Moscona and Hubby, 1963) that the NR is competent for GS induction long before the hormonal inducer becomes normally available. One way in which this was demonstrated was by injecting young chick embryos with adrenal corticosteroids such as cortisol (Piddington and Moscona, 1967). The premature supply of this hormone rapidly caused, already in 8-day embryos, a precocious induction of GS in the NR. Definitive evidence that this induction was due to a direct action of the hormone on the NR, and also that it did not require connection between the NR and the brain, came from experiments with isolated NR tissue (from chick and quail embryos) maintained in a defined (synthetic) culture medium. Addition of cortisol elicited a rapid induction of GS (Fig. 4). NR isolated from 8-day and older chick embryos were inducible; younger retinas (5 to 7 days) were not (Moscona and Moscona, 1979; Moscona and Degenstein, 1981a).

The cortisol-mediated precocious induction of GS in the NR requires transcriptional and translational processes and can be prevented by inhibitors of RNA and protein synthesis (Moscona, 1972; Moscona et al., 1980). The hormone rapidly enters NR cells and binds to specific receptors in the cytoplasm that are present in NR cells already before the seventh day of development (Koehler and Moscona, 1975); the hormone-receptor complexes translocate within 1 hour into the nuclei and bind to chromatin (Sarkar and Moscona, 1977). Shortly thereafter one can detect accumulation of polysomes with nascent GS and of mRNA for GS (Sarkar and Moscona, 1973; Soh and Sarkar, 1978). Within 1–2 hours following addition of the hormone, a rapid and pro-

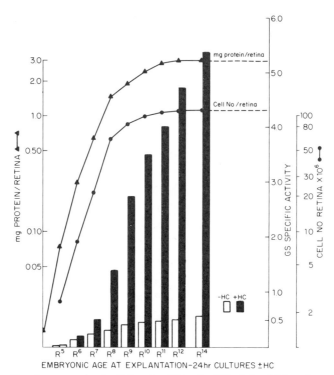

Fig. 4. Development of inducibility for GS in the NR of the chick embryo between 5 and 14 days of incubation: relation to embryonic age, and changes in cell number and in total protein per retina. Retinas dissected from embryos were cultured for 24 hours in medium with cortisol (+HC) or without it (−HC). The solid bars show the levels of GS activity induced in retinas of different embryonic ages. The open bars show the levels of GS in the absence of the steroid inducer. (From Moscona and Moscona, 1979.)

gressive increase in the rate of GS synthesis and accumulation begins, as demonstrated by measurements based on radioimmunotitration with GS-specific antiserum of *de novo* produced enzyme, as shown in Fig. 5 (Moscona *et al.*, 1972).

It should be noted that only in the embryonic NR is GS inducible precociously, very rapidly, and to this very high level, and that only 11-β-hydroxycorticosteroid hormones such as cortisol, corticosterone, aldosterone, and dexamethasone can induce GS in the NR of the chick embryo (Moscona and Piddington, 1967). Therefore, GS induction is an example of a specific "long-range cell interaction" between endocrine and target cells, resulting in a gene-regulated induction of a specific enzyme. This specificity is further underscored by the fact that, of the several classes of cells present in the NR, GS is induced and localized in only one type, Müller glia cells.

As mentioned above, NR shows competence for GS induction (inducibility) already by the eighth day of embryonic development; NR of 5- to 7-day embryos are not inducible, even though cortisol-binding receptors are present in the cytoplasm of these cells. However, this early period is critical because during it, cells in the NR are being programmed with competence for GS induction. Following this "period of competence acquisition," GS inducibility increases with embryonic age (Fig. 4) due, in part, to multiplication and further differentiation of induction-competent cells (Moscona and Moscona, 1979) (see also Fig. 13B). The NR develops induction competence also when it is isolated from 5-day embryos and maintained *in vitro* for 2 days. Since by the fifth day the NR had not yet become connected with the optic tectum, the development of induction competence depends on processes that are endogenous to the NR itself, and that can occur independently of connections with the brain.

The mechanism of competence acquisition is not yet known, but the following findings offer promising leads. If 5-day NR is treated for 12–24 hours with BrdU (bromodeoxyuridine; an analog of thymidine),

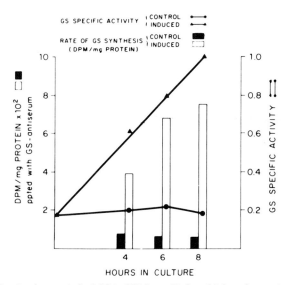

FIG. 5. Induction by cortisol of GS in NR from 12-day chick embryos; immunotitration of newly formed enzyme. Open bars show increases in the rate (per 15 minutes) of enzyme synthesis (expressed as net DPM precipitated by GS antiserum, per mg protein). Solid bars show controls. Steep line shows increase in enzyme activity in control NR. (For further details, see Moscona *et al.*, 1972.)

the development of induction competence is irreversibly blocked and the NR does not become at any time responsive to the hormonal induction of GS (Moscona and Moscona, 1979), although the cells contain cortisol receptors. The blocking of competence requires incorporation of BrdU into retina DNA specifically before the seventh day of development; in older retina cells that already are induction competent, incorporation of BrdU does not prevent GS induction. It has been suggested that, in the early NR, BrdU is incorporated into particular regions of DNA (Strom et al., 1978), and that this substitution permanently modifies certain genes, including those which control the development of induction competence. There is indirect evidence that this modification does not inactivate the structural gene(s) for GS, since the cells continue to produce base-line level of the enzyme and sometimes show spontaneous increases in GS activity in the absence of the inducer. Therefore, we suggest that BrdU alters regulatory DNA which directly or indirectly controls responsiveness to GS induction by the hormone. The existence of such regulatory mechanisms has been postulated on the basis of other findings (Moscona, 1972).

Another indication that BrdU modifies regulatory genes in the early embryonic NR comes from its effect on CA-C. As explained above, the cellular localization of this enzyme undergoes striking changes during the ontogeny of the NR; early in development CA-C is expressed in all the cells, then becomes "lost" from differentiating neurons and, finally, is confined only to Müller glia cells. Recently we found that treatment with BrdU prevents the loss of CA-C from non-glial cells, so that the enzyme continues to be expressed in most of the cells. Therefore, also in this case, it appears that Brdu does not modify or abolish the activity of the structural gene(s) for the enzyme, but rather of regulatory genes that differentially "turn off" CA-C expression in specific types of cells (Linser and Moscona, 1982b).

BrdU has still another important effect on cell differentiation in the early NR. It prevents the gene-controlled development on the cell surface of type-specific cell affinities. These affinity mechanisms determine mutual recognition between the various cell types that make up the NR, and they mediate selective association and histological organization of cells (Moscona, 1980). Failure of these mechanisms to differentiate prevents the various prospective cell types in the NR from becoming histologically positioned and organized into a normally developing retina tissue (Moscona et al., 1981); instead, they give rise to a highly malformed structure (Fig. 6) that consists of chaotically misorganized cells (Mayerson and Moscona, 1979). The simultaneous interference by BrdU (in 5–7 day NR) with the development of GS induction

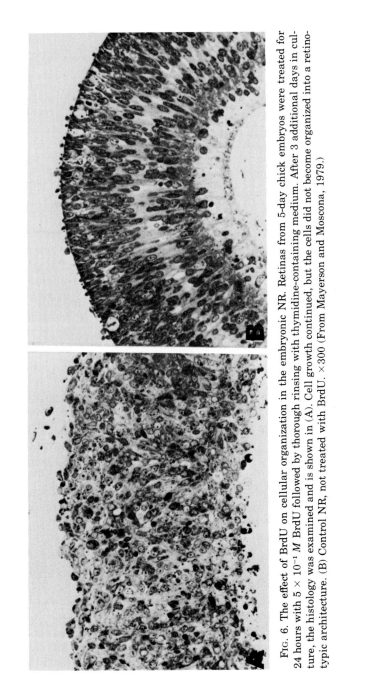

Fig. 6. The effect of BrdU on cellular organization in the embryonic NR. Retinas from 5-day chick embryos were treated for 24 hours with 5×10^{-1} M BrdU followed by thorough rinsing with thymidine-containing medium. After 3 additional days in culture, the histology was examined and is shown in (A). Cell growth continued, but the cells did not become organized into a retinotypic architecture. (B) Control NR, not treated with BrdU. ×300 (From Mayerson and Moscona, 1979.)

competence and of the mechanisms for normal cell organization may be due to effects that are independent, or that are in some way causally interrelated. In any case, it appears that both processes are controlled by DNA sequence(s) which at this specific developmental stage are susceptible to substitution of thymidine by BrdU and, therefore, to modification. This problem is being presently investigated and the theoretical possibilities were discussed elsewhere (Moscona and Moscona, 1979).

B. CELLULAR LOCALIZATION OF GS

GS is confined to Müller cells not only in the mature NR (Fig. 1), but also in the embryonic NR (Fig. 7), both during normal development and when the enzyme is precociously induced (Linser and Moscona, 1979). Immunostaining with anti-GS antiserum failed to detect GS outside of Müller cells at any stage of NR development. This is in marked contrast to CA-C; for, as described above, not only is CA-C expressed in the NR much earlier than the time at which GS becomes potentially inducible, but it is initially present in all the cells and becomes confined to Müller cells only in later stages.

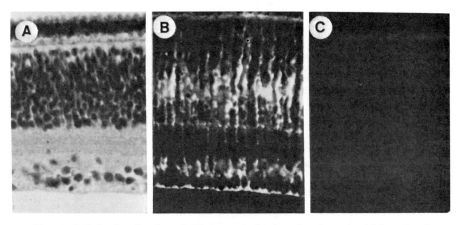

FIG. 7. Cellular localization of GS in cortisol-induced embryonic chick retina by immunostaining and indirect immunofluorescence. (A) Section of 13-day embryo retina stained with hematoxylin and eosin. (B) Thirteen-day retina induced *in vivo* with cortisol. Section was treated with anti-GS antiserum and FITC-GAR. Fluorescence is localized to Müller cells; at this stage of development, Müller cells do not yet show the extensive arborizations typical of later stages. (C) Section of control, noninduced 13-day retina treated as in (B); no immunofluorescence. All magnifications are ×350. (Modified from Linser and Moscona, 1979.)

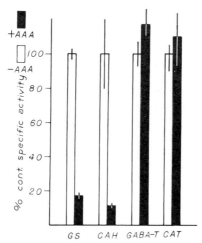

FIG. 8. Effects of pretreatment with α-aminoadipic acid (AAA) on levels of glutamine synthetase (GS), carbonic anhydrase (CAH), γ-aminobutyric acid transaminase (GABA-T), and choline acetyltransferase (CAT) in NR cells. Cell aggregates were prepared from 6-day embryo retina cells. After 4 days, AAA (200 μg/ml) was added to half the cultures for 48 hours. All the cultures were then transferred to cortisol medium for 48 hours and assayed for the enzymes. The specific activity for each of the controls (open bars) represents 100% and the experimental values (solid bars) are expressed accordingly. Each bar represents the mean of two or three determinations. (From Linser and Moscona, 1981b.)

The induction and localization of GS in Müller cells were further demonstrated by experiments with the gliatoxic agent α-aminoadipic acid (AAA) (Linser and Moscona, 1981b). If NR from 11- to 13-day chick embryos is treated with AAA for 1–2 days, there is no detectable effect on neurons; the levels of the neuronal enzymes cholinacetyltransferase and γ-aminobutyric acid transaminase remain virtually unchanged (Fig. 8). However, the majority of morphologically identifiable Müller cells are damaged or destroyed. In such glia-depleted NR, GS cannot be induced with cortisol, or only to a very low level, depending on the extent of the gliatoxic effect. Also the normal level of CA-C is markedly reduced, consistent with its presence in glia cells and their depletion.

The experiments with AAA revealed yet another aspect of Müller cell development. It was found that in early embryonic NR (up to 9 days) Müller cells (or their precursors) are not susceptible to the cytotoxic effect of AAA; the number of susceptible Müller cells begins to increase significantly only after the ninth day, in apparent correlation with the onset of their phenotypic maturation and cessation of their mitotic activity (Linser and Moscona, 1981b). Such a correlation is further indicated by the following results. If NR from 13-day or older embryos (i.e., postmitotic NR) is dissociated into single cells and these are plated in monolayer culture, mitotic activity is reinitiated in the Müller glia cells (Kaplowitz and Moscona, 1976); in addition, some of the phenotypic characteristics of these cells become altered (see below). Although such mitotically "reactivated" gliocytes are derived from definitive Müller cells that already are susceptible to AAA, they now become again resistant to AAA. This supports the suggestion that susceptibility to AAA in Müller cells develops as a function of their arrival at a postmitotic state and of their phenotypic maturation. It is of considerable interest that this developmental state can be "reversed" by removing the cells from their tissue contacts, as discussed further on.

C. CELL–CELL CONTACTS AND GS INDUCTION

One of the most significant and remarkable features of GS induction in Müller cells is that its expression requires, in addition to the hormonal inducer, also specific contact interactions with neurons. GS is not inducible in dissociated and separated NR cells, dispersed in suspension or in monolayer cultures (Morris and Moscona, 1970, 1971; Linser and Moscona, 1979). In such experiments, NR from 8- to 16-day embryos were dissociated by mild trypsinization, or by mechanical disruption into a cell suspension, and the cells were plated in culture dishes under conditions that favored their remaining monodispersed. Cortisol was added at plating time and GS activity was measured daily. Although the hormone entered the cells, there was no GS induction at any time in these monolayer cultures (Fig. 9). Similarly, GS could not be induced if the cells were maintained in suspension cultures under conditions that prevented them from adhering to each other.

In other experiments, we examined whether cells exposed to the hormonal inducer before they were dissociated retained GS inducibility after dispersion in monolayer. NR tissue from 10-day embryos was treated with cortisol for 2 days. The tissue was then dissociated and the dispersed cells were plated in cortisol-containing medium. The level of GS originally present in the cells declined rapidly, and there was no induction of GS. There was no evidence of a continuous loss of GS into the culture medium, or of a major reduction in overall protein synthesis. Therefore, the most likely explanation was that GS is not inducible in separated Müller cells.

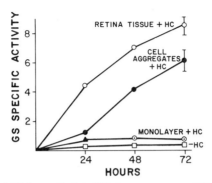

FIG. 9. Induction of GS by cortisol (+HC) in aggregates of NR cells, compared with absence of induction in cell monolayers. Also shown, GS induction in cultures of NR tissue. (From Moscona, 1974.)

Müller glia cells from postmitotic NR rapidly assume in monolayer culture a morphology of large flattened epitheliocytes referred to as LER cells (Kaplowitz and Moscona, 1976). Immunostaining with GS antiserum of cortisol-treated cultures of monodispersed NR cells failed to reveal accumulation of GS in the LER cells, or in any other cells (Fig. 10). On the other hand, LER cells immunostained with CA-C antiserum and continued to express this enzyme for several days (both in the presence and absence of cortisol; Linser and Moscona, 1981a). Therefore, their failure to express GS induction represented a differential response of the GS regulating mechanism to disruption of normal cell contacts.

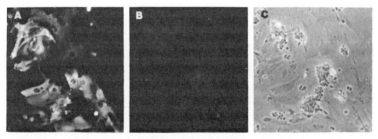

FIG. 10. Immunohistochemical examination by double-label immunofluorescence of CA-C and GS in monolayer cultures derived from embryonic NR cells. Retinas were isolated from cortisol-treated day-13 embryos, the fundal region was dissociated into single cells, and the suspension was plated on glass coverslips in medium with cortisol. (A) Immunostaining for CA-C, showing intense rhodamine fluorescence in most Müller glia-derived epithelioid cells. (B) Simultaneous immunostaining of the same cells for GS, showing only background fluorescein fluorescence, consistent with the absence of GS in these cells. (C) Phase-contrast micrograph of same. ×170. Results shown are for a culture maintained for 6 days with daily medium changes. (From Linser and Moscona, 1981a.)

More direct evidence that contacts between glia and neurons are a prerequisite for GS induction was provided by the following results. Cells dissociated from 10- through 12-day NR were plated in culture dishes at high densities that promoted cell–cell association and formation of cell groups; the resulting clusters consisted of LER epitheliocytes that were often closely juxtaposed with neurons, or were overlayed with neuronal processes. In such composite clusters, elevated GS could be immunohistochemically detected in LER cells (in the presence of cortisol), but only in those that were in close contact with neurons or neuronal processes (Fig. 11); LER cells that were not in direct contact with neurons did not show GS (Linser and Moscona, 1982a). Therefore, we conclude that contact-dependent interactions with neurons are a prerequisite for GS induction. Furthermore, this requirement is evidently not due to some "conditioning" factor that can readily diffuse from neurons through the culture medium.

Cluster-forming cultures of dissociated NR cells were examined for GS induction also by Dutt and Reif-Lehrer (1981). By means of an assay for enzyme activity, these investigators found that cortisol elicited a low level of induction in such cultures. Although these authors noted the presence of numerous cell clusters, they incorrectly equated their cultures with true monodispersed cell monolayers. This accounts for their erroneous conclusion that GS can be induced in totally separated NR cells in the absence of the appropriate cell contacts.

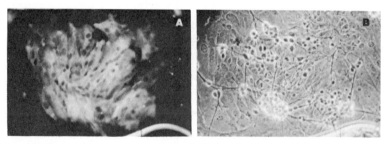

FIG. 11. Immunofluorescent analysis of GS localization in high-density monolayer cultures of NR cells derived from retinas of 10-day-old chick embryos. Retinas were dissociated with trypsin into cell suspensions, and the cells were plated at 1.3×10^6 cells/cm^2 in tissue culture dishes, in medium 199 with 10% fetal calf serum and cortisol (0.33 μg/ml). Medium was changed daily. After 7 days the cultures were fixed and examined for the presence of GS by indirect immunofluorescence, following treatment with GS antiserum. (A) Fluorescence indicating presence of GS in LER cells (Müller glia-derived cells) clustered with neuronal cells and cell processes, seen in the adjacent (B) phase micrograph of the same field. LER cells outside the area covered by the neuronal network do not stain ($\times$245). (Modified from Linser and Moscona, 1982a.)

That glia–neuron contact interactions are required for GS induction was further demonstrated by still another experimental approach. Neurons were depleted from high density monolayer cultures of NR cells by exposure to tetanus toxin, followed by complement-mediated lysis with antibodies to this toxin (Mirsky *et al.*, 1978). This resulted in an almost pure population of the Müller glia-derived LER cells. These cells immunostained for CA-C, but showed no GS induction in response to treatment with cortisol (Linser and Moscona, unpublished results). Therefore, inducibility of GS by cortisol in Müller cells is dependent on contact-mediated "input" for neurons.

D. GS INDUCTION IN CELL AGGREGATES

Conclusive evidence that contact-dependent cell interactions are a prerequisite for GS induction in the NR comes from studies on cell aggregates. In a representative experiment, a suspension of trypsin-dissociated NR cells from 8- to 10-day chick embryos is swirled in a flask on a gyratory shaker at 37°C. The cells regenerate on the surface cell–cell ligands and recognition sites lost during trypsinization; these determine cell affinities, and enable the different cell types to form selective contacts and to become histologically organized (Hausman and Moscona, 1979; Ben-Shaul *et al.*, 1979). The cells progressively reaggregate into multicellular clusters (Linser and Moscona, 1979) within which neurons and glia reestablish histological relationships and reconstruct a retinotypic tissue architecture. Such reconstructed retina tissue continues to differentiate histologically and biochemically in a manner closely approximating normal NR (Fig. 12). For example, CA-C expression shows developmental changes very similar to those in normal temporal pattern (our unpublished results), and so does the development of acetylcholine receptors (Vogel *et al.*, 1976). But the main point to be made here is that, while in separated cells GS is not inducible, it is inducible in such cell aggregates and is localized in Müller cells (Fig. 12) (Linser and Moscona, 1979). Therefore, dissociation of NR tissue into single cells does not cause a permanent, irreversible loss of GS inducibility; if the dissociated cells are allowed to reaggregate and reform histotypic contact relationships, GS inducibility is "restored" in Müller cells.

It is significant that GS inducibility in cell aggregates increases coordinately with restitution of histological cell relationships. Conversely, if reaggregated cells do not restitute normal retinotypic associations, GS is only marginally inducible, or not at all. A striking example of this is seen in aggregates of cells derived from older NR (13 day and older). Unlike the younger cells, cells dissociated from older

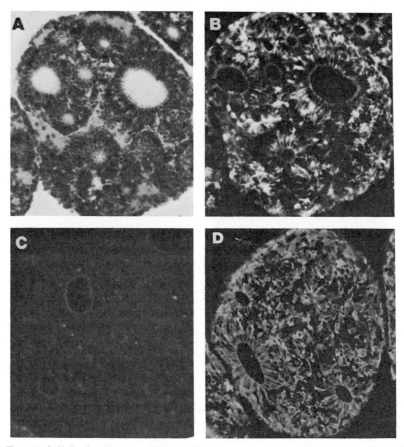

FIG. 12. Cellular localization of GS and CA-C in aggregates of chick embryo NR cells. (A) Section of cell aggregate stained with hematoxylin and eosin, showing reconstruction and development of NR tissue from dissociated cells. Note presence of multilayered retinal rosettes. Such advanced tissue reconstruction can be obtained only with cells dissociated from NR of embryos younger than 10 days. These aggregates were cultured in cortisol-containing medium to induce GS. (B) Same section as in (A) immunostained for GS; immunofluorescence shows presence of induced GS localized in Müller cells. (C) Section of a similar but noninduced cell aggregate (cultured in medium without cortisol), immunostained for GS. (D) Similar aggregate to (B) immunostained for CA-C. All magnifications are ×225. (Modified from Linser and Moscona, 1979.)

retina tissue no longer can effectively restore their original contact affinities required for restitution of retinotypic cell organization (Ben-Shaul *et al.*, 1980). Thus, glia cells dissociated from 13-day or older NR do not recover their normal affinity for neurons; in aggregates they tend to segregate from neurons and to cluster with each other mostly in the center of the aggregate. In the absence of normal glia–neuron contacts, GS is only marginally inducible, even though the cells are assembled in three-dimensional clusters (Fig. 13A). This effect is even more pronounced in aggregates obtained from still older cells, as shown in Fig. 13A. Thus, whereas in the intact NR, GS inducibility in Müller cells increases with embryonic age (Fig. 13B), replacement of normal cell contacts with abnormal contacts prevents induction.

Taken as a whole, the above results are consistent with the working hypothesis that contact-dependent cell interactions between Müller cells and retina neurons are a prerequisite for Müller cell responsiveness to GS induction by the corticosteroid inducer. The exact nature of such interactions and the type(s) of retina neurons specifically implicated remain to be elucidated. Presently, two possibilities are being examined. One is that these interactions involve metabolic cell cooperation, perhaps transfer of substances that function as regulators at some level of the mechanism of GS induction. Another possibility focuses on the role of the cell surface of Müller cells in the regulation of GS inducibility; it suggests that "signals" relayed from the cell surface sustain in the genome conditions permissive for GS induction, and that contact with neurons maintains the Müller cell surface in a state conducive to such signals. This conducive state may depend on the characteristics, topographic disposition, or "saturation" of membrane sites and cell ligands, or on activity of membrane-associated enzymes, etc. Abundant evidence from numerous systems points to the importance of the cell surface, cell shape, and specific cell contacts in various

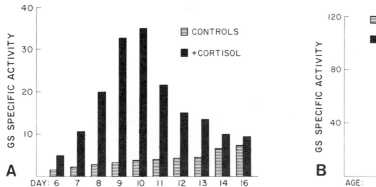
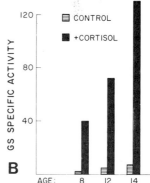

FIG. 13. (A) Changes in GS inducibility in aggregates of NR cells as a function of embryonic age of the cells at the time of their dissociation. The aggregates were assayed for GS activity after 48 hours in culture. (B) Age-dependent increase of GS inducibility in intact NR tissue; the NR was obtained from embryos at the ages indicated and was cultured for 48 hours in medium with or without cortisol. (From Moscona and Lee, 1982.)

regulatory and biosynthetic processes, including control of phenotypic expressions (e.g., Newell and Sussman, 1970; Moscona, 1974; Folkman and Moscona, 1978; Black and Patterson, 1980; Holton and Weston, 1982; Mangiarotti et al., 1982). In the case of Müller cells, cell separation results in changes in the cell surface, and alters the cells' microenvironment, thereby abrogating these permissive "signals" and rendering the cells noninducible. Following restoration of contacts with neurons (as in retinotypic cell aggregates), Müller cells can recover surface characteristics permissive for GS induction. Failure to restore normal contacts with neurons (as in aggregates of "older" NR cells) results in continued noninducibility.

Such a working hypothesis is buttressed by results from two related studies. The first is concerned with changes in cytoplasmic cortisol-binding receptors in separated NR cells; the second, with modification of the phenotype of Müller cells elicited by sustained separation from contact with neurons.

V. Cortisol Receptors

Cytoplasmic receptors that bind cortisol and translocate it into the nucleus are an essential component in the mechanism of GS induction in the NR; hence, they are one of the candidate targets for changes that affect this mechanism. We found that cell separation greatly reduces the level of these receptors (Saad et al., 1981).

NR (from 10-day chick embryos) was dissociated by trypsinization into a cell suspension and the cells were plated in culture dishes. The level of cortisol receptors (assayed as specific [^{3}H]cortisol-binding activity in cytosol preparations; Saad et al., 1981) was measured in intact tissue, in dissociated cells, and in monolayer cultures. Within 2–3 hours after cell dissociation the level of cortisol-binding receptors began to decline; by 24 hours after cell plating, receptor level in the monodispersed cells decreased to below 30% of that present in the intact tissue, and remained unchanged for the duration of these cultures (Fig. 14A and B). As described above, GS is not inducible in such cultures. It should be pointed out that, since the receptor assay measures cortisol-binding activity, it is not clear whether receptor decline in the separated cells is due to actual loss of receptors, or to inactivation of their hormone-binding properties. Also, it is not yet known if the loss affects neurons and glia, or only glia cells.

Trypsin (used for cell separation) was not the direct cause of receptor loss in the dissociated cells; a similarly rapid and persistent loss was obtained also if the cells were separated by methods which did not employ proteolytic enzymes, and also when the receptor assays were

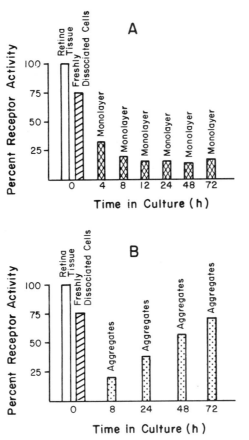

FIG. 14. Measurements of cortisol-binding receptors (receptor activity) in NR tissue from 10-day chick embryos, dissociated NR cells, monolayer cultures, and cell aggregates. (A) Decline in receptor level (expressed as percentage of level in retina tissue) in freshly dissociated cells, and in cell monolayers cultured for 4 to 72 hours. (B) Increase in the level of cortisol receptors in cell aggregates obtained from freshly dissociated NR cells (10-day embryos) and cultured for up to 72 hours. (Modified from Saad *et al.*, 1981.)

done in the presence of protease inhibitors. Therefore, receptor loss is not due to the agents used to separate the cells; it is triggered by disruption of the original cell contacts, i.e., by changes in the cell surface and within cells ensuing from cell separation.

This conclusion is supported by findings that receptor level returns to near normal if the cells are reaggregated. Cells dissociated from 10-day NR were reaggregated immediately, or after 24 hours in monolayer culture. Cortisol receptor assays showed that in the multicellular clusters the decline of receptors was reversed (Fig. 14B);

their level then continued to increase and in 72 hours reached 75% of values found in intact control NR tissue (Saad *et al.*, 1981).

The above results demonstrated that, in embryonic NR, disruption of cell–cell contacts and cell separation alter mechanisms which maintain the normal level of cytoplasmic cortisol receptors. Considering the role of these receptors in GS induction it is of interest that receptor decline in dispersed cells coincides with loss of GS inducibility, and that in histotypically reaggregated cells, receptor increase is correlated with restoration of inducibility. Although these are suggestive correlations, it is not certain that they represent a direct cause–effect relationships, i.e., that the reduced level of cortisol receptors is the primary reason for GS not being inducible in separated cells. This issue remains open for the following reason. Although the loss of receptors in separated cells is rapid and substantial, it is not complete and 20–30% of their original level remains. Theoretically, this amount should be amply sufficient for GS induction. Yet, the remaining receptors fail to mediate induction, even though they bind the hormone. At present, this cannot be satisfactorily explained, but the following exploratory possibilities arise. (1) Residual receptors in the dissociated cells may be confined only to the neurons and these are not inducible for GS. (2) The residual receptors may represent a subclass of cortisol-binding molecules that are not involved in GS induction. (3) Still other changes are elicited in Müller cells by disruption of normal cell contacts and these are directly responsible for preventing GS induction.

This third possibility raises an important suggestion. It implies that GS inducibility in competent Müller cells is controlled by a double mechanism which involves not only hormone receptors, but also requires responsiveness at the level of the genome; both are subject to regulation by cell–cell contact, but they are independently regulated of each other. In simplest terms this notion suggests that receptor level and genomic responsiveness to GS induction are separately controlled by different signals from the cell surface. Such a distinction is strongly supported by findings that an increase in receptor level does not always result in recovery of GS inducibility. This situation was found in aggregates of cells from NR of late embryos (14–16 days). For reasons explained earlier in this article, such "older" cells are unable to reconstruct in aggregates normal retinotypic histological relationships; instead of associating with each other, Müller cells and neurons become spatially segregated. In such aggregates, the level of cortisol receptors increases significantly above that in single cells; however, GS is only marginally inducible or not inducible.

These results lead to the following conclusions. Control of cortisol receptors in NR cells is less stringently dependent on the specificity of cell–cell contacts than is GS inducibility; hence, receptor loss due to cell separation is reversed also when the cells form atypical contacts, as in aggregates of older cells. On the other hand, restoration of GS inducibility requires specific juxtapositions between Müller cells and neurons; in their absence GS is not inducible even in the presence of a high level of receptors. Evidently, different features of the Müller cell phenotype are regulated by different aspects of cell contact, cell interactions, and cell surface properties.

All of the above points to the significance of contact-dependent relationships between neurons and Müller cells in the regulation of phenotypic characteristics of Müller cells. Considering the rapid changes that occur in these cells after their detachment from neurons, the question arises whether longer separation might not result in even more drastic modifications. The next section addresses this issue.

VI. Phenotype Modification of Müller Cells

As a rule, differentiated cells remain "committed" to their particular phenotype. However, there are important exceptions, for example, transformation of iris cells into lens cells in amphibians (Yamada, 1977; Reyer, 1977), and transdetermination of imaginal discs in *Drosophila* (Hadorn, 1966). These phenotypic conversions are initiated by perturbations in cell–cell relationships, or in the integrity of the given system. Their occurrence supports other evidence (Gurdon, 1977) that the genome of differentiated cells retains more information than it normally expresses; furthermore, it suggests that, under appropriate conditions, such latent information can become "activated" even in definitively "committed" cells, and can lead to phenotype alteration. Concerning the conditions that provoke this, of particular interest are changes in the cell surface elicited by modification of cell contacts. The work reviewed next indicates that the phenotype of definitive Müller cells can become "destabilized" by disruption of normal contacts with neurons, and that continued separation predisposes them to acquire features resembling those of lens cells (Moscona and Degenstein, 1981b). For the purpose of this discussion, phenotype modification is defined as a persistent change in differentiated cells that results in accumulation of products which normally are characteristic of another cell type.

In the course of normal embryogenesis, the lens develops from the head ectoderm and its cells accumulate crystallins and other lens characteristic proteins; the NR arises as an extension from the brain. Although the two tissues develop from different cellular antecedents, it has long been known that dissociated NR cells from 7-day chick embryos can undergo *in vitro* changes resulting in formation of lens-like multicellular bodies, or "lentoids" (Moscona, 1957). The formation of such lentoids is enhanced if the dissociated cells are cultured in monolayer for several days and then are reaggregated (Moscona, 1960). The presence of lens-specific proteins in lentoids derived from NR cells was demonstrated by immunostaining with antisera to lens antigens (Okada *et al.*, 1975; DePomerai *et al.*, 1977).

In their studies on lentoids, Okada and associates (Okada *et al.*, 1975; Nomura and Okada, 1979) used monolayer cultures of cells that were dissociated from NR of 3.5- to 4-day chick embryos; after 5 to 10 weeks they observed in these cultures spontaneously arising lentoid bodies that contained lens-type antigens. Because these cell cultures were derived from early, mostly predifferentiated embryonic NR, and because of the very long cultivation time, it could not be decided if the lentoids arose from some uncommitted retinal blast cells, or from a particular cell type. It has been tentatively suggested, on the basis of morphological observations, that the lentoids arose by transformation of neurons (Okada, 1980; Nomura *et al.*, 1980).

Our work showed that retina cells at later stages of differentiation were still capable of lentoid formation; and it suggested that Müller glia cells were the direct precursors of the lentoids. Therefore, we examined whether cells from postmitotic NR were able to give rise to lentoids, and what conditions were required (Moscona and Degenstein, 1981b). The experiments were conducted with cells dissociated from NR of 13- and 16-day embryos. The cells were monolayer cultured for 5 to 7 days; then they were collected and aggregated by rotation for 2 days.

Examination of the aggregates derived from 13-day NR cells showed that virtually each aggregate consisted of two regions. In the center it contained a "lentoid," i.e., a compact, well-demarcated spheroid core of oblong cells that immunostained with lens antiserum, or with antiserum to ∂-crystallin (the predominant protein of avian lens). The cells surrounding this core were smaller, rounded, did not react with these antisera, and were predominantly of neuronal origin (Fig. 15A).

Lentoids Arise from Modified Glia Cells

We now turn to the origin of the lentoids from Müller cells. It will be recalled that Müller cells dissociated from postmitotic 13- or 16-day NR

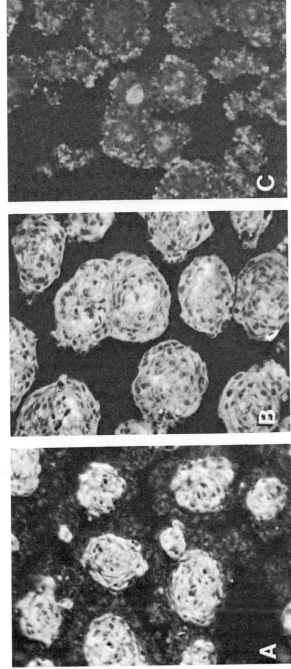

Fig. 15. Lentoid bodies in aggregates of cells derived from NR of 13- and 16-day chick embryos. Cells dissociated from the NR were cultured in monolayer for 7 days, then were collected and aggregated by rotation for 2 days. (A) Immunostaining with anti-lens antiserum of histological section of aggregates derived from 13-day NR cells. The central core (lentoid) which reacts with the antiserum consists of cells derived from Müller cells; the outer cells do not stain with the antiserum and are mostly of neuronal origin. (B) Aggregates similarly obtained from 16-day NR cells. Because of loss of neurons, these aggregates consist almost only of naked cores which stain with anti-lens antiserum. (C) Aggregates of cells originally obtained from 13-day NR after pretreatment with AAA in order to destroy most of the Müller cells. These aggregates show only small, weakly immunostaining cores that consist of residual Müller glia-derived cells. ×270. [(A) and (B) modified from Moscona and Degenstein, 1981b; (C) original figure.]

rapidly lose their normal contact affinity for neurons; in monolayer cultures they assume a shape of large epitheliocytes (LER cells), re-initiate mitotic activity, and lose their susceptibility to AAA. However, they continue to express CA-C which identifies them as derived from Müller glia cells. In aggregates, these CA-C containing cells converged in the center and formed the lentoidal cores. These observations established that the lentoid-forming cells represented a modified progeny of the original Müller cells (Moscona and Degenstein, 1982). It is noteworthy that normal, differentiating lens cells also express CA-C (Linser and Moscona, 1981a); therefore, the coexpression in lentoids of this enzyme together with lens-type proteins is consistent with the characteristics of lens phenotype.

The duration of precultivation in monolayer before the cells are collected and aggregated is an important factor in modification of their phenotype. If the cells were aggregated after only 2–4 days in monolayer, they formed central cores which, however, immunostained weakly with anti-lens antiserum. After 5–7 days in monolayer, the aggregated cells formed cores that showed pronounced immunostaining with this antiserum (Moscona and Degenstein, 1981b). Our observations strongly indicate that a large majority of the LER cells in these cultures undergo modification into lentoidogenic cells; there is no evidence to suggest that these cells arise from very few undifferentiated "blast cells" that might be present in the 13- or 16-day NR.

Monolayer cultures established from 16-day NR cells contained fewer neuronal cells than those from 13-day cells, mainly because of loss of neurons during medium changes. Cell aggregates obtained from these cultures consisted of almost bare lentoidal cores that were mostly devoid of outer cells (Fig. 15B). This result further corroborates the origin of the lentoid-forming cells from modified gliocytes; it also shows that gliocytes from late fetal NR are still capable of undergoing this modification.

The glial origin of the lentoidogenic cells was further confirmed by experiments with α-aminoadipic acid (AAA). As described earlier in this article, when AAA is applied to NR tissue it destroys only definitive postmitotic Müller cells. Thirteen-day NR was treated with AAA to deplete it from most glia cells; the tissue was then dissociated and the cells were maintained in monolayer for 5 days. Such cultures contained only sparce LER cells in addition to neurons (Linser and Moscona, 1981b). Accordingly, aggregates obtained from such cultures contained only few, small lentoids (Fig. 15C) (Moscona and Degenstein, 1982). In recent (unpublished) experiments, we were able to selectively destroy the neurons in monolayer cultures of 13-day NR cells by treatment with quinoline compounds, leaving the glia-derived cells intact. When these cells were aggregated, they formed typical lentoids. Taken as a whole, the above results conclusively established that the cells from 13- to 16-day NR which give rise to lentoids are derived by modification of definitive Müller gliocytes.

As to the conditions that lead to this modification of Müller cells, disruption of normal contacts with neurons clearly is a decisive initiating factor. The more immediate effects include loss of GS inducibility, decrease in cortisol receptors, and changes in contact affinities of the cells. The essential condition for the onset of the even more profound changes is sustained separation of the cells in a monodispersed state. It is not yet known whether this indicates a requirement for DNA and cell replication, or for some other changes that take place progressively when the cells remain separated. Expression of the altered phenotype is enhanced by contacts between the modified cells; aggregation of the cells by rotation is used because it facilitates and expedites formation of tissue-like cell contacts.

The above considerations lead to the following working hypothesis (Moscona, 1960; Moscona and Degenstein, 1981b, 1982).

1. The expression and stability of the phenotype of definitive, postmitotic Müller gliocytes (chick embryo NR) depend on histotypic relationships with neurons, mediated by surface contacts between these cells. Whether these contacts involve only interactions of surface molecules or also communication by junctions is presently unknown.

2. Disruption of cell contacts and continued separation of the gliocytes (in a monolayer) trigger modification of the cell surface and, in turn, result in changes in internal regulatory processes. These changes destabilize preexisting phenotypic controls, and predispose the cells to conversion into a lentoidogenic type.

3. The changes accompanying this conversion include (a) loss by the separated gliocytes of contact affinity for neurons and acquisition of homotypic affinity for each other; (b) loss of inducibility for GS, and decrease in the level of cortisol receptors; (c) changes in cell morphology; (d) reactivation of mitotic activity; (e) loss of susceptibility to the gliatoxin AAA; and (f) accumulation of antigens that cross-react with antibodies to lens antigens.

It remains to be determined how this syndrome of changes is implicated in irreversibly committing, at some point, the Müller glia-derived cells to a lentoidogenic conversion. As to the primary event, we associate it with modification of the gliocyte cell surface that results from their detachment and sustained separation from neurons. It is of obvious interest to identify the precise nature of these surface changes, and of the surface "signals" that determine normal expression and phenotypic stability of Müller cells on one hand, and their modification on the other.

It is not clear why definitive Müller glia cells tend to convert into lentoidal cells following detachment from neurons, i.e., "turn on" accumulation of lens-type products. One line for future exploration is suggested by the fact that antisera to lens crystallins can detect low levels of cross-reacting antigens also in the NR and in several other tissues (Clayton, 1970). It has been reported that the NR contains low levels of crystallin mRNA (Jackson et al., 1978; Clayton, 1982). Perhaps genes for lens proteins are ubiquitously "leaky" and their expression increases in Müller cells, and even in nonoccular cells (Kodama and Eguchi, 1982) following perturbation of controls that stabilize the original phenotype. However, it still remains to be unequivocally determined whether the lentoidal antigens that cross-react with antibodies to lens proteins are, in fact, completely identical to normal lens proteins.

Another attractive possibility is that accumulation of lens-like products in modified Müller cells is akin to the induction of stress or heat shock proteins (Ashburner and Bonner, 1979; Kelley and Schlesinger, 1982); in this case, the "stress response" is elicited by persistent cell separation. Of particular interest is the recent report that the amino acid sequence of certain heat shock proteins shows considerable homology to that of lens α-crystallin (Ingolia and Craig, 1982). The reason for this similarity is unknown, but this finding clearly deserves further investigation in light of the work described here.

Finally, the phenotype of normal lens cells is characterized not only by the presence of crystallins, but also of other lens constituents, membrane antigens, and cytoskeletal elements (Bloemendal, 1981). Thus, a definitive identification of the lentoidal cells must await detailed analysis of the spectrum and characteristics of their proteins, as well as of the molecular and metabolic changes that take place in Müller cells when they are separated from contact with neurons.

VII. Concluding Remarks

The unifying theme of this informal review is that, in embryonic NR, expression and stability of the phenotype of Müller glia cells depend on contact-mediated surface interactions with neurons. The corollary concept is that the cell surface plays a key role in these processes, not only because it is the site of identity determinants and cell ligands that enable selective contacts between cells (Moscona, 1980), but also because it conveys various "signals" that regulate intracellular processes ranging from gene activity and mRNA stability, to turnover of end products (Sussman and Schindler, 1978). As suggested here, such signals reflect the dynamic and specific characteristics of the given cell surface which, in turn, depend on cell contact conditions, state of cell differentiation, and microenvironmental factors. We have shown that disassociation of Müller cells from their normal contact relationships with neurons can rapidly cause a loss of some of their distinguishing features; and that restoration of normal cell contacts can reverse these losses. We have also shown that sustained separation of definitive Müller cells can result in profound and progressive changes, starting at the cell surface and ultimately leading to conversion of these cells into a lentoidogenic type. It is unlikely that contact regulation of Müller cell phenotype is a unique example of such a mechanism. A similar principle probably holds true in other neural and nonneural systems, albeit in different measure and detail.

The above notions lead to still broader implications. These have to do with failure (due to genetic or environmental causes) of surface mechanisms that regulate and maintain normal cell contacts and cell interactions during and after embryonic development. Contact disruption or contact abnormalities would interfere with cell responsiveness to specific inductions and, hence, with phenotype differentiation and expression and, in the longer run, with phenotype stability. It can be readily envisaged how this might result in congenital disorders, as others have pointed out (Bennett, 1975). In embryonic systems, even a localized failure of contact-dependent cell interactions could profoundly impair development; in the adult, it could lead to pathogenic changes. Taking this notion a step further, one should consider whether phenotype destabilization in differentiated mature cells, due to persistent disruption of normal cell contact relationships, might not result in changes conducive to neoplastic cell transformation; in fact, it is not inconceivable that cell-surface changes associated with neoplasia are an important part of the etiology, rather than an end symptom.

These considerations aim to focus attention on the role of specific cell contacts in the regulation of intracellular processes, and to encourage further exploration of the mechanisms at the cell surface that mediate morphogenetic cell contacts and developmental cell interactions. It is poignant to recall that, not too long ago, it was highly unorthodox to regard the cell surface as a dynamic, versatile, and heterogeneous system, subject to both genomic control and environmental modulation. Presently, this is an accepted axiom. Hence, it may now be less far fetched to suggest that the cell surface and cell contact-mediated processes exert, next to the genome, a decisive influence on cell differentiation and on phenotypic expression and stability of cells.

ACKNOWLEDGMENTS

The original research described here is part of a research program supported by Grant HD01253 from the National Institute of Child Health and Human Development, and by Grant 1-733 from the March of Dimes-Birth Defects Foundation.

REFERENCES

Ashburner, M., and Bonner, J. J. (1979). *Cell* **17**, 241–254.

Bennett, D. (1975). *Cell* **6**, 441–454.

Ben-Shaul, Y., Hausman, R. E., and Moscona, A. A. (1979). *Dev. Biol.* **72**, 89–010.

Ben-Shaul, Y., Hausman, R. E., and Moscona, A. A. (1980). *Dev. Neurosci.* **3**, 66–74.

Bhattacharjee, J. (1976). *Histochem. J.* **8**, 63–70.

Black, I. B., and Patterson, P. H. (1980). *Curr. Top. Dev. Biol.* **15**, 27–40.

Bloemendal, H. (1981). *In* "Molecular and Cellular Biology of the Eye Lens" (H. Bloemendal, ed.). Wiley, New York.

Cajal, S. R. (1973). *In* "The Vertebrate Retina" (R. W. Rodicek, ed.), pp. 838–852. Freeman, San Francisco, California.

Chader, G. J. (1971). *Arch. Biochem. Biophys.* **144**, 657–662.

Clark, A. M. (1951). *J. Exp. Biol.* **28**, 332–343.

Clayton, R. M. (1970). *Curr. Top. Dev. Biol.* **5**, 115–180.

Clayton, R. M. (1982). *Symp. Br. Soc. Cell Biol.* **4**, 83–120.

Coulombre, A. J. (1956). *J. Exp. Zool.* **133**, 211–225.

DePomerai, D., Pritchard, J., and Clayton, R. M. (1977). *Dev. Biol.* **60**, 416–427.

Dutt, K., and Reif-Lehrer, L. (1981). *Cell Biophys.* **3**, 1–17.

Folkman, J., and Moscona, A. (1978). *Nature (London)* **273**, 345–349.

Ghandour, M. S., Langley, O. K., Vincendon, G., and Gombos, G. (1979). *J. Histochem. Cytochem.* **27**, 1634–1637.

Giacobini, E. (1962). *J. Neurochem.* **9**, 169–177.

Gurdon, J. (1977). *Proc. R. Soc. (London) Ser. B* **198**, 211–247.

Hadorn, E. (1966). *In* "Major Problems in Developmental Biology" (M. Locke, ed.), pp. 85–104. Academic Press, New York.

Hamberger, A., Chiang, G. H., Nylén, E. S., Schiff, S. W., and Cotman, C. W. (1979). *Brain Res.* **168**, 513–530.

Hausman, R. E., and Moscona, A. A. (1979). *Exp. Cell Res.* **119**, 191–204.

Holton, B., and Weston, J. A. (1982). *Dev. Biol.* **89**, 72–81.

Ingolia, T. D., and Craig, E. A. (1982). *Proc. Natl. Acad. Sci. U.S.A.* **79**, 2360, 2364.

Jackson, J. F., Clayton, R. M., Williamson, R., THomson, I., Truman, D. E. S., and DePomerai, D. I. (1978). *Dev. Biol.* **65**, 383–395.

Kahn, A. J. (1974). *Dev. Biol.* **38**, 30–40.

Kaplowitz, P. B., and Moscona, A. A. (1976). *Cell Differ.* **5**, 109–119.

Kelley, M. P., and Schlesinger, M. J. (1982). *Mol. Cell Biol.* **2**, 267–274.

Kodama, R., and Eguchi, G. (1982). *Dev. Biol.* **91**, 221–226.

Koehler, D. E., and Moscona, A. A. (1975). *Arch. Biochem. Biophys.* **170**, 102–113.

Köhler, G., and Milstein, C. (1976). *Eur. J. Immunol.* **6**, 511–519.

Kuffler, S. W., and Nicholls, J. C. (1976). *In* "From Neuron to Brain: A Cellular Approach to the Nervous System" (S. W. Kuffler and J. G. Nicholls, eds.), p. 264. Sinauer, Sunderland, Massachusetts.

LaVail, M. M., and Reif-Lehrer, L. (1971). *J. Cell Biol.* **51,** 348–354.

Linser, P., and Moscona, A. A. (1979). *Proc. Natl. Acad. Sci. U.S.A.* **76,** 6476–6480.

Linser, P., and Moscona, A. A. (1981a). *Proc. Natl. Acad. Sci. U.S.A.* **78,** 7190–7194.

Linser, P., and Moscona, A. A. (1981b). *Dev. Brain Res.* **1,** 103–119.

Linser, P., and Moscona, A. A. (1982a). *In* "Molecular Approaches to Neurobiology" (I. R. Brown, ed.), pp. 179–193. Academic Press, New York.

Linser, P., and Moscona, A. A. (1982b). In preparation.

Mangiarotti, G., Bozzaro, S., Landfear, S., and Lodish, H. F. (1982). *Curr. Top. Dev. Biol.* **18,**

Maren, T. H. (1967). *Physiol. Rev.* **47,** 597–781.

Maren, T. H. (1976). *Invest. Ophthalmol.* **15,** 356–369.

Mayerson, P. L., and Moscona, A. A. (1979). *Differentiation* **13,** 173–184.

Meister, A. (1974). *In* "The Enzymes" (P. D. Boyer, ed.), Vol. 10, pp. 699–754. Academic Press, New York.

Meller, K., and Glees, P. (1965). *Z. Zellforsch. Microsk. Anat.* **66,** 321–332.

Mirsky, R., Wendon, L. M. B., Black, P., Stolkin, C., and Bray, D. (1978). *Brain Res.* **148,** 251–259.

Morris, J. E., and Moscona, A. A. (1970). *Science* **167,** 1736–1738.

Morris, J. E., and Moscona, A. A. (1971). *Dev. Biol.* **25,** 420–444.

Moscona, A. A. (1957). *Science* **125,** 598–599.

Moscona, A. A. (1960). *In* "Developing Cell Systems and their Controls" (D. Rudnick, ed.), pp. 45–70. Ronald, New York.

Moscona, A. A. (1972). *FEBS Proc.* **24,** 1–23.

Moscona, A. A. (1974). *In* "The Cell Surface in Development" (A. A. Moscona, ed.), pp. 67–99. Wiley, New York.

Moscona, A. A. (1980). *In* "Membranes, Receptors, and the Immune Response" (E. P. Cohen and H. Kohler, eds.), Vol. 42, pp. 171–188. Liss, New York.

Moscona, A. A., and Degenstein, L. (1981a). *Dev. Neurosci.* **4,** 211–219.

Moscona, A. A., and Degenstein, L. (1981b). *Cell Differ.* **10,** 39–46.

Moscona, A. A., and Degenstein, L. (1982). *In* "Problems of Normal and Genetically Abnormal Retinas." Academic Press, New York.

Moscona, A. A., and Hubby, J. L. (1963). *Dev. Biol.* **7,** 192–206.

Moscona, A. A., and Piddington, R. (1967). *Science* **158,** 496–497.

Moscona, A. A., Linser, P., Mayerson, P., and Moscona, M. (1980). *In* "Glutamine: Metabolism, Enzymology and Regulation" (J. Mora and R. Palacios, eds.), pp. 299–313. Academic Press, New York.

Moscona, M., and Lee, K. S. (1982). In preparation.

Moscona, M., and Moscona, A. A. (1979). *Differentiation* **13,** 165–172.

Moscona, M., Frenkel, N., and Moscona, A. A. (1972). *Dev. Biol.* **28,** 229–241.

Moscona, M., Degenstein, L., Byun, K. Y., and Moscona, A. A. (1981). *Cell Differ.* **10,** 317–327.

Musser, G. L., and Rosen, S. (1973). *Exp. Eye Res.* **15,** 105–109.

Newell, P. C., and Sussman, M. (1970). *J. Mol. Biol.* **49,** 627–637.

Nomura, K., and Okada, T. S. (1979). *Dev. Growth Differ.* **21,** 161–168.

Nomura, K., Tagaki, S., and Okada, T. S. (1980). *Differentiation* **16,** 141–147.

Norenberg, M. D. (1979). *J. Histochem. Cytochem.* **27,** 756–762.

Okada, T. S. (1980). *Curr. Top. Dev. Biol.* **16,** 349–380.

Okada, T. S., Itoh, Y., Watanabe, K., and Eguchi, G. (1975). *Dev. Biol.* **45,** 318–329.

Piddington, R. (1967). *Dev. Biol.* **16,** 168–188.

Piddington, R., and Moscona, A. A. (1967). *Biochim. Biophys. Acta* **141,** 429–432.

Reyer, R. W. (1977). *In* "Handbook of Sensory Physiology" (F. Crescitelli, ed.), Vol. VII/5, pp. 338–373. Springer-Verlag, Berlin and New York.

Riepe, R. E., and Norenberg, M. D. (1978). *Exp. Eye Res.* **27,** 435.

Saad, A. D., Soh, B. M., and Moscona, A. A. (1981). *Biochem. Biophys. Res. Commun.* **98,** 701–708.

Sarkar, P. K., and Moscona, A. A. (1973). *Proc. Natl. Acad. Sci. U.S.A.* **70,** 1667–1671.

Sarkar, P. K., and Moscona, A. A. (1977). *Differentiation* **7,** 75–82.

Soh, B. M., and Sarkar, P. K. (1978). *Dev. Biol.* **64,** 316–328.

Strom, C. M., Moscona, M., and Dorfman, A. (1978). *Proc. Natl. Acad. Sci. U.S.A.* **75,** 4451–4454.

Sussman, M., and Schindler, J. (1978). *Differentiation* **10,** 1–11.

Tapia, R. (1980). *In* "Glutamine: Metabolism, Enzymology and Regulation" (J. Mora and R. Palacios, eds.), pp. 285–298. Academic Press, New York.

Vogel, Z., Daniels, M. P., and Nirenberg, M. (1976). *Proc. Natl. Acad. Sci. U.S.A.* **73,** 2370–2374.

Yamada, T. (1977). "Control Mechanisms in Cell-Type Conversion in Newt Lens Regeneration." Karger, Basel.

CHAPTER 7

DEVELOPMENT OF THE HETEROGAMETIC GONAD: A MODEL SYSTEM FOR EMBRYONIC INDUCTION

Stephen S. Wachtel

DIVISION OF PEDIATRIC ENDOCRINOLOGY
NEW YORK HOSPITAL-CORNELL MEDICAL CENTER
NEW YORK, NEW YORK

I. Historical Perspectives in Development

A. INTRODUCTION

A major question of developmental biology is how the various tissues of the adult organism arise from the more or less homogeneous amalgam of the fertilized egg. It is useful and biologically valid to approach that question in terms of three related processes: *cellular differentiation* whereby new cell surface phenotypes appear, and thus

189

new classes of cells; *morphogenesis* during which cells of a particular class move together and compartmentalize in the formation of a particular tissue or organ; and *organogenesis* whereby cells of different classes associate in the formation of a particular tissue or organ.

Cellular differentiation may be viewed as a prerequisite of morphogenesis, and morphogenesis, as a prerequisite of organogenesis. Collectively, however, these processes are often referred to as "differentiation" or "organogenesis." Consequently one reads of the differentiation of a particular cell *and* of the differentiation of a particular gland—though this need not cause confusion when the terms are considered in their proper context.

Because cells communicate with their environment and with each other via the plasma membrane, it seems reasonable to assume that molecular components of the plasma membrane are critical to the various processes of organogenesis. It is hardly surprising therefore that the techniques of cell surface immunogenetics—inasmuch as they are concerned with antigenic differences at the level of the cell surface—have found wide applicability in the study of development. Antigenic cell surface components invoke formation of antibodies in individuals recognizing them as foreign or "non-self." Thus, for example, red blood cell antigen A invokes the formation of anti-A antibodies in type B or O individuals, who lack antigen A. Such antibodies can be used in serological tests to identify or trace the relevant cell surface components, and in biochemical tests, to characterize them.

In this article we shall consider several serologically defined cell surface systems, showing how they may contribute to the organogenesis of the mammalian testis. We shall emphasize recent studies of (1) the "male-specific" H-Y antigen and its gonadal receptor; (2) the β_2-microglobulin-major histocompatibility complex H-Y antigen anchorage site; and (3) the newly defined Sertoli cell-lineage antigen.

B. INDUCTION OF T-CELL DIFFERENTIATION

The term *induction* is used here to connote active inauguration of a particular differentiative program. An "inductor" or "inducer" thus is said to trigger the various processes of differentiation and organogenesis. Although the mechanisms of induction are poorly understood we nevertheless speak of permissive induction, or *initiation,* whereby a differentiative program is induced in cells already committed to that program; and instructive induction, or simply *instruction,* whereby a differentiative program is induced in cells that must be guided in the fulfillment of that program. These concepts will be developed below.

Differentiation of the T cells (thymus-dependent lymphocytes) requires some function of the thymus. The total population of T cells includes the thymocytes and the T-lymphocytes, which are derived from the thymocytes. T cells are characterized by selective expression of serologically defined plasma membrane antigens which comprise the thymocyte surface phenotype. Let us consider the antigens that are denoted Thy1, TL, Ly1, Ly23, and Ly5. With the exception of Ly5, which occurs on most hemopoietic cells (Scheid and Triglia, 1979), none is present in the prothymocyte, the immediate precursor of the thymocyte; TL is found only on thymocytes; Ly1 and Ly23 are found only on T cells. Thus the prothymocyte is [TL$^-$Thy1$^-$Ly1$^-$Ly23$^-$Ly5$^+$], but when it arrives in the thymus after its migration from the bone marrow or spleen, the prothymocyte is induced to differentiate, and the result is expression of the new surface phenotype [TL$^+$Thy1$^+$Ly1$^+$Ly23$^+$Ly5$^+$] in a new cell, the thymocyte. A later stage of differentiation involves transformation of the thymocyte into T-cell subsets. As a consequence of that differentiation, TL ceases to be expressed and Thy1 is expressed in considerably reduced amounts; the Ly antigens are differentially expressed according to cell type and function (Table I).

The T-lymphocytes are classified broadly according to helper, cytotoxic, and supressor functions: helper T-lymphocytes promote antibody synthesis in B cells; cytotoxic T-lymphocytes mediate destruction of cells that are antigenically foreign; and suppressor T-lymphocytes inhibit antibody production. So it is noteworthy that T-lymphocytes exhibiting helper function are Ly1$^+$; and T-lymphocytes exhibiting cytotoxic and suppressor functions are Ly23$^+$ (and may be separable by "new" markers such as Qa-1 and I-J); whereas cells that are part of a

TABLE I

Surface Phenotype of Lymphocytes and Epidermal Cells of the Mouse[a]

	TL	Thy1	Ly1	Ly23	Ly5	Skn1[a]	Skn2	H-2	H-Y
Pro-thymocyte	−	−	−	−	+	−	−	+	+ (?)
Thymocyte	+	+	+	+	+	−	−	+	+
Helper T cell	−	±	+	−	+	−	−	+	+ (?)
CS[b] T cell	−	±	−	+	+	−	−	+	+ (?)
Epidermal cell	−	+	−	−	−	+	+	+	+

[a] Skn1 and Skn2 (formerly Sk1 and Sk2; Wachtel et al., 1977), coded by segregating genes, are selectively expressed in epidermal cells and brain; TL is found in some mice but not in others (as is Rh in man); Thy1 is part of at least two differentiative programs. H-2 and H-Y are not properly classified as differentiation antigens, being found in all or nearly all tissues of the (male) mouse.

[b] CS, cytotoxic suppressor T lymphocyte. After Wachtel (1983); with permission.

pool that may represent an intermediate stage of T-lymphocyte differentation are Ly123 (reviewed in Boyse and Cantor, 1979).

The point of this discussion is that the prothymocyte is induced to become a thymocyte by the thymic hormone, *thymopoietin,* and that this differentiation (which does not involve cell division) is associated with the appearance of a series of cell surface *differentiation alloantigens.* Subsequent differentiative events (which may involve cell division) bring about more selective expression of these cell surface molecules, such that particular cell surface phenotypes can be strictly correlated with particular functions. *But T-cell induction is permissive.* Appearance of the T-cell antigens can be induced not only by thymopoietin, but also by cAMP, bacterial endotoxin, ubiquitin, and, in general, by agents that engage β-adrenergic receptors. Moreover T-cell markers can be induced in spleen and lymph node cells from congenitally athymic mice (Scheid *et al.,* 1975). So the prothymocyte is committed before it takes up residence in the thymus.

Differentiation alloantigens are known for skin (Boyse *et al.,* 1970) and for embryonic cells. It may be inferred that selective expression of surface phenotype—and thus selective gene action—is a characteristic of all cell sets, and indeed, of all differentiated cells (Table I).

C. INDUCTION OF THE OPTIC LENS

As another example of induction, let us consider the development of the optic lens, which follows a more or less similar pattern in all vertebrates. The embryonic brain is divided into three sections—forebrain, midbrain, and hindbrain—by constrictions that appear in the cephalad aspect of the neural tube. An *optic vesicle* emerges on each side of the forebrain and grows laterally until coming in contact with the ectoderm. The part of the optic vesicle in contact with the ectoderm invaginates, forming the double walled *optic cup*; this gives rise to various parts of the eye. The inner wall of the cup becomes the retina, for example, and the rim of the cup becomes the perimeter of the pupil; the optic cup retains its connection with the forebrain via the optic stalk; this becomes the optic nerve.

The lens is induced in the cells of the ectoderm immediately overlying the optic cup. At about the same time that the optic cup develops, a "thickening" appears in the ectoderm. This is the presumptive lens. The cells of the presumptive lens now form a hollow vesicle which rounds off and breaks away from the epithelium (the remaining surface epithelium will develop as part of the clear corneum). Within the vesicle, the cells elongate and synthesize the lens-specific crystallins, the nuclei degenerate, and the cytoplasm becomes transparent.

Evidently development of the lens is induced by a signal or signals emanating from the optic cup (reviewed in Balinsky, 1970). Thus removal of the optic vesicle precludes development of the lens, and heterotopic transplantation of the optic vesicle under, say, flank epidermis, triggers development of a lens in the flank. These results indicate moreover that induction of the lens is *instructive*. Indeed, if the epidermis overlying the optic vesicle is removed and replaced with epidermis from another part of the body (head or flank, for example), development of a lens is induced in the transplanted cells.

Despite the long-held belief that physical contact between optic cup and target tissue is a prerequisite of development of the lens, there are reasons for believing that the inducer of the lens is in fact a *diffusible protein*. Thus in the chick embryo, the lens is induced even when the optic vesicle and target epidermis are separated by a slice of agar (McKeehan, 1958); and in *Xenopus,* radioactive label is detected in the induced lenses of normal host embryos after transplantation of optic cups that have been labeled with [^{14}C]phenylalanine (Sirlin and Brahma, 1959). [The situation may be rather more complicated; in some amphibian species the lens may develop—to an extent—even after the optic cup has been removed, and "free lenses" have been triggered by physiologically irrelevant inducers (guinea pig thymus for example). So the eye cup may provide one of several inductive signals in this system.]

In summary, then, differentiation of the thymocyte and development of the optic lens are induced by diffusible "proteins." In the former case induction is permissive, and in the latter case it is instructive (with the qualification noted above). The inference is that differentiative events, in general, are induced by reaction of diffusible macromolecular "inductors" with their target cells.

D. CELLULAR AGGREGATION IN MORPHOGENESIS

Further to the observation that silicious marine sponges "in confinement under proper conditions" could degenerate spontaneously, and that individual surviving cells could aggregate to reconstitute "perfect sponges," Wilson (1908) described regeneration of tissues of the sponge *Microciona prolifera* after experimental disruption. He cut the tissues into small pieces, and then forced the pieces through a fine bolting cloth. Having been thus released, individual cells migrated along the substratum where they came into contact with other free cells; the result was formation of little conglomerates. When he dispersed the cells on glass slides and coverslips, Wilson could follow the regenerative process microscopically. Under those conditions, he described active organization of functional miniature sponges.

Wilson's observations generated a series of similar studies in laboratories utilizing tissues from "higher" organisms. Perhaps best known are the reaggregation experiments performed by Aaron Moscona some 22 years ago. Moscona (1961) obtained cell suspensions from tissues of the embryonic chick and mouse by mechanical dissociation, after incubation of the tissues in Ca^{2+}- and Mg^{2+}-free medium containing dilute trypsin. The cells were placed in flasks, and the flasks rotated at low g to promote collision and aggregation.

After 24–48 hours the resulting clusters were studied histologically with the following results: (1) cells from a particular tissue organized themselves into patterns characteristic of the tissue from which they had been derived; dispersed cells from the neural retina of the chick embryo organized concentric aggregates or "rosettes" characteristic of the retina *in situ,* for example, and dispersed cells from the mesonephros of the chick embryo organized tubular and glomerular aggregates with stromal mesenchyme; (2) when cells of chick and mouse embryo were cultured together, the cells sorted out and formed aggregates *according to tissue* but not species. Thus in cultures containing limb-bud mesoblasts from chick and mouse embryos, and in addition, "third party" liver cells from the chick embryo, the aggregates contained well-delineated regions of chimeric mouse–chick cartilage with chick and mouse cells interspersed—and separate regions of chick liver cells; (3) the tendency toward strict histotypic aggregation was lost in cultures containing normal cells from one species and neoplastic cells of the other. When cells of the chick embryonic liver were cultured with cells from a mouse melanoma, the initial aggregates were spherical, consisting of a central core of neoplastic cells and an outer layer of liver cells. But with further culturing, the neoplastic cells invaded the outer layer of chick liver cells, thereby obliterating the regional integrity of the initial architecture.

In other, related studies, Weiss and Taylor (1960) deduced that histotypic aggregation of dispersed cells was conducted in the absence of exogenous cues. Liver, mesonephros, and skin from chick embryos of from 8 to 14 days of age were pooled and dissociated, and the resulting cell suspensions were washed and grafted onto the chorioallantoic membranes of other chick embryos. The grafts were allowed to remain in place for 9 days at which time they were fixed and sectioned. Histologic analysis disclosed that the cells had reconstituted characteristic, distinct, and well-organized tissues and organs, even in the "indifferent" environment of the chorioallantoic membrane.

On the basis of the observations of Moscona and of Weiss and Taylor, it may be concluded that (1) the cell–cell interactions of morphogenesis and organogenesis are conducted with respect to intrinsic directive (the information for aggregation and association is contained in the cells themselves); (2) the informational signals for organization of embryonic structures operate at the cell surface; and (3) the signals are phylogenetically conservative.

At first glance, the results of the reaggregation experiments cited above seem to contradict the results of earlier studies purporting to show that morphogenetic movements are induced by external cue. Yet the distinction between internal and external directive may be less than appropriate, for one group of cells could provide inductive signals to another neighboring group; and the question arises whether the aggregating system in isolation may subsume the blueprint for complete organogenesis. Suffice it to say that differentiated cells of the embryonic organ rudiment seem to contain all of the signals and instructions required for successful arrangement of *that* organ.

E. DEVELOPMENT OF THE TESTIS

In mammals the indifferent embryonic gonad appears as a stratification of the coelomic epithelium on the urogenital ridge next to the mesonephros. Testicular organogenesis commences with the arrival of the primordial germ cells. In embryos of the mouse and rat these are found embedded in the epithelium of the primordial gonad (hence "germinal epithelium") at about the eleventh or twelfth day of gestation. Cellular proliferation now causes a swelling, called the *gonadal ridge*; this consists of two distinct regions: peripheral cortex (epithelium) and central medulla (mesenchyme). At this stage the primordial germ cells, recognizable by their dense dark cytoplasm, are found throughout the developing gonad. Now the primary sex cords appear in the medulla (perhaps having invaded the medulla from the cortex or from the mesonephros, perhaps having arisen *in situ*). The primary sex cords become the seminiferous tubules of the testis. They appear later and then retrogress in the developing ovary.

According to Jost (1972), the first signs of testicular differentiation occur at 13 days of gestation in the rat. A few cells in the medulla differentiate in the absence of mitosis; they are recognized by their characteristic clear "swollen cytoplasm." These early Sertoli cells now begin to move together and to aggregate. They surround and encase the primordial germ cells, thereby generating the characteristic architecture of the testicular tubule. Other Sertoli cells appear, and other tubules. Jost *et al.* (1981) describe the entire process as a "wave of differentiation" moving irrevocably through the developing medulla.

Now the Leydig cells appear among the undifferentiated elements of the interstitium, and the tunica albuginea emerges as the tough outer envelope of the cortex. The Sertoli cells secrete H-Y antigen, anti-Müllerian "hormone," and androgen binding protein, and in response to endocrinological dictate, the Leydig cells secrete androgen.

In summary, then, testicular organogenesis may be viewed as comprising this fundamental sequence of events: (1) differentiation of the Sertoli cells; (2) morphogenesis of the seminiferous tubules (encasement of germ cells); (3) differentiation of the Leydig cells; and (4) appearance of the tunica albuginea.

Although it could be argued (Witschi, 1965) that testis and ovary arise from alternative regions of the primordial gonad—medulla and cortex, respectively—there are reasons for believing that the cells which organize the seminiferous tubule and those which organize the ovarian follicle are derived from the same precursors. If that is true (discussed in Section III,D) then induction of the seminiferous tubule must be an instructive process; organogenesis of the XX testis (which occurs in perhaps one out of 20,000 human males) would hardly be plausible in cells committed to pathways of ovarian development. It follows that the inducer of the seminiferous tubule actually directs the characteristic cylindrical aggregation of the primordial Sertoli cells.

But if the factors that govern morphogeneses are cell surface components, and if they are phylogenetically conservative—being tissue-specific but not species-specific—then the inducer of the seminiferous tubule must be a phylogenetically conservative cell surface component, or a molecule that promotes synthesis of other, phylogenetically conservative cell surface components.

II. H-Y Antigen in Development

A. H-Y ANTIGEN: INDUCER OF THE TESTIS

By definition, transplantation antigens are cell-surface components. These invoke characteristic allograft reactions when they are present in the cells of a graft and absent in the cells of the host; the graft is recognized as foreign, and the result is antibody production and/or rejection. Inasmuch as the allograft reaction depends on genetic disparity of donor and host, and on polymorphism of donor and host cell surface components, one might not expect to find conservative cell surface components among the armamentarium of transplantation antigens. Yet one such cell surface component has been discovered—because it is present only in males.

Among mice and rats, several highly inbred or so-called "isogenic" strains have been developed by successive generations of brother–sister mating. Isogenic strains are like populations of identical twins; genetic heterogeneity has been eliminated and skin grafts exchanged between members of the same inbred strain are accepted—even as skin grafts exchanged between identical twins are accepted.

The exception is the male-to-female graft. Rejection of male-to-female skin grafts was described in inbred strains of the mouse by Eichwald and Silmser in 1955, and in inbred strains of the rat by Billingham and Silvers in 1959. The failure of male-to-female grafts was attributed to occurrence of a male-specific histocompatibility antigen determined directly or indirectly by the Y chromosome, which has no analog in females; for that reason the antigen was called "H-Y." Whether the structural genes for H-Y antigen are on the Y chromsome, or on another chromosome that is regulated by the Y, is a question that is currently being debated. The answer is irrelevant to the present discussion. Wherever the structural genes for H-Y may be situated, it is remarkable that they are not polymorphic. H-Y antigen is the same in all mice, and in all rats, and the H-Y antigen of the mouse is the same as the H-Y antigen of the rat (Silvers and Yang, 1973).*

Male-grafted female mice produce antiserum containing H-Y antibodies that can be used to identify H-Y antigen in serological tests (Goldberg et al., 1971; Scheid et al., 1972). Thus identify or cross-reactivity of male antigens of mouse and rat can be demonstrated in vitro: H-Y antiserum of the mouse loses its ability to kill H-Y$^+$ mouse target cells after absorption with cells of the male rat. But mouse H-Y antiserum also loses its reactivity after absorption with cells from males of the rabbit or guinea pig or human, and, indeed, after absorption with cells from members of the heterogametic sex (XY) of every vertebrate species so far tested, including amphibians and fish (reviewed in Wachtel, 1983).

Inasmuch as mutation is intolerable in genes of critical significance, widespread phylogenetic occurrence of H-Y signaled persistence of a critical function. Absence of H-Y in half the members of each species implied moreover that occurrence of the molecule is critical to the species but not to the individual. For those reasons in particular, and in view of the role of cell-surface components in morphogenesis and

---

* The question of H-Y alleles is raised by Hildemann et al. (1970) (and see discussion Wachtel, 1977).

organogenesis, we proposed that H-Y antigen induces cells of the indifferent gonad to organize a testis in male heterogametic species such as mouse and man, and an ovary in female heterogametic species such as the chicken and quail (Wachtel *et al.,* 1975).

Sex determination may be perceived as an ordered process commencing with the establishment of genetic sex at fertilization, proceeding with the "translation" of genetic sex into gonadal sex, and culminating in the translation of gonadal sex into body sex (Jost, 1970). Development of the gonad is sometimes called primary sex determination, and development of body sex is sometimes called secondary sex determination. In mammals the secondary sex characteristics are induced by secretions of the testis and their metabolites. In the presence of testosterone (and its receptor) the body is masculinized despite karyotype or gonadal type, and in the absence of testosterone (or its receptor) the body is feminized despite karyotype or gonadal type (Jost, 1970). Hence the sex-determining role of the Y chromosome is concerned only in the organization of the testis, and hence the sex-determining role of Y chromosome-associated H-Y antigen should be concerned only in the organization of the testis.

But that allows a corollary—that testicular architecture should be associated with the presence of H-Y antigen despite karyotype or secondary sex phenotype. Accordingly the putative sex-determining role of H-Y was first evaluated by surveying its expression in individuals whose gonadal phenotype did not correspond with karyotype or secondary sex phenotype. The results of several such studies are reviewed elsewhere (Wachtel, 1983). Suffice it to say that XX males and XX true hermaphrodites of mouse, goat, dog, and human were typed H-Y$^+$ [a useful example is the study of Winters *et al.* (1979) in which H-Y was detected in cells from the testicular portion but not ovarian portion of a human ovotestis], and that XY fertile females of the wood lemming were typed H-Y$^-$ [Herbst *et al.* (1978) discovered alternative X chromosome banding patterns in XY males and females of that species indicating occurrence of an X-linked gene in suppression of H-Y].

It would be incorrect on the basis of these correlations to assume that expression of H-Y is a *secondary* manifestation of testicular organogenesis. H-Y is detected in mouse embryos of the eight cell stage, in fertile P/+ nanny goats (obligate carriers of "recessive" testis-determining genes), and in androgen-insensitive females exhibiting the syndrome of testicular feminization (reviewed in Ohno, 1979). One is left with the conclusion that H-Y is concerned in some aspect of *primary* sex determination.

B. H-Y Is Necessary for Testicular Reaggregation *in Vitro*

First direct evidence of a role of H-Y in primary sex determination was provided by Ohno *et al.* (1978b) in mice, and independently, by Zenzes *et al.* (1978c) in rats, both groups using the aggregation system described by Moscona (1961). Cells of the neonatal XY testis were dispersed, treated with normal serum or with H-Y antiserum, and then placed in rotary culture for periods up to 48 hours. Untreated cells and cells that had been exposed to normal serum formed long tubular aggregates, but cells that had been exposed to H-Y antiserum formed spherical aggregates resembling the follicles of the young ovary. Ohno *et al.* (1978b) surmised that H-Y antigen had been "lysostripped" from the XY Sertoli cells—which now behaved like follicular cells. The inference was that newly formed H-Y antigen–antibody complexes had migrated to the polar caps of the cultured testicular cells, and that they had been internalized and then ingested by autophagic lyosomes. [In other similar experiments (Müller and Urban, 1981) cylindrical aggregation was impeded by H-Y antibody, but there was no tendency toward follicular organization.]

Although the anatomical figures of Ohno *et al.* (1978b) and Zenzes *et al.* (1978c) are open to subjective interpretation (Short, 1979), the foregoing observations, if substantiated, would indicate that continuous expression of H-Y is required for organization of the seminiferous tubule. H-Y may thus instruct Sertoli cells in the organization of the tubule by providing the linkages whereby those cells associate (see Section IV,D below).

C. The XX/XY Chimeric Male Mouse: Evidence for Dissemination and Binding of a Testis-Inducing Signal

It is possible to fuse embryos of the mouse by combining blastocysts or by injecting cells of one dissociated blastocyst into the blastocoele of another intact blastocyst. Of the resulting *chimeric* embryos, 25% should be XX/XX, another 25% should be XY/XY, and 50% should be XX/XY. One might expect a high incidence of hermaphroditism among the XX/XY chimeric portion, but the fact is that about three-quarters of all XX/XY mice become males and about one-quarter become females; hermaphroditism is rare, with an incidence of about 1 or 2% (McLaren, 1976). In that connection, it is worth noting that testicular development predominates in rotary culture systems incorporating cells of the neonatal XY testis and cells of the neonatal XX ovary. When the proportion of XY testicular cells was as low as 20%, testicular reaggregation occurred in two instances, and ovotesticular reaggregation (tubules *and* follicles) occurred in one instance. When the proportion of XY testicular cells exceeded 20% testicular reaggregation was observed in all cases (Urban *et al.*, 1981). *The implication is that XY cells of the XX/XY chimeric gonad release a diffusible hormone-like factor that induces testicular organogenesis in neighboring XX cells.*

To evaluate the question whether H-Y antigen is secreted by XY gonadal cells, and bound in XX gonadal cells, Ohno *et al.* (1978a) studied the gonad of an XX/XY chimeric male mouse "produced" by combining embryos of the BALB (XX) and C3H (XY) inbred strains. Germinal tissue of the unambiguous testis contained C3H cells only; nongerminal tissue (Sertoli cells and Leydig cells) consisted of XX and XY cells in equal proportions—as revealed by staining for GPI, which has different electrophoretic mobilities in the BALB and C3H strains. Despite the relatively high frequency of XX cells, nongerminal tissue of the chimeric testis absorbed as much H-Y antibody as corresponding tissues from XY males of either "parental" strain. But H-Y antibody was not absorbed in XX cells of the chimeric epidermis or spleen. It could be inferred that XY gonadal cells do indeed release H-Y, which is bound in XX gonadal cells.

D. The Gonad-Specific H-Y Antigen Receptor

It is now evident that H-Y is released by Sertoli cells (Zenzes *et al.*, 1978a). The molecule may be obtained in soluble form in the supernatant fluid of mouse testicular cell preparations, in the medium of newborn rat testicular cell cultures, and in rat epididymal fluid. Soluble H-Y is also present in the medium of "Daudi" cells (cultured from a human male lymphoma—see Section III,C below).

Soluble H-Y is bound specifically in ovarian cells but not in cells of the somatic tissues. When XX cells of the rat ovary were reacted with epididymal fluid, they became H-Y$^+$, and they absorbed H-Y antibody in serological tests. When XX cells of the rat brain, epidermis, kidney, or liver were reacted with epididymal fluid, they remained H-Y$^-$ and did not absorb H-Y antibody (Müller *et al.*, 1978a).

More recently XX cells of the bovine fetal ovary and of mouse adult spleen and epidermis were exposed to radioactive Daudi-secreted H-Y. Enumeration of radioactive label disclosed selective binding of H-Y in the ovarian cells (Nagai *et al.*, 1979). And in the female heterogametic species, *Xenopus laveis,* the South African clawed frog, selective binding of H-Y was observed in the homogametic testis. Thus ZZ testicular cells acquired the H-Y$^+$ phenotype on exposure to the supernatant fluid from mouse testicular cell preparations, whereas ZZ somatic tissues did not. Uptake the H-Y was obviated by prior reaction of the testis supernatant with specific H-Y antibody (reviewed in Wachtel, 1983).

The inference is that there is a gonad-specific receptor for H-Y (H-W) antigen, and that reaction of H-Y and its receptor signals a differentiative program culminating in organogenesis of the heterogametic gonad—which may be testis or ovary, depending on the species. Binding of exogenous H-Y is thus readily demonstrable in the homogametic gonad, because the receptor is vacant, and less readily demonstrable in the heterogametic gonad, because the receptor is saturated. The question how a particular molecule could induce alternative programs will be addressed in Section IV,C below.

E. INDUCTION OF THE XX TESTIS *in Vitro*

Inductive function of soluble H-Y antigen has been demonstrated *in vitro*. (1) When incubated in rotary culture with H-Y antigen, dispersed XX ovarian cells of the neonatal rat formed tubular aggregates; the histology was similar to that found in control cultures containing aggregates of untreated XY testicular cells. But tubular reaggregation of the XX cells was impeded by H-Y antibody; after addition of H-Y antibody the XX cells organized follicular structures similar to those found in untreated XX controls (Zenzes *et al.*, 1978b; Müller and Urban, 1981). (2) When indifferent gonads of the XX fetal calf were cultured intact in medium containing concentrated sources of human H-Y from Daudi cells, testicular transformation was observed after 3 days, commencing with the appearance of tubular structures and culminating after 5 days with the appearance of a structure resembling the tunica albuginea; Leydig cells and germ cells were not observed (Ohno *et al.*, 1979; and see Nagai *et al.*, 1979). [Germ cells are not required for testicular organogenesis, which proceeds in their absence (Coulombre and Russell, 1954).]

It is worth mentioning that H-Y-induced transformation of the XX neonatal ovary is associated with the appearance of gonad-specific cell surface molecules. The LH/hCG receptor is found in the XY rat testis at birth, but it is not found in cells of the XX ovary until 6–8 days after birth. So it is remarkable that the LH/hCG receptor is prematurely induced in rat neonatal XX ovarian cells exposed to epididymal fluid in rotary culture (Müller *et al.*, 1978b). Although it is not unambiguously established that H-Y antigen is responsible for precocious appearance of the LH/hCG receptor (another soluble factor could be involved), H-Y is present in epididymal fluid.

III. Other Cell Surface Structures in Development

A. THE MAJOR HISTOCOMPATIBILITY COMPLEX

The major histocompatibility complex (MHC) is a system of closely linked genetic loci including genes that determine the formation of "strong" transplantation antigens; transplants exchanged between MHC-incompatible donor and host are destroyed with maximal intensity. The MHC of the mouse is referred to as the H-2 (histocompatibility-2) system and the MHC of man is called the HLA (human leukocyte antigen) system. Five regions have been identified by recombination in the mouse. They are given in linear order as H-2K, H-2I, H-2S, H-2D, and H-2L—or simply as K, I, S, D, and L. The I region is further divisible into the *subregions* A, B, J, E, C which seem to be involved in controlling various aspects of the immune response. A simple H-2 map is thus denoted K-IA-IB-IJ-IE-IC-S-D-L. (For more detailed genetic information consult Murphy, 1981.) The K and D loci at opposite ends of the H-2 complex, corresponding to HLA-A and HLA-B in man, mediate synthesis of serologically detectable cell surface glycoproteins of 45,000 molecular weight (MW). Antigenic specificity of the 45,000-MW chain is known to reside in the polypeptide moiety. The 45,000-MW chain spans the lipid portion of the plasma membrane such that the COOH terminus is free at the interior, and the NH_2 terminus is exposed at the cell surface. Each NH_2 terminus is associated noncovalently with a molecule of β_2-microglobulin (β_2m) (Fig. 1). The smaller β_2m (12,000 MW) is coded by a gene that is not linked to the MHC.

When they are extracted from the plasma membrane with detergent, MHC molecules can link up covalently in solution to form heavy chain dimers and light chain dimers. But when they are first reacted with papain, or if they are reacted with papain after extraction with detergent, a soluble fragment of the heavy chain is recovered—in association with the light chain (β_2m). It follows that cell surface H-2 may occur as a heavy chain–light chain dimer, or perhaps as two heavy chains and two light chains, or perhaps as some other combination of heavy and light chains. Whatever the precise arrangement of H-2 and β_2m, it seems certain that MHC components are anchored in the internal portion of the plasma membrane, and it is apparent that the externalized parts of the MHC heavy chains can interact with one another, with β_2m, and possibly with other cell surface components.

There is evidence that certain amino acid sequences are the same in K and D molecules, raising the question whether H-2K and H-2D loci are derived from a common ancestral gene. There is evidence too for

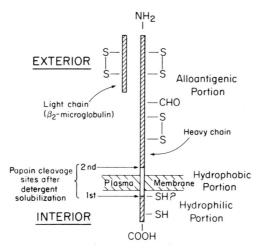

FIG. 1. Hypothetical arrangement of MHC heavy chain and β_2m in the plasma membrane. The precise physical relationship of β_2m and the heavy chain is not known. After Strominger et al. (1977); reprinted by permission.

homology of sequence in K/D and immunoglobulin (Ig) variable regions (Terhorst et al., 1977)—and for homology of sequence in human β_2m and Ig constant domains (Peterson et al., 1972). So it may be asked whether MHC heavy and light chains, and Ig molecules are all coded by loci derived from a common ancestral gene (Bodmer, 1972). The point is that reaction of Ig (antibody) and antigen is a function of the tertiary structure of the Ig molecule. Thus immunoglobulin-like sequences of β_2m-MHC cell surface components may generate immunoglobulin-like affinity of the presumptive carrier for other cell surface components—including H-Y antigen.

B. H-Y AND THE MAJOR HISTOCOMPATIBILITY COMPLEX

There is in fact considerable evidence of association of MHC antigens and "minor" histocompatibility antigens—especially H-Y—and there is evidence of association of MHC and viral antigens as well. When cytotoxic T cells from C57BL female mice are primed in vivo and sensitized in vitro with target cells from C57BL male mice (H-2D^b), for example, the killer cells lyse only target cells bearing H-Y and H-2D^b (Gordon et al., 1975). Susceptibility of H-Y incompatible target cells to lysis by female killer T cells is in general H-2 restricted, such that H-Y may be "recognized" only within the context of a particular MHC haplotype. Evidently the same is true in man (Goulmy et al., 1977).

As another example (B10 × B10.BR)F$_1$ hybrid female mice (H-2^b/ H-2^k) reject skin grafts from B10.BR males (H-2^k) more rapidly than they reject skin grafts from B10 males (H-2^b). But B10 and B10.BR are *congenic* strains—highly inbred strains differing from one another only with respect to a single locus—in this case, H-2. Since the only difference between the two graft donors in this system is H-2, and the only difference between either donor and host is H-Y, it may be concluded that H-2 influences the immunogenicity of H-Y by virtue of some functional relationship between the two molecules (Wachtel *et al.*, 1973).

On the basis of those and other, similar observations, Ohno (1977) proposed that β_2m-MHC cell surface dimers serve as the nonspecific anchorage sites or carriers for H-Y, and indeed for all "organogenesis-directing" proteins. According to that proposal, newly synthesized H-Y, lacking the capacity for direct integration in the plasma membrane, is anchored there in close physical association with β_2m and the MHC heavy chain. Dissemination of H-Y could accordingly be viewed as a consequence of the need to *displace* other inducers that compete for the nonspecific anchorage sites of the plasma membrane. Inasmuch as XX/XY chimeric gonads can sometimes become unambiguous ovaries, one might argue for the existence of an X chromosome-determined ovary inducer molecule that is able to override the tendency of XY cells to organize a testis. If the ovary inducer and the testis inducer utilized the same plasma membrane anchorage site (and/or if specific binding of one inducer inhibited specific binding of the other), dissemination of H-Y might be necessary to overcome the residual inclination toward ovarian development in any XY gonad.

Early and ubiquitous ("constitutive") expression of H-Y, and its dissemination, could be viewed as a secondary consequence of the need to escape regulation, as occurs in the nonmammalian vertebrates. Whether that need is predicated on possible sex-reversing effects of maternal estrogen *in utero* remains to be clarified. Estrogen *can* sex-reverse the developing testis of the opossum, *Didelphis virginiana* (Burns, 1961). (Is that one of the reasons why the marsupial fetus forsakes the womb for the pouch?) Gonadal organogenesis and synthesis of H-Y seem to be influenced by endocrinological, environmental, and even psychosocial cues in the more primitive species. Two examples will suffice: (1) In chicks and quails, exposure of the primordial ZZ gonad to estrogens causes development of an ovotestis; this is associated with the *de novo* appearance of H-W antigen (Müller *et al.*, 1980); (2) in certain marine fish (*Anthias squamipinnis*), removal of a male from a large social group causes sex reversal in a female member of the same group (Shapiro, 1980); H-Y has not been studied in these fish. But hormone-mediated sex reversal has not been reported in any eutherian species.

Of all loci in the mammalian genome, the MHC is notable for extensive polymorphism; 56 alleles have been reported at H-2K of the mouse, and 45 alleles at H-2D, occurring together in some 2500 combinations (see Klein, 1979). Thus Ohno (1977) extended his ontogenetic "strategy of competitive displacement" to include parasitic viruses, by suggesting that viruses have learned to mimic organogenesis-directing molecules with their own viral antigens, thereby competing for a foothold among the β_2m-MHC molecules of the plasma membrane. Development of extensive polymorphism of MHC antigens could accordingly represent a means of escaping susceptibility to viral infection resulting from affinity of particular viral antigens and particular MHC haplotypes. [Compare that scheme with the *altered self hypothesis* of Zinkernagel and Doherty (1974) according to which MHC restriction of viral-infected target cells (in T-cell-mediated cytotoxicity tests *in vitro*) is due to formation of a complex of viral and MHC antigens, or to sterical changes in MHC cell surface components induced by neighboring virus particles, and according to which it is the altered MHC antigen itself that invokes the immune response.]

Indeed syngeneic antisera directed against an adenovirus-infected rat cell line were found to immunoprecipitate cell surface components having molecular weights of 45,000, 19,000, and 12,000. Antisera directed against β_2m or MHC (heavy chain) antigen immunoprecipitated cell surface components with the same molecular weights. It was assumed that viral-determined antigen, MHC antigen, and β_2m had formed a ternary complex on the surface of the transformed cells. Evidently the ternary complex was recognized by cytotoxic T cells, because T-cell-mediated cytotoxicity was abolished by either of the two antisera (Kvist *et al.*, 1978).

C. DAUDI CELLS SECRETE H-Y ANTIGEN

If β_2m-MHC components are required for stable cell surface expression of H-Y, then expression of the presumptive inducer should be unstable in cells lacking β_2m-MHC. Daudi cells, cultured from a human (male) Burkitt lymphoma, have lost cell surface β_2m and HLA. So it is remarkable that Daudi cells absorbed considerably less H-Y antibody in serological tests than was absorbed by corresponding β_2m(+) HLA(+) cells cultured from other male lymphomas. Furthermore when Daudi cells were cocultured with β_2m(+) HLA(+) cells of the HeLa D98 line, β_2m supplied by the latter caused restored expression of HLA in the (HeLa × Daudi) somatic cell hybrids; and that was correlated with restored expression of H-Y (Beutler *et al.*, 1978).

Surely the data favor the proposition that H-Y utilizes the β_2-m-HLA anchorage site in human cells—but there are other data suggesting that MHC and H-Y antigens are not always associated on the plasma membrane (see for example Fellous *et al.*, 1978; Flaherty *et al.*, 1979; reviewed in Hall and Wachtel, 1980). Yet H-Y is secreted by cultured Daudi cells. Thus bovine fetal ovarian cells become H-Y$^+$ on exposure to Daudi culture medium—and as we have already seen, Daudi-secreted proteins induce testicular architecture in XX indifferent gonads of the fetal calf *in vitro*.

By growing Daudi cells in medium containing radioactive amino acids, one obtains labeled macromolecules in the supernatant, including radioactive H-Y antigen (^{3}H:H-Y for example). As noted above (Section II,D), this has been used in the demonstration of gonad-specific binding of H-Y. It has been used also in preliminary biochemical characterization of the secreted molecule (Nagai *et al.*, 1979). Early indications are that Daudi-secreted H-Y is a molecule of 15,000–18,000 MW, corresponding to mouse Sertoli cell membrane bound H-Y, which has approximately the same molecular weight (Hall and Wachtel, 1980).

D. Sertoli Cell Differentiation Alloantigen

Given the presence of the primordial germ cells (PGC), Leydig cell precursors and Sertoli cell precursors in the central blastema of the indifferent gonad, and given that the PGC are H-Y$^-$, whereas the Sertoli cells and Leydig cells are H-Y$^+$ (Zenzes *et al.*, 1978a), it is self-evident that H-Y alone could not direct the "sorting-out" processes by which the various cell types are compartmentalized in the developing testis. Other signals would be required. Since XY testicular (Sertoli) cells lysostripped of H-Y seemed to aggregate in the manner of follicular cells in the reaggregation experiments described above, Ciccarese and Ohno (1978) asked whether Sertoli cells of the testicular tubule and granulosa cells of the ovarian follicle might be derived from the same precursor, and, if so, whether these cells might carry a common differentiation alloantigen.

In fact, female mice immunized with Sertoli cells (from the germ cell-negative testes of H-2-compatible Sxr/−,XX male mice) produced two antibodies: H-Y antibody, and another antibody reactive with Sertoli cells and granulosa cells. After absorption with cells of male spleen or epidermis (to remove H-Y antibodies) sera from the Sertoli cell-sensitized females retained cytotoxicity for Sertoli cells *and* ovarian follicular cells, but not luteal cells; the H-Y antibody-depleted sera were unreactive with PGC and Leydig cells. Yet cytotoxicity of the antisera for Sertoli cells could be abolished by absorption with ovarian follicular cells. (As for the question of how females could readily produce this autoantibody, the authors proposed disappearance of the follicular cell antigen after puberty.)

Other experiments (Ciccarese and Ohno, 1978) revealed that T-cell-mediated lysis of Sertoli target cells is not H-2 restricted. Female killer T cells sensitized *in vivo* and primed *in vitro* with Sertoli cells could lyse Sertoli cells in cell-mediated cytotoxicity tests, irrespective of the H-2 haplotype of the target cell. The implication is that the Sertoli-follicular cell differentiation alloantigen is not expressed in association with MHC antigens. But differentiation alloantigens— functioning ostensibly in cell–cell recognition—need not be involved in the tactics of competitive displacement, and thus need not be disseminated, and thus have no reason for association with β_2m-MHC antigens.

IV. Mechanisms and Hypotheses

A. INDUCTION OF THE MAMMALIAN TESTIS

Consider the following points in review: (1) There are genes for H-Y on the mammalian X and Y chromosomes; mutation of either X- or Y-situated H-Y genes may preclude synthesis of H-Y thereby blocking normal development of the XY presumptive testis [other H-Y genes may occur on unidentified autosomes—see Ohno (1979) and Wolf *et al.* (1980) for discussion of the genetics of primary sex determination]. (2) H-Y can occur as a "stable" component of the plasma membrane, hence its recognition as a transplantation antigen, and as a free molecule in solution, hence its presumptive role as inducer. But if H-Y transplantation antigen is the same as soluble H-Y, we may assume that the molecule is bound to the membrane in association with another membrane component. An alternative possibility—that H-Y is sheared from the membrane by an enzyme—would seem unlikely, given evidence that H-Y is bound to the membrane of somatic cells in association with β_2m-MHC cell surface components. (3) Apparently there is a gonadal receptor for H-Y antigen. Soluble H-Y is bound specifically in Leydig cells and in Sertoli cells, but not in germ cells or in cells of the extragonadal tissues. (4) In the normal male, H-Y is secreted only in Sertoli cells (Zenzes *et al.*, 1978a), which according to Jost *et al.* (1981) are among the first "new" cells to appear in the developing testis. (5) Sertoli cells of the testicular tubule and granulosa cells of the ovarian follicle share a common differentiation alloantigen, implying a common lineage of the two cell types. (6) Primordial germ cells are H-Y antigen negative.

On the basis of these considerations, and on the basis of our earlier discussion, the following scheme may be envisioned (Fig. 2): under direction of X and Y chromosome-situated H-Y genes, primordial Sertoli cells in the central blastema of the indifferent gonad produce H-Y

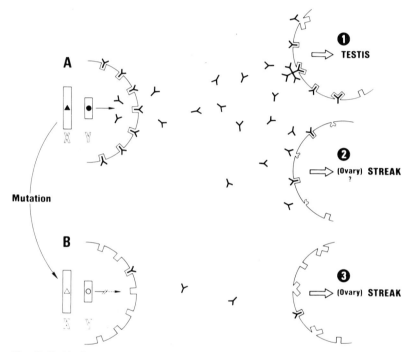

FIG. 2. Testicular organogenesis and its abnormalities. (A) Given normal function of X and Y chromosome-situated H-Y genes, H-Y is produced in normal quantity and disseminated in Sertoli cell precursor. (1) H-Y (including endogenous H-Y) is bound in β_2m-MHC carriers (single indentures) and specific receptors (bifurcated recesses) in target cell, which is now induced for testicular organogenesis. Bound H-Y may occur as a polymer (see Wachtel, 1983). (2) H-Y is not bound in mutated receptor. Despite the presence of β_2m-MHC-associated H-Y, cell bearing mutated receptor cannot participate in normal testicular organogenesis. In the functional absence of H-Y, the XY gonad is induced for ovarian development. In humans the XY ovary degenerates, giving rise to the syndrome of XY gonadal dysgenesis in phenotypic female with H-Y+ cellular phenotype. (B) Mutation of X or Y chromsome-situated H-Y genes precludes normal synthesis of the inducer. (3) In the absence of a threshold quantity of H-Y, the XY gonad is induced for ovarian development as above. In humans the XY ovary degenerates, giving rise to the syndrome of XY gonadal dysgenesis—in this case in a phenotypic female with H-Y- cellular phenotype (see Section IV, B). After Wachtel (1983); reprinted by permission.

antigen. the newly synthesized H-Y saturates avilable β_2m-MHC nonspecific anchorage sites, displacing other "irrelevant" inducer molecules, including those which could direct ovarian organogenesis. The disseminated molecule is taken up nonspecifically in the anchorage sites of neighboring cells; it is bound specifically in the receptors of neighboring Sertoli cell precursors and Leydig cell precursors. According to Ohno (1977), specific binding of H-Y in Sertoli cell precursors induces increased production and dissemination of the H-Y molecule itself. According to Müller *et al.* (1978b), specific binding of H-Y in Leydig cell precursors may cause synthesis of the LH/hCG receptor.

At the same time that the Sertoli cells aggregate, the germ cells must be incorporated into the "lumen" of the tubule, and the Leydig cells must be excluded. Since the germ cells are H-Y⁻ and ostensibly receptor-negative as well (Zenzes *et al.*, 1978a), their participation in the morphogenesis of the tubule must be negotiated by cell surface signals other than H-Y. It follows that extratubular sorting-out and aggregation of the Leydig cells is also mediated by signals other than H-Y. One might propose that these signals are provided by cell surface differentiation alloantigens—but there is really little evidence to support that proposal. Suffice it to say that organization of the seminiferous tubule, of the interstitium, and of the tunica albuginea, must involve several differentiative and morphogenetic events, and possibly several inductive signals, in a complex system of inductive signals.

Let us assume that reaction of H-Y and its gonadal receptor actually induces differentiation of the Sertoli cell, and that this differentiative step is accompanied by cell-type-specific programs—including synthesis of anti-Müllerian "hormone" (which blocks development of the internal female genitalia), expression of H-Y antigen, and production of other molecules that remain to be discovered. And let us consider the possibility that H-Y, or another Sertoli cell product, induces differentiation of the Leydig cell, and that this step, too, is accompanied by cell-type-specific programs—including expression of the LH/hCG receptor, synthesis of androgen, which induces development of the internal male genitalia, and production of other molecules that remain to be discovered. From that perspective, *the early organogenesis of the testis—and indeed the full cascade of differentiative events in primary and secondary sex-determination leading to final acquisition of the male phenotype, could be set in motion by a single inducer molecule.*

B. ABNORMALITIES OF PRIMARY SEX DETERMINATION

If H-Y is the inducer of the testis, then the several abnormalities of gonadal sex determination represented in such conditions as true hermaphroditism and XX and XY sex reversal can be explained as errors in the synthesis, dissemination, and binding of H-Y.

Although true hermaphroditism—occurrence of testicular and ovarian tissue in the same individual—might be perceived as a natural consequence of XX/XY chimerism in the gonad, the fact is that most human true hermaphrodites have a female karyotype (46, XX). Thus XX true hermaphroditism, like XX male sex reversal, must involve the abnormal presence of Y chromosomal genes as in a translocation or abnormal "switching-on" of X-linked or autosomal genes as in a *constitutive* mutation. As for the question why a particular XX^{H-Y+} gonad develops as a testis, and another, as an ovotestis, we have already pointed out that the ovotestis is characterized by mosaic expression of H-Y (Winters *et al.*, 1979). As for the question why a disseminated inducer should not reach and sex reverse *all* cells of the developing XX^{H-Y+} gonad, one might argue that disseminated H-Y may or may not reach all cells of the gonad, and that it is competing with factors that promote ovarian differentiation in either case. It follows that a certain threshold synthesis of H-Y is required to ensure general dominance of the testicular phenotype. The inference is that the degree of sex-reversal of the XX^{H-Y+} gonad is related to the proportion of cells bearing functional H-Y genes (Urban *et al.*, 1981). That could be related in turn to the proportion of cells bearing *lyonized* H-Y mutants, assuming that mutation of an X-linked gene could influence synthesis of the testis inducer in the XX primordium. The syndrome of XY true hermaphroditism is rather more difficult to explain, given the tendency of XY ovaries to degenerate (see below). It could be supposed that XY cells—bearing residual ovary-inducing genes—are induced to organize the female gonad in cases of subthreshold production of the testis inducer. Accordingly subthreshold production of H-Y could be due to mutation or loss of H-Y genes in a critical population of cells in the primordial gonad.

Development of the unambiguous XY ovary—fertile as in the wood lemming, or degenerative as in the human (Simpson, 1976)—is explained in terms of *functional absence* of the testis inducer, or according to our model, in terms of failure of reaction of H-Y and its gonadal receptor. The indifferent XY gonad thus would be induced for ovarian differentiation in each of the following conditions: (1) *deletion or inactivation of H-Y genes,* in a female with the $H-Y^-$ cellular phenotype; (2) *mutation of H-Y genes,* in which case the H-Y phenotype would be determined by the extent to which the variant molecule could react with H-Y antibody [Iwata *et al.* (1979) reported a Daudi-secreted H-Y variant reactive with H-Y antibody but unreactive with its receptor];

(3) *mutation of the H-Y receptor,* in a female with the H-Y$^+$ phenotype, H-Y being expressed in association with β_2m-MHC cell surface components in somatic and gonadal cells. (Certain mutations of the β_2m/ MHC nonspecific carrier might conceivably favor membrane anchorage of one inducer molecule over anchorage of another—but gross changes of MHC structure could be expected to disrupt organogenesis in general, thereby blocking survival of the embryo.)

In humans, two X chromosomes are required to sustain the ovary. In subjects lacking the normal X pair, ovarian development proceeds normally during early gestation, but the ovary degenerates and is represented by a streak of fibrous tissue devoid of follicles, at around the time of birth or shortly thereafter. Thus lacking the X-pair, XY gonads that fail to become testes may start out as ovaries, but these degenerate as described above, giving rise to the syndrome of 46,XY gonadal dysgenesis. In man the condition is characterized by a high incidence of gonadal malignancy, with some 25% of cases developing gonadoblastoma or dysgerminoma.

Our scheme requires two major classes of XY gonadal dysgenesis: one caused by failure of the testis inducer and the other, by failure of its gonadal receptor (Fig. 2). So it is worth pointing out that two classes have now been defined serologically: one that is H-Y$^-$ and another that is H-Y$^+$. Remarkably gonadal malignancies have so far been confined to the H-Y$^+$ class (Simpson *et al.,* 1981; Wachtel, 1983).

C. ORGANOGENESIS OF THE HETEROGAMETIC OVARY

We have reviewed evidence that H-Y actively directs the morphogenesis of the seminiferous tubule (Section II,B). But mammalian H-Y also promotes follicular reaggregation in dispersed ZZ testicular cells of the chicken (Zenzes *et al.,* 1980). How can one antigen direct alternative and disparate morphogenetic events?

First, H-Y and H-W (as it is called in the ZZ/ZW species) may represent common amino acid or carbohydrate sequences in larger macromolecules with alternative differentiative functions. Then the alternative XY and ZW programs of gonadal organogenesis could be attributed to differences in other polypeptide sequences. (That argument is weakened by observations suggesting conservation of the H-Y/H-W receptor.) Second, it is conceivable that H-Y and H-W are the same, but that they are *permissive* inducers—that the response to the "two" molecules is different because the responding cells are committed to alternative pathways. In support of that contention, one might argue that any instructive phases of gonadal induction are governed by molecules other than H-Y/H-W, but synthesized under the direction of

H-Y/H-W. Third, according to the same general scheme, it could be proposed that H-Y and H-W are identical or equivalent, but that they govern different aspects of gonadal organogenesis—that H-Y triggers the process (differentiation of the Sertoli cells), whereas H-W is only a part of the process. We have already said that avian ZZ embryonic gonads are induced for ovarian development by estrogen, and that one of the consequences is *de novo* expression of H-W.

Finally let us consider the following conjectural analysis (Ohno and Matsunaga, 1981): we have pointed out that immature germ cells of the mammal are H-Y$^-$; they do not become H-Y$^+$ until late pachytene or thereafter, and they remain receptor-negative throughout. In contrast, germ cells of the ZW chick have already attained late pachytene and diplotene shortly after hatching. It may be supposed that they become H-W$^+$ at about the same time that ZW follicles appear (about 2 weeks after hatching). The point is that follicular organization seems to require the presence of a central germ cell. Inasmuch as H-W is involved in that event, H-W$^+$ germ cells could participate. Given an instructive function of the inducer, H-W-positive/receptor-positive granulosa cells could aggregate about a central H-W$^+$ germ cell; and the resulting interactions would generate the spherical architecture of the follicle—not the cylindrical architecture of the tubule (see discussion in Wachtel, 1983). The foregoing argument is complicated however by the observation that ZZ follicular aggregation could be induced *in vitro*—ostensibly in the absence of H-W$^+$ germ cells (Zenzes *et al.*, 1980).

D. A MODEL INDUCTIVE SYSTEM

The various cells of the zygote become differentiated shortly after fertilization. Some cells may contain more yolk than others; some are internalized having no direct interface with the "environment"; some are exposed partly to other cells and partly to the environment; and so on. Initial changes of cellular phenotype leading to the appearance of new classes of cells may thus be induced by simple physical cues. Later differentiative events may be triggered when different classes of cells come into contact with one another. On the basis of the information reviewed above, it is evident that one cell may release a diffusible molecule that can be taken up in another neighboring cell—and it is evident too that the diffusible molecule can induce changes in the target cells leading to appearance of a new surface phenotype. Changes in surface phenotype can further be correlated with changes in cellular functions—in particular those relating to cell–cell communication and physical interplay.

As an example let us consider a hypothetical "lens-inducer" that is produced in cells of the optic vesicle. The molecule is disseminated, and it is bound in target cells of the overlying epithelium. On engaging its specific receptor, the inducer triggers production of cell-type-specific proteins including the lens-specific crystallins and perhaps other, cell surface molecules—differentiation alloantigens that remain to be defined. Reaction of the inducer and its receptor may trigger production of the inducer itself. Upon further dissemination, more cells are induced and more inducer is synthesized, the differentiative wave being limited by factors that remain to be elucidated in this system (availability of specific receptors and competitive inducers, in the gonad).

Organization of the optic lens like the organization of the gonad involves two developmental phases: differentiation of new cell types and physical interaction of the differentiated cells in the elaboration of new structure (morphogenesis). Could a single inducer directly mediate both phases? Could a cell surface molecule provide the means whereby cells aggregate in the formation of a particular structure? Perhaps. According to the strategy of competitive displacement, increased dissemination of the inducer leads to saturation of available β_2m-MHC anchorage sites; the inducer drives out irrelevant inducers thereby promoting unambiguous development (of the lens, for example). But the "active site" (receptor binding site) of the inducer molecule would still be free for reaction with the specific receptor. A macromolecule attached to the nonspecific carrier of one cell could thus bind the specific receptor of another cell, and that interaction could serve to link the cells (Fig. 3). The characteristic aggregation of cells in the optic lens could therefore be mediated by the same molecule that induces differentiation of those cells. An alternative possibility is that a given inducer may polymerize (Fig. 2, 1) thereby providing identical arms for reaction with multiple receptors (Nagai *et al.*, 1979).

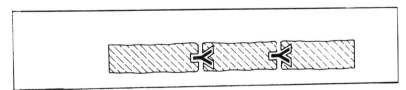

FIG. 3. Inducer-mediated linkage of cells in organogenesis. Inducer molecule (H-Y) that is bound to β_2m-MHC carrier (single indenture) in one cell can react with specific receptor (bifurcated recess) in another. Instruction for development of distinct morphology is thereby contained in the arrangement of β_2m-MHC and specific receptors in a given cell type.

A final point: if a given differentiative event is triggered by a particular inducer produced in a particular differentiated cell—then production of the inducer itself is a consequence of a preceding differentiative event triggered by a preceding inducer. In other words the inducer is a specialized product of a specialized cell. One differentiative step thus induces another, and embryogenesis may be perceived as a succession of differentiative steps culminating in the development of the whole organism. Then the inducer of the testis is a product of the fertilizing spermatozoon.

ACKNOWLEDGMENTS

Supported in part by grants from the National Institutes of Health (AI-19456, HD-17049) and the Dwight School Foundation.

REFERENCES

Balinsky, B. I. (1970). "An Introduction to Embryology." Saunders, Philadelphia, Pennsylvania.

Beutler, B., Nagai, Y., Ohno, S., Klein, G., and Shapiro, I. M. (1978). *Cell* **13**, 509–513.

Billingham, R. E., and Silvers, W. K. (1959). *Transplant Bull.* **6**, 399–406.

Bodmer, W. F. (1972). *Nature (London)* **237**, 139–145.

Boyse, E. A., and Cantor, H. (1979). *Arthritis Rheum.* **22**, 1153–1160.

Boyse, E. A., Lance, E. M., Carswell, E. A., Cooper, S., and Old, L. J. (1970). *Nature (London)* **227**, 901–903.

Burns, R. K. (1961). *In* "Sex and Internal Secretions" (W. C. Young, ed.), Vol. 1, pp. 76–158. Williams & Wilkins, Baltimore, Maryland.

Ciccarese, S., and Ohno, S. (1978). *Cell* **13**, 643–650.

Coulombre, J. C., and Russell, E. S. (1954). *J. Exp. Zool.* **126**, 277–295.

Eichwald, E. J., and Silmser, C. R. (1955). *Transplant Bull.* **2**, 148–149.

Fellous, M., Gunther, E., Kemler, R., Wiels, J., Berger, R., Guenet, J. L., Jakob, H., and Jacob, F. (1978). *J. Exp. Med.* **147**, 58–70.

Flaherty, L., Zimmerman, D., and Wachtel, S. S. (1979). *J. Exp. Med.* **150**, 1020–1027.

Goldberg, E. H., Boyse, E. A., Bennett, D., Scheid, M., and Carswell, E. A. (1971). *Nature (London)* **232**, 478–480.

Gordon, R. D., Simpson, E., and Samelson, L. E. (1975). *J. Exp. Med.* **142**, 1108–1120.

Goulmy, E., Termijtelen, A., Bradley, B. A., and van Rood, J. J. (1977). *Nature (London)* **266**, 544–545.

Hall, J. L., and Wachtel, S. S. (1980). *Mol. Cell. Biochem.* **33**, 49–66.

Herbst, E. W., Fredga, K., Frank, F., Winking, H., and Gropp, A. (1978). *Chromosoma* **69**, 185–191.

Hildemann, W. H., Morgan, M., and Frautnick, L. (1970). *Transplant Proc.* **2**, 24–31.

Iwata, H., Nagai, Y., Stapleton, D. D., Smith, R. C., and Ohno, S. (1979). *Arthritis Rheum.* **22**, 1211–1216.

Jost, A. (1970). *Philos. Trans. R. Soc. London Ser. B* **259**, 119–130.

Jost, A. (1972). *Arch. Anat. Microsc. Morphol. Exp.* **61**, 415–438.

Jost, A., Magre, S., and Agelopoulou, R. (1981). *Hum. Genet.* **58**, 59–63.

Klein, J. (1979). *Science* **203**, 516–521.

Kvist, S., Ostberg, L., Persson, H., Philipson, L., and Peterson, P. (1978). *Proc. Natl. Acad. Sci. U.S.A.* **75**, 5674–5678.

McKeehan, M. S. (1958). *Anat. Rec.* **132**, 297–306.

McLaren, A. (1976). "Mammalian Chimaeras." University Press, Cambridge.

Moscona, A. A. (1961). *Exp. Cell. Res.* **22**, 455–475.

Müller, U., and Urban, E. (1981). *Cytogenet. Cell. Genet.* **31**, 104–107.

Müller, U., Aschmoneit, I., Zenzes, M. T., and Wolf, U. (1978a). *Hum. Genet.* **43**, 151–157.

Müller, U., Zenzes, M. T., Bauknecht, T., Wolf, U., Siebers, J. W., and Engel, W. (1978b). *Hum. Genet.* **45**, 203–207.

Müller, U., Guichard, A., Reyss-Brion, M., and Scheib, D. (1980). *Differentiation* **16**, 129–133.

Murphy, D. B. (1981). *In* "The Role of the Major Histocompatibility Complex in Immunobiology" (M. E. Dorf, ed.), pp. 1–32. Garland STPM Press, New York.

Nagai, Y., Ciccarese, S., and Ohno, S. (1979). *Differentiation* **13**, 155–164.

Ohno, S. (1977). *Immunol. Rev.* **33**, 59–69.

Ohno, S. (1979). "Major Sex-Determining Genes." Springer-Verlag, Berlin and New York.

Ohno, S., and Matsunaga, T. (1981). *In* "Levels of Genetic Control in Development," pp. 235–246. Liss, New York.

Ohno, S., Ciccarese, S., Nagai, Y., and Wachtel, S. S. (1978a). *Arch. Androl.* **1**, 103–109.

Ohno, S., Nagai, Y., and Ciccarese, S. (1978b). *Cytogenet. Cell Genet.* **20**, 351–354.

Ohno, S., Nagai, Y., Ciccarese, S., and Iwata, H. (1979). *Rec. Prog. Hormone Res.* **35**, 449–476.

Peterson, P. A., Cunningham, B. A., Berggard, I., and Edelman, G. M. (1972). *Proc. Natl. Acad. Sci. U.S.A.* **69**, 1697–1701.

Scheid, M. P., and Triglia, D. (1979). *Immunogenetics* **9**, 423–433.

Scheid, M., Boyse, E. A., Carswell, E. A., and Old, L. J. (1972). *J. Exp. Med.* **135**, 938–955.

Scheid, M. P., Goldstein, G., and Boyse, E. A. (1975). *Science* **190**, 1211–1213.

Shapiro, D. Y. (1980). *Science* **209**, 1136–1137.

Short, R. V. (1979). *Br. Med. Bull.* **35**, 121–127.

Silvers, W. K., and Yang, S.-L. (1973). *Science* **181**, 570–572.

Simpson, J. L. (1976). *In* "Disorders of Sexual Differentiation. Etiology and Clinical Delineation" (J. L. Simpson, ed.), pp. 260–302. Academic Press, New York.

Simpson, J. L., Blagowidow, N., and Martin, A. O. (1981). *Hum. Genet.* **58**, 91–97.

Sirlin, J. L., and Brahma, S. K. (1959). *Dev. Biol.* **1**, 234–246.

Strominger, J. L., Mann, D. L., Parham, P., Robb, R., Springer, T., and Terhorst, C. (1977). *Cold Spring Harbor Symp. Quant. Biol.* **41**, 323–329.

Terhorst, C., Robb, R., Jones, C., and Strominger, J. L. (1977). *Proc. Natl. Acad. Sci. U.S.A.* **74**, 4002–4006.

Urban, E., Zenzes, M. T., Müller, U., and Wolf, U. (1981). *Differentiation* **18**, 161–168.

Wachtel, S. S. (1977). *Immunol. Rev.* **33**, 33–58.

Wachtel, S. S. (1983). "H-Y Antigen and the Biology of Sex Determination." Grune & Stratton, New York.

Wachtel, S. S., Gasser, D. L., and Silvers, W. K. (1973). *Science* **181**, 862–863.

Wachtel, S. S., Ohno, S., Koo, G., and Boyse, E. A. (1975). *Nature (London)* **257**, 235–236.

Wachtel, S. S., Thaler, H. T., and Boyse, E. A. (1977). *Immunogenetics* **5**, 17–23.

Weiss, P., and Taylor, A. C. (1960). *Proc. Natl. Acad. Sci. U.S.A.* **46**, 1177–1185.

Wilson, H. V. (1908). *J. Exp. Zool.* **5**, 245–258.

Winters, S. J., Wachtel, S. S., White, B. J., Koo, G. C., Javadpour, N., Loriaux, L., and Sherins, R. J. (1979). *N. Engl. J. Med.* **300**, 745–749.

Witschi, E. (1965). *Arch. Anat. Microsc. Morphol. Exp.* **54,** 601–611.

Wolf, U., Fraccaro, M., Mayerova, A., Hecht, T., Zuffardi, O., and Hameister, H. (1980). *Hum. Genet.* **54,** 315–318.

Zenzes, M. T., Müller, U., Aschmoneit, I., and Wolf, U. (1978a). *Hum. Genet.* **45,** 297–303.

Zenzes, M. T., Wolf, U., and Engel, W. (1978b). *Hum. Genet.* **44,** 333–338.

Zenzes, M. T., Wolf, U., Gunther, E., and Engel, W. (1978c). *Cytogenet. Cell Genet.* **20,** 365–372.

Zenzes, M. T., Müller, U., Aschmoneit, I., and Wolf, U. (1978a). *Hum. Genet.* **45,** 297–303.

Zinkernagel, R. M., and Doherty, P. C. (1974). *Nature (London)* **251,** 547–548.

INDEX

CONTENTS OF PREVIOUS VOLUMES

221

Volume 16: Neural Development, Part II. Neural Development in Model Systems

Volume 17: Neural Development, III. Neuronal Specificity, Plasticity, and Patterns